A GUIDE TO WORSHIP IN CENTRAL LONDON

A GUIDE TO WORSHIP IN CENTRAL LONDON

Compiled
by
The London Central YMCA
Places of Worship
Researcn Team

Edited
by
Howard Willows

Illustrated
by
Paul Zervos

distributed by Fowler Wright Books
Burgess Street, Leominster, HR6 8DE

Published by London Central YMCA
112 Great Russell Street, London, WC1B 3NQ
First published 1988
ISBN 1-871559-00-6

British Library Cataloguing in Publication Data

A guide to worship in central London.
1. London. Central London. Religions. Public worship
I. London Central YMCA, Places of Worship Research Team II. Willows, Howard
291.3'09421

ISBN 1-871559-00-6

Printed in the UK by
Anchor Press Ltd, Tiptree, Essex

CONTENTS

PREFACES TO A GUIDE TO WORSHIP IN CENTRAL LONDON

'One of London's great treasures are not only the religious buildings but the communities which worship in them.

This guide will enable visitors to add exciting dimensions to their stay in London and will undoubtedly contribute to richer memories and greater friendships.

I hope the guide will be a success and I congratulate the YMCA on such an imaginative and helpful project.'

Rabbi Hugo Gryn, *West London Synagogue of British Jews*

'Here at last is a comprehensive guide to the many places of worship in our multi-faith city.

For worshippers, as well as those seeking to strengthen their spiritual life, this book will be of real value.'

Lord Soper, *West London Methodist Mission*

'It is not unreasonable to maintain that to conform to an age and a society characterised by increasing secularism, religion should be, more than ever, ready to provide a stability without which our society can only deteriorate.

A vast majority of worshipping men and women who feel a deep need for worship will find in this book a place which will meet that need.

As for Muslims, the prescribed procedure of Islam is inviolably woven into their creed.'

Dr A A Mughram Al-Ghamdi,
Director General, The Islamic Cultural Centre

A PREFACE FROM THE SPONSORING BODY – LONDON CENTRAL YMCA

Why a [illegible] there not [illegible]

[illegible]

[illegible]

[illegible] Christians [illegible] the Churches in London [illegible] therefore, it will be helpful [illegible] the work.

Some may question why an organisation such as the YMCA is apparently condoning other faiths. It is vital to us that a really Christian respect [illegible] really welcome, including [illegible] worship he prefers. We share the [illegible] hindering others from practising their religion.

So there seemed a demand for such a guide. How could it be met?

In other aspects of our work, the YMCA is very much aware of the many unemployed young people in our society. If the need for a guide could be met by some of them – then the 'process' as well as the 'product' would be useful.

A PREFACE FROM THE SPONSORING BODY – LONDON CENTRAL YMCA

Why a Guide to the Places of Worship in London? Are there not enough already? Who will use it?

While there are a great number of guide books to the secular places of interest in London, it seemed to us that religious centres were relatively neglected. Perhaps this is partly due to morale being so low amongst the Christian Churches, that we often forget that there are more people seeking Churches on a Sunday than there are people looking for football grounds on a Saturday.

But apart from our citizens resident in London, this guide has chiefly in mind the 24 million visitors who come to London each year and who stay for at least one night. Despite occasional fluctuations in the figures the trend for these numbers is increasing, and the length of their stay increases. London is now one of the major tourist attractions of the world and tourism is one of our major growth industries.

In presenting this guide we hope it will be particularly helpful to those concerned with meeting these visitors and in making them welcome and in helping them to respond in an informed way when faced with the question 'where can we worship'.

Of the 24 million visitors, 9 million come from overseas. Many are from societies less secularized than ours, where worship is an accepted part of life. The request for places to worship will be more frequent amongst these than with our own population and of course many of the 9 million visitors come from countries where faiths other than Christianity are dominant. So our guide is not one to the Churches of London but to 'places of worship'. We hope, therefore, it will be helpful to those of all faiths of the world.

Some may question why a Christian foundation such as the YMCA is apparently commending other faiths. It seemed to us that a really Christian response was to make 'the stranger in our midst' really welcome, including helping him to find the place of worship he prefers. We share the view that 'the Gospel is not commended by hindering others from practising their religion'.

So there seemed a demand for such a guide. How could it be met?

In other aspects of our work, the YMCA is very much aware of the many unemployed young people in our society. If the need for a guide could be met by some of these – then 'the process' as well as 'the product' would be useful.

The YMCA therefore asked the Manpower Services Commission if they could find the monies to fund a group of young unemployed people to tackle this task. We are grateful that they gladly agreed. And we record our thanks to our colleague Charles Nunn, now retired, who 'set the wheels in motion'.

As the project proceeded, our own enthusiasm for it was increased by the mounting enthusiasm of the group of young people who undertook it. We admired their dedication and skill and thank them for the result. We are delighted that most of them have now found permanent employment.

While we hope this guide will be useful to those who meet visitors to London as well as to those who live here, we hope it will also be useful to those 'on the move' in another sense. Those who are seeking a faith that they have not yet found. We hoped this guide may be helpful to them in their search.

GENERAL INTRODUCTION

This book is an unprecedented directory of over 400 places of worship ranging from cathedrals to basement rooms, all to be found within a few miles of each other, representing eight major faiths as well as over 40 distinct Christian Churches, denominations and groups. The compilers have no religious axe to grind: our aim is not to judge or grade the following entries, but to present a picture of the religious life of London in the hope it will prove to be interesting, informative and of real benefit, especially to those new to London, those lacking a spiritual home, and those tourists wishig to look further than stone-deep.

The idea behind such a book germinated at London's Central YMCA and took shape as an MSC-funded research project set up by the team Co-ordinator, Heather Douglas. Our basic criterion for inclusion was simply that a place of worship (that is, one recognised as such by a bona fide religious group and in regular use) be located (more or less) within the confines of the London Transport map provided for tourists. We have, however, strayed some distance beyond these geographical boundaries for two reasons: firstly, in order to bring to wider attention places of exceptional interest or singularity, such as the Buddhapadipa Temple in Wimbledon; and secondly, to obtain a more representative sample of certain significant groups who have been unable (or have not felt the need) to secure premises in this central area. Thus, the Pentecostal churches of Brixton, for example, are included. This approach also enables us to examine in a wider context how places of worship interact with, and adapt themselves to, their immediate environment. We also decided to create entries for those groups we came across of no fixed abode who nonetheless worship regularly at a venue within our boundaries; after all, a church, strictly speaking, is nothing more than a body of people.

This leaning towards people rather than buildings is the only element of bias we have deliberately embraced. Ultimately, we have tried to portray within each entry a *living place of worship*, as well as the national monument, aesthetic masterpiece, bustling social centre, or whatever else it may be. Visual descriptions have been kept brief for the most part, and where we do dwell on architectural features it is more likely to be for some lesser-known "gem" than such places as Westminster Abbey which has been more than adequately delineated elsewhere.

Personal interviews with priests, rabbis, vicars, imams, monks or other representatives, backed up with any available documentary research, were the primary source of information. The interviewee then had an opportunity to check a report before it was edited into the final version for publication, thus greatly reducing the risk of our perpetuating errors. The overwhelming majority of those we contacted were most helpful, some well beyond the call of duty, and sympathetic to our aims. Some groups proved simply too hard to track down. Also, a few declined to take part, usually on the grounds that they did not wish to rub shoulders with people of other persuasions. This has to be set against the wealth of inter-faith and ecumenical initiatives undertaken by many groups featured in these pages.

I would like to thank all those who have helped and supported this project: our champions at the YMCA, especially Alex Cloke and Geoffrey Palmer, who revived our hopes when it seemed the work would never come to fruition; John Holmes, for his help and expertise; and, of course, the researchers themselves for all their efforts and enthusiasm. In editing their contributions I have sought to avoid imposing a rigid uniformity and to allow something of their personal impressions and individual styles to come through. What we have produced is, I feel, a credit to the project team—all of whom, in order to be eligible to work on an MSC scheme such as this, had been unemployed for some time. Many have gone on to find jobs in publishing, the leisure industry and the voluntary sector, which only goes to show what a waste of valuable human resources their joblessness represented.

Howard Willows, *Editor*

THE LONDON CENTRAL YMCA

PLACES OF WORSHIP RESEARCH TEAM

Heather Douglas (Co-ordinator)
John Harmar-Smith
Steve Hornibrook
Debbie Lowe
Victor Seedman
Howard Willows (Editor)
and briefly Erica Fellows-Smith
Yvonne Gordon
Christine Hipkiss
John C Kerr
David Ricketts
Graeme Stirling
Paul Zervos (Illustrator)

Thanks also to Chris Riseley

A NOTE ON THE TEXT

The places of worship have been arranged alphabetically within their religious or denominational grouping, thus allowing each section to be preceded by a brief introduction outlining something of the history and beliefs of the group. There is an index of names of places of worship and groups (both official name and any other commonly used) at the back of the book.

While every effort has been made to ensure the accuracy of the information, it is possible that some minor errors will have slipped through and that some details will have gone out of date. If a second edition proves possible, we will of course provide an opportunity for representatives of all the places of worship featured to amend and update the entries.

ILLUSTRATIONS

1 THE BAHA'I FAITH

Baha'is are so called after a young Persian who, in 1863, took the name Baha'u'llah ('glory of God') and proclaimed himself to be the Messenger of God foretold by an earlier venerated figure, the Bab or 'gate', some twenty years before. The Bab's followers largely accepted Baha'u'llah, and his teachings, although originating within Islam, soon came to constitute a new faith. As a result, Baha'is were much persecuted and Baha'u'llah himself spent 40 years in prison.

Baha'u'llah saw divine revelation as an unfolding process involving such figures as Moses, Krishna, Zarathustra, Buddha, Christ and Muhammad, and culminating in himself. He is claimed to be the Promised One of all religions whose message transcends cultural and religious barriers.

The central tenet of the Baha'i faith is the oneness of God, of religion and of mankind. Social and religious ideals are closely linked; Baha'is are to work for an end to prejudice and repression, and for an age of unity and peace under a federal world government. Baha'is are involved with equal rights concerns, while remaining free of political ties, and the Baha'i International Community, a nongovernmental organisation, is accredited with consultative status at the UN Economic and Social Council. Spiritual development is based on prayer and meditation, and Baha'is fast from sunrise to sunset from 2nd to 21st of March.

Still strong in its native Iran, despite everything, the Baha'i faith has spread throughout the world, and there are over 130 National Spiritual Assemblies. In Britain, there are perhaps 2,000 Baha'is of whom around 500 live in London.

The Baha'i Centre

27 Rutland Gate, SW7 □ Telephone: 584 2566 □ Bus:74, 264 □ Tube:Knightsbridge □ Parking: on street, meters □ Contact: Ms Jan Mughraby, or anyone at Centre □ Available: most times, especially Thursday evenings

As yet there is no Baha'i place of worship, no *Hazrut al Qud*, in Britain. Every 19 days (their solar calendar has 19 months of 19 days), Baha'is meet in a small worship room at the Baha'i Centre. Set in a quiet Knightsbridge square, the Centre has a bookshop and library, and is the meeting place of the National Spiritual Assembly, an elected dministrative body.

At the simple services, readings may be taken from any of the major religious texts, such as the Upanishads, the Bible, or Baha'u'llah's own writings. This is not mere eclecticism, but an indication of the Baha'i acceptance of all religions as part of one divine process. As there is no clergy, any member present may read from the scriptures. There are communal prayers, and time for meditation.

Conscious of representing the new international religion, Baha'is gear their work towards modern issues such as sexual equality, industrial co-operation and race relations. The Centre promotes racial harmony and inter-cultural understanding by means of floats, information buses and inter-race weekends.

Baha'is do not proselytise, not even within their own families, but visitors are most welcome, especially to the informal open evenings each Thursday.

Services: Prayers and readings every 19 days. Informal open evenings every Thursday □ Wheelchair: steps, help required □ Other details: bookshop, library, etc □ Visiting: all welcome, especially Thursday evenings

2 BUDDHISM

It can be argued that Buddhism is not a religion at all but a philosophical way of life offering salvation or *nirvana*, an end to the suffering that permeates all worldly life. If many of the following entries appear more like centres for evening classes than places of worship, it must be remembered firstly that Buddha was a teacher and Buddhism tries to follow his teachings, and secondly, that the fellowship generated in these organisations (equivalent to the Sangha of monks) is itself an element in combatting greed and delusion.

Buddha is not a proper name, but denotes a state of enlightenment, of knowing the true nature of things. The person we think of as the Buddha was only one of many. He was Siddhartha Gautama, who lived in India in the 6th century BC. He renounced the world, and saw everything in relation to the three marks of existence; these are change, suffering, and the difficult concept of 'no-self' which means that nothing, including the individual, endures. Simplistically speaking, it is necessary to study the *Dhamma* (teachings) to see things as they really are and escape the delusions which bind us to the world of illusion.

Most of the major Buddhist traditions are represented in Britain and a brief outline of each may prove useful. The Theravada school, developed in Ceylon and SE Asia, has the smallest scriptural canon, and tends to be characterised by the path of the individual disciple towards Buddhahood. The Mahayana school differs here in that it presents the ideal of the Bodhisattva, one who postpones enlightenment in order to help others. Mahayana proved more flexible and travelled better, giving rise to Tibetan and Zen Buddhism. The Tibetan tradition incorporates the magical device of the *tantra*, procedures of stylised meditations and the evocations of deities dependent upon a *guru* or *lama*. Zen, best known in its Japanese forms, features paradoxical questions, meditation and sudden enlightenment.

Buddhism in the West has had a slow and tentative awakening (the 1960s' 'hip' appropriation of Zen notwithstanding) and it is still finding its feet. Having said this it should be remembered that the Buddhist Society dates back to 1907; furthermore, Buddhism is reckoned to be the fastest growing religion in Britain, differing radically from the other World Faiths such as Islam and Sikhism, also on the increase in this country, in that the vast majority of new adherents are Westerners. The full range of the Buddhist experience, from academic, Western-oriented study to the devotional worship of orange-robed monks, is available in London today.

For more information, contact any of the places listed here.

The British Buddhist Association

57 Farringdon Road, EC1 □ Telephone: 242 5538, 286 5575 □ Bus: 63, 221, 243, 259 □ Tube: Farringdon □ Parking: difficult □ Director: Mr A Haviland-Nye □ Address: 39 Elgin Avenue, W9 □ Tel: 286 5575 □ Available: office hours □ Other contacts: Ven Dr M Vajiragnana, Mrs I R Quittner, J G Robertson

The Association exists to spread awareness of the Buddha's teachings, the

Dhamma, by providing systematic instruction. This approach, which is the traditional one of southern or Theravada Buddhism, involves an intellectual effort to comprehend the Dhamma, as well as living a Buddhist life and meditating. The Association was opened in May 1974 on Vesaka Day, the day on which the Buddha's enlightenment is celebrated and on which he was born and died.

Most of the staff work on a voluntary basis and the Association is financed by its supporters who pay about £5 per month, according to their means. Supporters are entitled to attend afternoon seminars with eminent Buddhists. There are also regular devotions, meditations and festivals to which supporters may bring guests.

Mr A Haviland-Nye, one of the founders and the Association's Administrative Director, holds lecture/discussion meetings at the Working Men's College in Mornington Cresent. The syllabus in basic Buddhism requires a year's commitment, but a 6-week introductory course is held in premises in Maida Vale where there are a pleasant shrine room and facilities for meditation. Among the courses then available are ones bringing Buddhism right up to date by considering its meaning in modern society in the light of comtempory attitudes.

Sessions: Monday 7–9pm Basic Buddhism (Working Men's College, Crowndale Road, NW1; fee £28.50); Tuesday & Thursday 7.30–9.30pm Introduction to Buddhism (9A Andover Place, NW6; fee £3 per session); Wednesday 7.15pm Group meditation, Sutta readings and Discussion (for supporters and invited guests only) □ *Wheelchair: no access* □ *Visiting: open office hours for enquiries; prospectus available*

The Buddhapadipa Temple

14 Calonne Road, Wimbledon, SW19 □ *Bus: 80, 93* □ *Tube: Wimbledon* □ *Parking: on street* □ *Secretary: The Venerable Phra Khru Silanandra* □ *Address: at the Temple* □ *Tel: 946 1357*

Set in peaceful grounds near Wimbledon Common, complete with ornamental lake, orchard and tree-lined avenue, the Buddhapadipa Temple is a remarkable sight. The large white building, mounted on a stepped podium, is built in an exuberant Thai style, with the gable ends fashioned, to startling effect, into flames of red and gold leaf. In front of the Temple is a substantial house, once a family home, which now contains a meditation hall, kitchens, a bookshop, and accommodation for the resident Sangha of nine Thai monks. As in their native land, the monks are entirely provided for by the Thai community.

Master craftsmen, brought over from Thailand specifically for the task, have covered the interior of the Temple with murals depicting the life of Buddha and his Enlightenment. Particularly powerful is the scene where he is seated under the Bo tree and is assaulted by the Mara demons, vividly portrayed in all their ferocity. The small shrine room houses a gold Buddha-rupa of the 16th century, and is used as a quiet place of meditation and prayer.

In all, the Temple, financed by the Thai Embassy partly in response to the growing interest in Buddhism in Britain, took 2 years to complete and cost almost £1m. The opening ceremony in 1982 was attended by members of the Royal Family of Thailand, Princess Alexandra and many distinguished Buddhists. There are many visitors, largely Westerners hoping to learn more about the Faith.

The Buddhapadipa Temple, SW19

The majority of worshippers are Thais, along with people from Hong Kong, Burma and Malaysia. There is a group of Westerners who form the Lay Buddhist Association and who meet here regularly for meditation and the teaching of the Dhamma in Pali. In return, they help teach the monks English. Phra Khru Silanandra himself speaks many languages, and is able to help all the ethnic groups. Anyone is welcome to the classes, although the activities are never publicised except by word of mouth.

On invitation the monks will give talks and help organise retreats, and they can perform ceremonies of blessing for marriages. The major Buddhist festivals are observed at the Temple, and to mark the New Year of the ancient calendar (13 July) thousands of Thais come to pay their respects and to take part in the festivities, the sporting events and the feasting.

Sessions: Weekdays 6–7am, 6–8pm, Saturdays 4–6.30pm, Sundays 3–5pm, Puja, chanting & meditation □ Classes: Tuesdays, Thursdays, Saturdays, Sundays (for times enquire at Temple) □ Wheelchair: steps up to Temple □ Other details: some accommodation □ Visiting: generally open (except Mondays)

The Buddhist Society

58 Eccleston Square, SW1 □ Telephone: 834 5858 □ Bus: 11, 39 □ Tube/BR: Victoria □ Parking: on street □ General Secretary: Ron Maddox □ Address: c/o Society □ Available: office hours □ Other staff: librarian, secretary, etc

The history of the early days of Buddhism in this country could by and large be described as the history of the Buddhist Society. Formed as the Buddhist Society of Great Britain and Ireland in 1907 it was a scholarly organisation, as led by its President, Professor Rhys-Davies. The Society responded to the awakening interest of British scholars to the newly-translated texts in the ancient Pali language, known as the Pali Canon. By the time the First World War came to its close, membership had seriously declined and the Society was not to revive until 1924, with a new name (the Buddist Lodge) and a new President (Christmas Humphreys). It was the hard work of Humphreys, a great pioneer of the western interpretation of Buddhism, which led to the foundation of a new Society.

The present premises, in a converted mansion in Eccleston Square, Victoria, were officially opened in 1959. The Society occupies the basement, ground and first floors, while the rest of the building is sub-let. On the ground floor is a meeting room, the office, and an excellent library covering all aspects of Buddhism, plus works on alternative medicine and oriental studies. Upstairs are two shrine rooms which have pleasant prospects over the tree-lined square, and in the basement is a hospitality room enabling members to gather informally over refreshments.

The Society is a busy yet relaxed place and staff are always pleased to assist. Schools, for instance, often refer here for general information; GP's inquire about sending patients to learn meditation in order to help them cope with stress; and other work has included correspondence with people in prison.

There is a regular programme of day and evening classes to cover aspects of Buddhism as it has developed historically in different lands, and this includes basic Buddhism and Buddhist meditation. Zen is the most popular class, and always guaranteed to be full. A free introductory course is held from time to time, there is an annual summer school, and for those unable to attend classes the Society produces a correspondence course with a characteristic Buddhist emphasis on practical questions of life. There are frequent lectures by distinguished invited speakers.

Members have full use of the Eccleston Square facilities, and additionally receive copies of the quarterly journal *The Middle Way* which has a section on forthcoming events. The Buddhist Society Book Service will provide a comprehensive book list on receipt of a stamped, addressed envelope.

Sessions: Wednesday 6.30pm Monthly public lecture; Tuesday 6.30pm Public class, 'Introducing Buddhism'; plus many classes and sessions for members only □ *Wheelchair: no access* □ *Other details: library, bookstall, hospitality room* □ *Visiting: open 2–6pm Monday–Saturday*

Dharmadhatu Buddhist Centre

27 Belmont Close, SW4 □ *Telephone: 720 3207* □ *Bus: 35, 37, 45, 88, 137* □ *Tube: Clapham Common* □ *Parking: on street* □ *Co-ordinators: Jane Hope, Kay Crinnean* □ *Available: telephone Centre for appointment*

The Dharmadhatu Centre represents the Tibetan tradition of *Kagyu-pa*. The centre is under the direction of the Venerable Chogyam Trungpa, who founded the Samye-Ling Centre in Scotland, the first Tibetan meditation centre in the West. Since 1970 he has lived in the USA and the Dharmadhatu forms part of a worldwide association of meditation and study centres called Vajradhatu, run by American-trained teachers.

The centre runs regular study programmes and discussion groups, with seminars on such topics as the relationship between Buddhism and contemporary Western psychology; there are also film shows and the occasional open day. The centre runs a secular (non-Buddhist) training programme called *Shambhala,* which teaches the use of meditation as a device to open oneself up to experience, to expand awareness and to respond positively to opportunity. Some may wish to go further, to take the refuges and become committed Buddhists.

The centre is based in former Methodist church premises which are rented from the Society of Oddfellows. The meditation hall is spacious, and offers a choice of cushions or chairs; there is a small shrine. Those who attend cover a wide range of occupations and ages.

There is no obligation to become a member but those who do pay £15 per month and are obliged to meditate for 18 hours monthly. Everyone is allotted a meditation instructor, and a private interview is conducted before training begins.

Sessions: Monday 7am–9.30am Meditation; Wednesday 7.30am–9.30am Meditation (beginners), 7pm Study programme; Sunday 10.30am–1.30pm Meditation, 2.30pm Discussions; 1st Sunday of month 9.30am–7.30pm Nyinthun (all day meditation); Festivals according to Tibetan calendar □ *Children: creche* □ *Wheelchair: good access* □ *Visiting: open for classes and events only; leaflets available*

Friends of the Western Buddhist Order, West London Centre

7 Colville Houses, W11 □ Telephone: 727 9382 □ Bus: 7, 15, 15A, 52, 52A □ Tube: Ladbroke Grove, Westbourne Park □ Parking: on street □ Contact: Mr Wilson □ Address: at Centre □ Available: at meeting times

The FWBO Centre at Notting Hill was opened in 1985. Originally a house used as a residence for male members of the Order, it is now being renovated to enable more activities to be carried out here.

The most important room in the house for its inhabitants is the shrine room where meditations are held. These attempt to cultivate breath awareness and the boundless virtue *(Brahma Vihara)* of friendship, both of which are regular Buddhist practices though not exclusive to Buddhism. The shrine room is quiet and peaceful with a large Buddha statue (made by one of the Order members) as the only decoration. It is an unusual figure inasmuch as it has Western features and hair. This ties in with the FWBO's basic tenet, 'to present the teachings of Buddhism in a way that is most suited to modern Western society'. In this the FWBO has parallels with the Buddhism-with-a-social dimension that has developed in Japan. However, while in Japan such groups as Sokka Gakkai offer Buddhism for businessmen, in Britain it tends to be the disaffected and disillusioned who are attracted.

Although a small charge is made for all classes (except Wednesday lunchtime which is free), concessions are available for the unwaged and no-one would be refused in cases of genuine need. The FWBO enjoys registered charity status; this group is supported by lay donations and course fees, but also has two 'Right Livelihood' businesses including a Notting Hill health food shop. Classes include study groups on aspects of the Dhamma, massage, and Iyengar yoga (focusing on posture work). Devotional *puja* is a regular feature.

Sessions: Tuesday 7pm Open meditation (beginners); Wednesday 1–2pm Open meditation (beginners); 7pm Buddhism and meditation courses; Thursday 7pm Friends' night (study, meditation & puja); Friday 7pm Open yoga night; plus retreats, workshops, study—ring for details □ Wheelchair: many steps; help available □ Visiting: open meeting times only; leaflets, books available

London Buddhist Centre of the Friends of the Western Buddhist Order

51 Roman Road, E2 □ Telephone: 981 1225 □ Bus: 8, 8A, 106, 253 □ Tube: Bethnal Green □ Parking: on street □ Co-ordinator: Dharmachari Ian Waddle □ Address: at centre □ Available: opening times (see below) □ Other contacts: someone always available during opening times

The London Buddhist Centre is situated on the ground floor of a converted fire station on the corner of Roman Road and Globe Road in Bethnal Green. When

London Peace Pagoda, Battersea Park

first rented by the FWBO in 1975, the building was a burnt-out shell—ironically enough for a fire station. After three-and-a-half years of work by members of the residential community, the completely re-built Centre was opened in December 1978.

The FWBO is a Buddhist sect founded in 1967 by a Westerner ordained as a Buddhist monk with the name Sangharakshita. From modest beginnings in Monmouth Street, the movement has grown to include 25 centres throughout Europe as well as two retreat centres. The FWBO places great emphasis on the Sangha, or community, and on friendship, so while around 50 people at the Centre are ordained members, many more are Friends who come for classes and lectures here.

The room which once housed the fire-engines is now the larger of the Centre's two shrine rooms, used for meditation classes. Introductory classes on the basic principles of meditation are available to all irrespective of their interest in, or commitment to, Buddhism. Certainly this enables the FWBO to claim a great degree of openness, but it does mark off their approach as idiosyncratic. Sangharakshita's argument in his many books and taped lectures is that Buddhism has to be interpreted if it is to gain a foothold in the West.

As well as lectures on Buddhist topics, the Centre also offers classes in yoga (Iyengar method), Alexander technique, and, no less attractive to its young clientele, sessions on massage and dance. These take place at 'Bodywise', 119 Roman Road. The FWBO lifestyle is further manifested in their 'Right Livelihood' co-operative businesses, which include a building co-op, a gift shop, a wholefood shop and a cafe.

Sessions: Monday–Friday 1pm Friends' meditation; Monday 7pm Dhamma study (by invitation); Tuesday & Friday 7pm Friends' night; Wednesday & Thursday 1pm Introductory meditation class; Wednesday 7pm Introductory meditation class; Friday 7pm Meditation course; Weekend meditation days, retreats and events—ring for details. Yoga, massage and dance classes—ring for details □ Children: creche by arrangement □ Wheelchair: easy access □ Other details: reading space, study rooms, etc □ Visiting: open 10am–5pm Monday–Friday.

London Peace Pagoda

Battersea Park, SW11 (Chelsea Bridge entrance) □ Bus: 137 □ BR: Battersea Park □ Parking: carpark in park □ Contact: monks & nuns via Caretaker's Lodge, Battersea Park, SW11

Until 1985 the only Pagoda in London was the 18th century whimsy ornamenting Kew Gardens, and it was an unsafe structure at that. For the Peace Pagoda in Battersea Park we have a real Japanese monastic order to thank, Nipponzam Myhoho by name. This is a Buddhist sect of recent origin which, under its founder Nichidatsu Fujii, has constructed seventy similar shrines for peace around the world.

The decision of the GLC to approve plans and offer the riverside site has been acclaimed as an adventurous and happy one. The Pagoda is a cheerful building and is visible for some distance along the river, against a backdrop of trees in the park. It was inaugurated following a walk from Canterbury to Westminster Abbey along the old Pilgrims Way on Hiroshima Day, 1985.

Inevitably, the Pagoda has been assimilated by the Peace Movement which has its own strong tradition of marches, while the monks themselves are content to walk in procession on the first Friday of every month to St James, Piccadilly. They maintain the hope that Buddhism will once again grow to be a force in its native India, for only then, they believe, will true peace come to the world. The monks evidently seek to live harmoniously amidst London's multi-faith community. They follow a daily round of chanting and collecting alms, they fast regularly, and take care of the Pagoda.

Their building combines traditional design with modern construction methods, being an octangonal structure in reinforced concrete. Its two cantilevered roofs are covered with traditionally Japanese dark silver-grey tiles. These are supported by timber columns, made from the trunks of 500-year-old Douglas Firs, and the whole is decorated lavishly with stucco and gold leaf. Even the wind-bells surmounting the roof are gilded, and they make a most tranquil sound. The sacred geometry of pagodas is not something we are equipped to explain, but one thing at least is for sure: that this is an utterly clam building, fully in keeping with Buddhist traditions.

Sessions: Daily 5am–7am Chanting, Daily 5pm–7pm Nam Myhoho Renge Kyo *and Lotus Sutra, drums* □ *Special celebrations: Hiroshima and Nagasaki Day (July)* □ *Wheelchair: steps up to Pagoda; easy access to Shrine Room* □ *Other details: books available* □ *Visiting: all times*

London Zen Society

10 Belmont Street, NW1 □ *Telephone: 485 9576* □ *Bus: 24, 31, 68* □ *Tube: Chalk Farm* □ *Parking: on street* □ *Resident Monk: Mr Jojun* □ *Address: at centre* □ *Available: ring for appointment*

Writing about Zen is perhaps a paradox, given the Zen teaching that words are futile. All things partake of the nature of emptiness to such an extent that they are inexpressible and can only be pointed at. This is illustrated in the tale of the sermon without words, in which Buddha merely plucked a flower and one of his disciples 'saw'. All this underlies two features of Zen: its simplicity and its emphasis on a special discipline beyond the sphere of the written Dhamma.

These Zen characteristics are practised by the London Zen Society, founded in 1969 by the Zen Master Sochu Suzuki Roshi, the Abbot of Ryutaku-ji in Mishima, Japan. He still visits occasionally to supervise a class, as do other Zen Masters, though normally classes are taken by the resident monk Jojun.

The simplicity of Zen appeals to people from all walks of life. Musicians, actors, office-workers come here; even a Catholic deacon attends. The house is neat, and natural colours and materials predominate. Its lounge is the shrine room with a well-polished floor, hangings on the wall, and a small Buddha figure backed by a screen. The regular two-hour sittings are divided into three periods of sitting quietly, or *zazen;* during the intervals Zen walking is practised. After the final sitting, Mr Jojun supervises a period of chanting. He then personally serves tea, and answers questions as necessary from the participants. When a Zen master visits, sittings lasting up to seven days are held and can include a formal interview or *san-zen* with the individual aspirant. Sitting continues all day, with breaks for meals and work.

The Society also offers weekend sessions, usually held on the second week of each month. Vegetarian food is provided and there is a fee for accommodation at the centre. Membership is £6 per month; however, non-members are permitted to attend visiting teachers' sessions at a fee of £7 per day. The Society welcomes newcomers and people of all religions and age groups.

Sessions: Monday–Friday 6–8am Zazen, 6–8am Zazen (Wednesday is beginners' night) □ *Facilities: mats and cushions provided* □ *Wheelchair: no access* □ *Other details: sleeping quarters* □ *Visiting: ring to enquire*

Manjushri London Centre

10 Finsbury Park Road, N4 □ *Telephone: 359 1394* □ *Tube: Finsbury Park* □ *Buses: 19, 106, 236* □ *Contact: Geshe Namgyal Wangchen* □ *Address: 10 Finsbury Park Road, N4* □ *Telephone: 359 1394* □ *Available: afternoons, evenings* □ *Other staff: two resident staff members*

Manjushri London Centre was started by Lama Thubten Yeshe in 1978 who, until his death in 1984, was the 'spiritual guide of the Foundation for the Preservation of the Mahayana Tradition'. The Centre is now estabished in a terraced house in Finsbury Park and has a new resident teacher Geshe Wangchen (Geshe-la). Geshe Wangchen is a Tibetan Buddhist monk who studied for about eight years in Drepung Monastery near Lhasa, leaving when Tibet was taken over by the Chinese. He continued his studies in the re-established Drepung Monastery in south India for twelve years. Among Tibetan Buddhism there are four traditional sects; Geshe Wangchen belongs to the Yellow Hat Sect founded by Lama Tsong Khapa. This tradition places emphasis on maintaining personal morality, inner awareness, tranquility and compassion and love toward all fellow beings.

The programme is based on a one year course, and each year a new programme is produced. However, in every programme the essential topic is meditation on calming and stabilising one's mind, so one is encouraged to attend basic meditation classes before one becomes involved in courses which deal specifically with Buddhist ideas and philosophy. Once comfortable in the basics of meditation, one can attend more detailed sessions which discuss and evaluate Buddhist texts. Those who have received the appropriate initiations are invited on retreats to study and practise together, including sessions on prostrations and mandala offerings, etc., but should contact the Centre about arranging this before turning up. People are requested to give donations toward the running costs of the Centre. If people cannot afford to give donations they are still welcome, but all classes have a fee which is payable at the event.

Sessions: Monday 7.30pm Basic meditation; Thursday 2.30pm Basic meditation; Sunday 6.30pm Buddhist meditation; Tuesday 7.30pm Discussion; plus other courses on specific texts, weekend retreats, etc □ *Children: creche available at Thursday class* □ *Weelchair: very difficult, winding stairs* □ *Other facilities: small collection of books* □ *Visiting: usually open during day; leaflets available*

Rigpa Meditation Centre

44 St Pauls Crescent, Camden, NW1 □ *Telephone: 485 4342* □ *Bus: 29, 239, 253* □ *Tube: Camden Town* □ *Parking: on Agar Grove* □ *Contact: anyone at centre*

There are four principal schools in Tibetan Buddhism, representing four separate lines of spiritual transmission. They all, however, represent a fusion of 'classical' Buddhism with indigenous Tibetan elements; the result is termed *Vajrayana* Buddhism. Of these sects, perhaps the best known is the most recent, the Gelugpa school headed by the Dalai Lama. Rigpa (meaning 'awakening wisdom') belongs to the oldest of these sects, the *Nyingma*.

This London centre is part of an international association of Buddhist meditation centres throughout Europe and the USA which was set up by the Venerable Sogyal Rinpoche. All the teaching here is under his direction. Sogyal Rinpoche is an open and energetic Tibetan Lama with a keen understanding of the Western mind. The emphasis is on meditation and study.

Sogyal Rinpoche also gives seminars on death and dying, and healing through meditation. These seminars attract a wide audience covering care-givers, therapists and professionals—not necessarily Buddhist—as well as the general public. Teachers from other Tibetan traditions, Zen and other Buddhists are also invited to lecture at Rigpa.

Meditation sessions take place upstairs at the centre, and classes, focusing on *shamatha* ('peacefully remaining') meditation—including breath awareness—are held on Thursday evenings. However, Rigpa also runs a number of special programmes, weekend courses and workshops, which teach more advanced practices.

The upstairs shrine room is colourfully and richly decorated in Tibetan style. There are original Tibetan *thankas* (wall hangings) depicting Buddhas, Bodhisattvas, protectors and tantric symbols; and two shrines. The Rigpa centre has somehow contrived to find itself situated next door to rehearsal studios, in such a way that meditation sessions occasionally coincide with those of musical hopefuls tuning up. This offers a truly tantric challenge to the concentration. For those of a more peaceful disposition, there are Easter retreats in Britain and summer retreats in France.

Sessions: Thursday 7.30pm Meditation classes; Weekend courses and workshops; Festivals according to Tibetan calendar □ *Facilities: amplification, mats* □ *Wheelchair: no access* □ *Visiting: by arrangement with secretary*

3 CHRISTIANITY AND RELATED GROUPS

In this section are included all the recognised Trinitarian Christian Churches and denominations found in central London, as well as other groups who adhere to most tenets of orthodox Christianity or who recognise Christ to be of central importance to their faith.

Baptist Churches

The modern Baptist movement has two distinct origins. In 1609 John Smythe introduced the baptism of mature believers as a sign of membership to his church in Amsterdam; three years later some of his followers, led by Thomas Helwys, came to England to form the first of the churches that became known as the General Baptists. The other branch was formed by a breakaway group of the Calvinist Separatist church in London, led by Henry Jacob, in 1635. Retaining their Calvinist theology, they became known as Particular Baptists. By the 1800s sections of the General Baptists had drawn close to the Particular Baptists who had softened their Calvinistic attitude; in 1812 they united as the Baptist Union of Great Britain. Today the Baptists form one of the largest Protestant communions and can claim well over 15 million members worldwide.

Despite many associations, both formal and informal, each local church is autonomous, and it is difficult to generalise about Baptist beliefs and practices; each local group has a distinct character. Services, though generally simple and evangelical in style with the congregation taking an active role, are often open to experiment.

Obviously, as the name states, it is baptismal theory that characterises the denomination. The most important feature is that there is no baptism of infants for it is argued that it is only as an adult that one can make the decision to be faithful to the teachings of a church. Baptism is by total immersion.

Further information is available from Baptist Church House, 4 Southampton Row, WC1 Telephone: 242 7815.

Abbey Road Baptist Church

16a Abbey Road, NW8 □ Telephone: 289 0706 □ Bus: 159 □ Tube: St Johns Wood □ Parking: small forecourt and street □ Minister: Rev G Marshall □ Address: 7 Mays Court, Grooms Hill, SE10 □ Telephone: 853 3063 □ Available: at church office most days □ Other staff: school principal, Val Lawrence

Abbey Road Baptist Church lies opposite the EMI Studios made famous by the Beatles in the 1960s. It has a listed, red-brick, Byzantine facade and originally had two towers. The church dates back to 1883 when Rev William Stott, encouraged by a group of believers, decided to build a chapel. Stott became well known when he began preaching in Hyde Park, and he was invited to speak at the Eyre Arms Assembly Rooms. Soon after this the Abbey Road site was purchased from the

Eyre Estate by an agent, who was told it was 'not a yard for dissenters at any price'.

The congregation grew rapidly, and amongst the members were some who initiated a savings scheme to enable people to buy their own homes. Together they formed the Abbey Road Building Society. By 1925 the building society was the largest in London, and it later amalgamated with another society, the National. Now, as the Abbey National, it is one of the largest building societies in the UK.

The Abbey Road Missionary School for the English Language began in 1962 after Rev Barnard, the pastor at the time, invited foreign students around to his home to practise English. Although the school leases a large part of the church buildings the school is undenominational. Students are made welcome from all churches and missionary societies. The school is residential, providing full board for 60 or 70 students.

At the Sunday service the atmosphere is lively and spontaneous, with 60–70 people present. When not attending their own churches, language school students often worship here, creating a truly international congregation. The music is a mixture of favourite hymns and modern songs while the accompaniment ranges from an organ to a small ensemble of harp, cello, drums and other percussion instruments. Tea and coffee are served in the foyer afterwards.

Services: Sunday 10.30am □ Facilities: amplification □ Children: creche □ Wheelchair: flight of steps; help available □ Visiting: open 9am–5pm

Bloomsbury Central Baptist Church

235 Shaftesbury Avenue, WC2 □ Telephone: 836 6843 & 240 0544 □ Bus: 1, 7, 8, 14, 19, 22, 24, 25, 29, 38, 55, 73, 134, 153, 176 □ Tube: Tottenham Court Road □ Parking: difficult, except Sunday □ Minister: Rev Barrie Hibbert □ Address: at chapel □ Available: phone for appointment □ Assistant Minister: Rev Barbara Stanford

Before 1844 and the Nonconformist Chapels Act, Baptists and other Dissenters were obliged to worship, if not secretly, then at least inconspicuously. Chapels were small and tucked away out of sight. Bloomsbury Chapel, built in 1848, was the first Baptist place of worship that looked like a church; its size and grandeur affirmed the newly secured status of its worshippers. Located on Shaftesbury Avenue near New Oxford Street, it is the most central Baptist church in London.

Overlooking a busy street, the facade is uncluttered, and dominated by a large rose window flanked by two tall towers. The interior, once rather dark and dreary, was re-arranged and brightened up in 1962. The small rear gallery, originally used by children of the Shaftesbury Society, was removed, allowing in light from the rose window for the first time. Also, a bright modern sanctuary was created within the old shell, and the pews arranged radially around a raised pulpit area. A wide gallery with seating for 400 was left in place, but it is seldom used nowadays.

At the time it was built, the church lay between two totally opposing areas: Bloomsbury with its elegant houses, and the terrible slums of St Giles. Today, the church still has an awareness of the whole spectrum of society and the congregation may include homeless people, sleeping rough in the area, as well as worshippers from the wealthier suburbs—some even travelling from as far afield as Leatherhead and St Albans. On average 150 to 200 attend the main Sunday service. The church's attractions are various: its central position both in London and in Baptist history, the standard of preaching to be heard here, the emphasis on family worship, and indeed, on the level of practical assistance, the provision of cheap—and some free—meals in the Friendship Centre beneath the chapel. A major part of the church's time is spent running these community rooms with the catering facilities staffed by voluntary helpers under the guidance of Assistant Minister Barbara Stanford. Above the chapel is another set of rooms, known as the Institute, which provides venues for study groups and lectures. The Japanese Christians worship at this church.

Services: Sunday 11am & 6.30pm □ Facilities: amplification, deaf loop, large print & braille texts □ Children: creche for Sunday services □ Wheelchair: ramps available □ Other details: large & small meeting rooms at variable rates; Friendship rooms □ Visiting: open all day Sunday; Friendship rooms open Tues & Wed

Brandon Baptist Centre

Redcar Street, SE5 □ Bus: 36, 36A, 36B, 185 □ Tube: Oval □ Parking: car park □ Contact: Mrs Ruth Dowley, 115 John Ruskin Street, SE5 or Mr & Mrs D Watkins, 4 Bonser Street, SE5

Built in 1975, in response to the many needs of an inner city area dominated by housing estates, this multi-purpose building is both a community centre and a place of worship. The Baptist congregation here originally worshipped in the Calvary Chapel, established in 1890.

Three services are held on Sundays in the spacious main hall. Informality, openess and friendliness are the feature of worship, and this approach has proved most attractive to this community. The main service of the day is split in half; in the first half the congregation worship together, and in the second half they are split into smaller groups, one for the adults and the others for children according to age. The evening service, slightly more traditional, is shared with invited groups from other chapels on the last Sunday of each month. Lay participation is fundamental to the services; anyone is invited to take part or discuss issues raised. Prayer and Bible Study groups meet at private homes.

Weekday community activities are many and varied, and provide a very necessary opportunity for young and old alike to share their talents, thoughts and problems. The building's facilities, beside the main hall, include a kitchen, a large entrance hall with video and table games, a snooker room, and three small rooms used mainly for after-church meetings (one of which has video facilities). An old people's day centre operates four days a week; a youth club and women's group also use the centre regularly and there are a host of other meetings and events.

Services: Sunday 10.15am (Communion 2nd and 4th Sundays.), 11am Family Service (Communion 3rd Sunday every 2nd month), 6.30 pm; Alternate Tuesdays 7.30pm □ Facilities: amplification □ Children: groups during Family Service □ Wheelchair: designed for wheelchair access; toilets for disabled □ Other details: hall and extensive facilities □ Visiting: open for services and various activities only

Christ Church and Upton Chapel, SE1

Christ Church and Upton Chapel

Kennington Road, SE1 □ Telephone: 633 0617 □ Bus: 3, 12, 53, 59 □ Tube: Lambeth North □ Parking: street □ Minister: Rev Graham Powell □ Address: at church □ When available: ring for appointment

Appropriately enough, two distinct architectural elements make up this interesting church which has a joint congregation of both Baptists and URC members. The Victorian Gothic Christ Church was damaged in 1940 but the Lincoln Tower (so named after the American President) survived and was declared a protected building. Eventually a multi-purpose new church building designed by Mr P J Darvall was attached to the tower, and opened in 1960. The chapel itself, with the pews arranged around the pulpit and communion table, recalls the design of the first building (c. 1780) in the congregation's history, which had sixteen sides 'so that the Devil should not get in at the corners'.

The Christ Church congregation has always been nonconformist but there have never been any formal ties with a recognised denomination. There have been ministers appointed here who were Baptist or Congregationalist. Since 1972 the church has been affiliated to the Baptist Union and in membership with the United Reformed Church.

Upton Chapel refers to the other half of this ecumenical union. In 1785, a group of 12 Baptists split with their minister and formed their own congregation under a Rev James Upton. In 48 years of his ministry their numbers had increased to around 400. They acquired their own chapel, and prospered until the second World War, when the building was destroyed. So, in 1941 the Baptists had a minister but no chapel, while at Christ Church there was a building but no minister, and amalgamation was the obvious answer. Initially the congregations worshipped separately but they soon merged under one minister.

Today, as with many nonconformists, the church is keen to experiment. The evening service in particular is kept informal, and may include film shows, dialogue between minister and worshippers, or lay testimonies. At the end of the more formal morning service, the children from the Junior Church join in to share what they have learnt.

The remainder of Darvall's building is given over to a wide range of activities. The large basement is used for a youth club, for example, and other rooms and a hall can be hired for various community purposes. A lunch-and-discussion group, comprising mainly young office workers, meets here every Thursday. True to its ecumenical traditions, the church works closely with other Lambeth churches and contributes to the monthly Review, along with the local Anglicans, Catholics, Methodists and Salvation Army. The church, together with other churches in the North Lambeth District Council of Churches, has become part of a Local Ecumenical Project through the signing and outworking of a Covenant in February, 1986.

Services: Sunday 11am & 6.30pm □ Facilities: amplification, deaf loop □ Children: Junior Church, Sunday 11am; also Youth Club □ Wheelchair: level access to lower hall from carpark, toilets for disabled □ Other details: hall, gymnasium, committee rooms, etc. □ Visiting: open service times or by arrangement with the resident warden

Shoreditch Tabernacle

Hackney Road, E2 □ Telephone: 739 8120 □ Bus: 5, 6, 8, 22, 35, 47, 48, 55, 67, 78 □ Tube: Old Street □ Parking: Church car park □ Joint Pastors: Rev Paul and Lyn Henstock □ Address: at church □ Available: any time

In 1986 this church celebrated its 150th anniversary; the Providence Chapel, their first church, was opened in 1836. A succession of very hard-working pastors since then have faced the dual problem of the continual poverty of Shoreditch's population, resulting in restricted financial support from the congregation, and the tendency of people to move out of the area once they could afford to do so, resulting in a fluctuating congregation.

The emphasis of the church's work naturally lay on the spiritual and practical means to alleviate poverty in Shoreditch; the hugeness of the task put incredible strains on the clergy, both mentally and physically. The church was for many years in debt, finding that the grandness of design of the buildings constructed was not matched by the hoped-for future growth in the size of the congregation. Being in the 'front line' of the Blitz during the Second World War did not help either—the second building on the site, the Tabernacle opened in 1879, was damaged by a flying bomb and was eventually torn down in 1960. The more practically built replacement, smaller and of simple design, is well suited to the needs of the present congregation. There is a large hall and a smaller hall to cater for the various church and outside activities.

After the war, the trend of people moving to other areas continued; evacuees whose houses were destroyed did not return; the permissiveness and relative prosperity of post-war life led to new pursuits other than church-going—all these were factors in the decline of the Tabernacle's influence. More recently, however, the influx of newcomers to the area has maintained the church's existence. The congregation, from a very low point in the mid-1970s, has increased tenfold in the last ten years and now numbers around 75 each Sunday.

There is a 50-strong Bengali school that uses the church's classrooms four afternoons a week. Nigerian and West Indian Christians now make up the bulk of the congregation.

Services are informal, especially the evening service, with much lay participation, through testimonies and open prayer. The church runs a women's group, a youth group, a mother and toddlers group, and Boys and Girls Brigades. Next door to the church is the Mildmay Mission Hospital, which provides medical care under Christian auspices for about a dozen patients. The combination of medical and spiritual havens working so closely together epitomises what is a very valuable asset for Shoreditch.

Services: Sunday 11am (3rd Sunday, 10.30am, Holy Communion), 6pm (1st Sunday, Holy Communion) □ Facilities: amplification, deaf loop, large-print hymnbooks □ Children: Sunday School and creche 11am □ Wheelchair: 2 shallow steps □ Other details: two halls, classrooms, etc. □ Visiting: open for services only

Vernon Baptist Chapel

Vernon Square, Kings Cross, WC1 □ Telephone: 837 3976 □ Bus: 17, 18, 45, 46, 63, 221, 259 □ Tube: Kings Cross □ BR: Kings Cross Midland □ Parking: difficult □ Ministers: Revv Humphrey Vellacott & Bob Stephen □ Address: at church □ Available: at church most days

The Vernon Chapel is set back away from a busy, congested street and dominates a small pleasant square, almost hidden behind what must be the only trees in this heavily built-up area.

Up until the early 1980s the congregation had been steadily decreasing. The energies of the two incumbents have therefore centred on bringing worshippers back to the chapel. Part of this was the transformation of the interior from its traditional Baptist layout to a brighter, more congenial place of worship that would be more inviting especially to young families.

Photographs of the original interior of the 1850s show a dark chapel with a large pulpit and broad gallery. The gallery and pews have gone, the roof has been lowered and thick carpeting laid throughout. The imposing pulpit is no longer used except to house a screen and overhead projector used during sermons. A glass screen divides off the back of the chapel to form a comfortable area for a creche. The amplification is extended into this area so families can stay together during a service without the children disturbing the rest of the congregation.

The Sunday morning service is thus termed 'All Age Worship—from tiny tots to senior citizens'. Evening services are more informal, with refreshments following. One of the Ministers holds a consulting session on Monday nights. There is also a Women's Meeting on Mondays, and Prayer and Bible Study on Wednesday evenings.

Underneath the chapel is a large hall which is slowly being renovated, and with the large kitchens will make ideal community rooms. The development of community activities in such a needy area can proceed in the near future, now that the congregation has been revived.

Services: Sunday 11am and 6.30pm; Monday 2.30pm Meeting for Women, 7pm Minister's consulting session; Wednesday 8pm Prayer—Bible Study—Discussion □ Facilities: amplification, Braille books □ Children: creche, Sunday school □ Wheelchair: good access □ Other details: study, hall, kitchens □ Visiting: service times only

Westbourne Park Baptist Church

Porchester Road, W2 □ Telephone: 727 6019 □ Bus: 7, 15, 27, 28, 31 □ Tube/BR: Royal Oak; Paddington □ Parking: on street, meters □ Minister: Rev Paul S Jackson □ Address: as church □ When available: any time by appointment □ Other Staff: K. Biggs, Church Secretary

The church was built in 1877 but reconstructed in a bold, modern style in 1962 after severe wartime damage. Above the baptistry hangs a 'flowing water' motif, and there is some fine coloured glass in the east front, which is by Margaret Traherne (who worked on Coventry Cathedral). The area is very mixed: well-maintained Bayswater housing stops abruptly at the Great Western Railway and

Westbourne Park Baptist Church, W2

the M40 flyover. At the other side is Harrow Road with tower blocks, a council estate, and Victorian streets which show their age rather less gracefully than those of Porchester Road.

Most young singles and some elderly people come to Sunday services. There has been a steady decline in numbers since the turn of the century, but this is thought to have been halted with the arrival of Rev Paul Jackson in 1986. He has made outreach a priority, and aims to counter the loneliness and social problems endemic on the Warwick Estate. In his combination of preaching of the Gospel and practical care he is following in a great tradition at Westbourne Park, whose first minister, Dr John Clifford, was a national figure. Dr Clifford was even asked to stand for Parliament for Paddington North but declined, asserting that a strong pulpit would 'render the best national service'.

These days a midweek meeting, a 'mums 'n' tots' group, and some house groups are just some of the ways in which the church serves the community. There may be no more great campaigns about national education as in Dr Clifford's day, but this remains a concerned group of Christians. Services are a mix of traditional and formal (Sunday morning) and more informal (Sunday evening). On the third Sunday morning in the month Communion is celebrated. Prayers for the bread and wine are offered by the serving Deacons, who join the minister when requested. The bread is eaten when received, but the wine is retained and drunk together, as is the custom of the Baptist Church. Open prayer, testimony, meditative readings, responsive readings, solos and duets are sometimes included in the Evening Service.

Services: Sunday 11am, 6.30pm □ *Facilities: amplification, deaf loop, Braille bibles* □ *Children: creche, Sunday 11–12 noon* □ *Wheelchair: easy access* □ *Other details: recreation hall, coffee-room, etc* □ *Visiting: open 7am–5pm*

The Christian Community

The Christian Community was founded in Dornach, Switzerland in 1922 and is based on the teachings of the Austrian-born Rudolf Steiner (1861–1925). His system of religious beliefs is called Anthroposophy and has features from theosophy and Indian religions; a central aim is to develop cognition of the spirit world. Dr Steiner lectured extensively and attracted many supporters, amongst whom was a group of theological students who saw in the Anthroposophical Society the genesis of a movement for religious renewal within Christianity.

A former Lutheran priest was installed by Steiner as the head of the Christian Community and the first 'Act of Consecration of Man', as Steiner termed the Communion service, took place on September 16th 1922. It was not until 1929 that a service was held in Britain, and the first British priests were ordained in 1931. Since then the movement has grown steadily, chiefly among the white middle-class, and there are now 14 churches here.

All services include Communion and are led by a priest; no prayer books are used and hymns are not always sung but there is always music—on the piano and perhaps flute. Children are not admitted to services but most churches hold special children's services, usually twice a month. Counselling is an important part of the Community's work. Further information is available from either of the churches included here.

The Christian Community, Belsize Park

34 Glenilla Road, NW3 □ Telephone: 722 3587 □ Bus: C11, 268 □ Tube: Belsize Park □ Parking: on street □ Priest: Pearl Goodwin □ Address: as church □ Telephone: as church □ Available most days

The first centre for the Christian Community in England, founded in 1931, has been based in Glenilla Road since 1944. In the late 1940s the present church, designed by Kenneth Bayes, was built. The church is in a similar style to the 2nd Goetheanum in Dornach, Switzerland—the Anthroposophical Centre designed by Rudolf Steiner. The idea behind the building is that by having no straight lines, the building will be more in harmony with nature, thereby facilitating worship and helping to encourage the more harmonious aspects of man's nature to develop. The whole exterior is painted salmon pink, and although the building's design is less flamboyant than the prototype, its attractive oddness is emphasised by the juxtaposition with the many ordinary houses in this residential road.

Inside, the lilac walls, curved ceiling and lingering fragnance of incense help to create a calm atmosphere. The altar painting (in the style advocated by Steiner) of the Crucifixion and Resurrection, is by the Swedish artist Arne Klingborg.

The adults' service, The Act of Consecration of Man, on Wednesdays and Sundays is attended by 30 to 40 people and there is also a children's service every other Sunday. After each Sunday morning service, the congregation move to the main meeting room in the house next door. After a short break when tea is served, either the resident or a visiting priest gives a talk on a subject ranging from 'Christ in the 20th century' to 'health and creativity'. A number of books and leaflets on the Christian Community are available from a small bookshop in the meeting room, and a library stocks a selection of books ranging from the Anthroposophical Society to recent publications on the Christian Community.

During the week the centre is busy with craft and study groups and individual counselling sessions, given by the resident priest. There are also a number of conferences throughout the year. In addition, the Glenilla Arts Foundation organises an annual programme of concerts by young professional musicians, open to the public as well as members. This initiative springs from the Community's conviction that 'music especially can instil a healing element in our lives.'

A small garden at the back of the house is often used in summer for garden parties, picnic lunches and for just sitting quietly enjoying nature.

Services: Sunday 10.30am Act of Consecration of Man, 11.35am Children's service every second week; Wednesday 11am □ Wheelchair: not difficult (no steps to church) □ Children: children's service as above; creche can be arranged when necessary □ Other details: small bookstall □ Visiting: open for services or visit by appointment

Temple Lodge

51 Queen Caroline Street, W6 □ Bus: 9, 11, 27, 33, 72, 73, 91, 220, 283, 295 □ Tube: Hammersmith □ Parking: on street □ Priest: Mrs Evelyn Capel □ Address: at Lodge □ Available: from 9am to 9pm □ Other Staff: Mr Capel

Temple Lodge, just a few minutes walk from Hammersmith tube, is in Queen Caroline Street on the other side of the Hammersmith flyover. To find it, look out for the Christian Community bookshop at the front of the house, which has a bold sign giving directions to the Angel Gate Vegetarian Restaurant inside.

A house dating back to the 18th century, Temple Lodge has gone through several changes with walls being knocked down and rebuilt and rooms added. The main extension was originally built as an artist's studio for Frank Brangwyn in 1907 and was used as a builder's yard by a subsequent owner. When the Christian Community moved into the Lodge in 1969, they restored the studio and hired it out for a while before redecorating it for use as their chapel. The altar painting of the Holy Trinity is by Dutch painter Collot d'Herbois and is in the style advocated by Steiner. Services held twice weekly attract a dedicated congregation of around 50, many of whom previously belonged to mainstream Christian denominations, but were dissatisfied with them. To get to the chapel, ask at the bookshop or, if closed, go through the small courtyard to the side entrance. There are plans to build a new chapel in the rear garden when the funds are raised.

As well as chapel, restaurant and bookshop, the building also houses a library, meeting room and Bed and Breakfast accommodation for 14 guests. The Lodge is busy 7 days a week; study groups, art and craft workshops and private consultations are an important part of the activities. There are also occasional recitals and exhibitions of work by artists concentrating on spiritual expression.

Services: Sunday 10.45; Thursday 10.45 Act of Consecration of Man □ *Children: own services* □ *Wheelchair: level access* □ *Other details: small library; vegetarian restaurant; bookshop (no set hours—will open on request, including Sunday)* □ *Visiting: most days*

Christian Science

Christian Science was founded by Mary Baker Eddy (1820–1910), and the first church, now known as the Mother Church, was formed in Boston, USA, in 1879 by Mrs Eddy and 15 students. Their aim was to 'organise a church designed to commemorate the word and works of our Master, which should reinstate primitive Christianity and its lost element of healing'.

Mrs Eddy's own search for healing had been long. She had tried various methods, but none had provided a complete and lasting cure. Being a deeply religious woman however, she found comfort in reading the Bible, especially the New Testament, and it was on one such occasion that she experienced a complete cure. This led to her forming the Christian Science movement with its method of healing through prayer alone.

Christian Science maintains that the mental and spiritual life comprises reality while matter is illusion. God did not invent matter, nor all the ills that flesh is heir to, and thus redemption from sin involves freedom from the material and mortal state. This process is described as gaining 'the mind of Christ', and the cure of disease purely through prayer is a necessary element. Many converts to the Church first come seeking physical healing.

Each Christian Science church is democratically run with members being elected every three years to positions including president, clerk, reader, librarian and usher. The church auditoriums are free of normal Christian symbolism and are used for free lectures. Also on the premises will be a Sunday school and nursery, various committee rooms and usually a reading room where the writings of Mrs Eddy, the Christian Science Monitor, and other material may be read, borrowed or bought as appropriate. If not on the premises, the reading room will be located nearby.

Sunday services worldwide are kept to a set pattern, with readings from the Bible and the Christian Science text book, *Science and Health with Key to the Scriptures* by Mrs Eddy, and hymns, one of which will be sung by a soloist. The Wednesday evening service also contains readings and hymns, but the second half is set aside for accounts of healing and gratitude, given spontaneously by members of the congregation, and are generally known as midweek evening testimony meetings.

New churches are formed when congregations become too large at an existing church. This applies to the founding of all the London churches after First Church. Free literature can be found outside any Christian Science church.

First Church of Christ, Scientist, London

Sloane Terrace, SW1 □ Telephone: 730 8584 □ Bus: 11, 19, 22, 137 □ Tube: Sloane Square □ Parking: difficult □ Clerk: Mr Mobsby □ Available: telephone church for appointment

Christian Science was first introduced in London in 1890 by visiting Americans. The first British resident Christian Scientist was Mrs Blanche Ward, who moved from Bedford to London in 1894. At first she held services in her home, then in hired rooms. Soon however, because of growing interest, the Jewish synagogue in Bryanston Street was purchased and, in 1897, it was declared the First Church of Christ, Scientist, London.

Numbers continued to grow, and soon a site to build a much larger church was sought. In 1902, the present site was purchased. An old Wesleyan chapel stood on the grounds at the time and was used for worship until the new church was opened in 1905. Built in white Portland stone to a 20th century Byzantine design, it is easily recognisable by its square clock tower.

The auditorium, which gives one the feeling of having entered an Edwardian theatre, can seat 1,200, including seating in the gallery. The sloping floor, rising 10 feet from the base of the platform to the back of the church, and the cantilever gallery surrounding the auditorium on three sides combine to create this theatrical effect.

A notable event, bringing together Christian Scientists from all parts of the world took place on December 8th 1984. The event was a video conference, transmitted live from Boston via satellite. Christian Scientists from the Home Counties and London gathered at First Church; screens were placed in the auditorium and Sunday school room. The aim of the conference was not only to enable members worldwide to listen to a talk on current issues from the Mother Church, but to bring them all together in prayer.

Services: Sunday 11am; Wednesday 7pm Testimonial meeting □ Facilities: amplification, deaf loop □ Children: Sunday school 11am (up to 20 year olds) □ Wheelchair: lift at Wilbraham Place entrance □ Other details: Reading Room, 156 Fulham Road (open 11am–7pm except Sun 2–6pm and Wed 11am–6pm) □ Visiting: by arrangement

Second Church of Christ, Scientist, London

104/108 Palace Gardens Terrace, W8 □ Telephone: 229 2682 □ Bus: 12, 27, 28, 31, 52, 88 □ Tube: Notting Hill Gate □ Parking: on street □ Clerk: Mr Tony Kennan □ Available: all day Wednesday, Mon & Fri mornings □ Other staff: Librarian (229 2717)

Soon after Christian Science was introduced to London, enthusiasm grew rapidly. First Church found it difficult to cope with the increasing numbers, so members left to form a new congregation. Although Second Church was formed in 1902, rented halls were used until 1911, when the present site in Palace Gardens Terrace was purchased. At first an empty Swedenborgian church on the site was used, until Second Church, designed by Sir John Burnett and Partners, was completed in 1925, delayed because of the First World War.

One of the most pleasing features of Second Church is the garden in front, which allows the red brick Byzantine edifice to be seen in full. The auditorium, with seating for 1,000, has an unusual shape: the front and central block of seats are surrounded by the sides and back rows, which slope to form a kind of gallery. The Sunday school seats 500 and was very popular among the children during the early days.

Through the garden, at No 8 Palace Gardens Terrace, is the Christian Science Committees on Publication for Great Britain and Ireland, and The Christian Science Nursing Activities (UK) office.

Services: Sunday 11am, 7pm; Wednesday 7.30pm Testimonial meeting □ Facilities: amplification, deaf loop (front row) □ Children: Sunday school 11am □ Wheelchair: level access □ Other details: Reading Room, 104 Palace Gardens Terrace (phone for opening times) □ Visiting: by arrangement

Third Church of Christ, Scientist, London

7 Curzon Street, W1 □ Telephone: 449 1271 □ Bus: 9, 14, 19, 22, 25, 38, 55 □ Tube: Green Park □ Parking: on street □ Contact: clerk □ Available: telephone church for appointment □ Other staff: Librarian (449 1275)

Perhaps the best known Christian Science in London, Third Church refuses to be overawed by its exclusive Mayfair location. It has an imposing white facade with Tuscan columns and a giant niche, culminating in a splendid baroque tower.

Third Church was formed as a congregation in 1905 but the building designed by Lanchester & Rickards was not completed until 1910. With seating for 1,500 it was the largest of all the Christian Scientist churches in London and it was often full. At the dedication service in 1914 some 2,000 people are recorded as having attended.

Services continued throughout the war, and the basement hall, complete with canteen, was opened as a shelter during air raids. One night 700 people stayed here. It escaped bomb damage but during 1979 and 1980 the interior of the church was radically altered to designs by Graham Herbert. The original grand auditorium made way for offices and flats, while a new small auditorium was built

Third Church of Christ, Scientist, London, W1

on the first floor. It is a comfortable carpeted hall with seating for 100 to suit present day congregations. The Sunday school was moved to the top floor, though the Reading Room was unchanged.

A Wednesday lunchtime service, first held in 1928 and the only midday service at any London Christian Science Church, remains popular, attracting people who work in the area. Third Church also give lunchtime organ recitals. The recitals are free and are advertised by word of mouth only.

Services: Sunday 7pm; Wednesday 12.15pm, 7pm Testimonial meeting □ Facilities: amplification □ Children: creche; Sunday school (up to 20 years) □ Wheelchair: lift to auditorium □ Other details: Reading Room (open Mon–Fri 11am–3.30pm, Wed until 6.45pm; closed weekends) □ Visiting: open service times only

Seventh Church of Christ, Scientist, London

8 Wright's Lane, W8 □ Telephone: 937 3389 □ Bus: any along Kensington High St □ Tube: Kensington High Street □ Parking: on street □ Clerk: Miss Jones □ Available: telephone church for appointment □ Other staff: Miss Hooper (Librarian)

In December 1914, Seventh Church, consisting of 69 members from First Church, first met in a rented hall in Kensington. In 1919, the Wrights Lane site was purchased, and a temporary building was erected until the proposed permanent church was built. The church, originally with seating for 1,000 in the auditorium, was designed by architect and Christian Scientist Paul Phipps. Building began on the permanent structure in 1924, and was completed and dedicated in 1929.

In 1986 the church underwent a mammoth re-building programme. The new design now uses only 1/3 of the original church building. The remaining 2/3 have been developed into a block of flats. During re-development a primary school in Earl's Court housed the twice weekly services, and the Reading Room, which was originally in a leased shop in Kensington High Street, was moved to College House, opposite the church in Wrights Lane. The Reading Room is presently housed in the church, but it is hoped that by the 1990s, a premises in Kensington High Street will once again be leased.

The re-designed church was opened on 21st December 1986. A flight of steps leads up to the auditorium on the first floor, and a lift is available for those who prefer to use it. The newly designed auditorium has seating for 200.

Services: Sunday 11am; Wednesday 7pm Testimonial meeting □ Facilities: amplification □ Children: Sunday school 11am □ Wheelchair: lift to auditorium; toilet for disabled □ Other details: Reading Room (times to be arranged) □ Visiting: by arrangement

Eighth Church of Christ, Scientist, London

20 Acre Lane, SW2 □ Telephone: 274 3260 □ Bus: 3, 59, 95, 109, 133, 159, 196 □ Tube: Brixton □ Parking: car park (up to 20 cars) □ Clerk: Mrs Simpson □ Available: telephone church for appointment

Eighth Church as a congregation was formed in 1921 and held services in a temporary structure on the site until a large red brick cruciform church, with seating for 500, was completed ten years later. Badly damaged during the war, it was re-designed in 1946/7 by Oswald P Milne. It now seats 250 and no longer has transepts, but it does have an integral Reading Room. The church stands opposite Brixton Town Hall, only a few minutes from the tube station.

Reflecting the make-up of the local population, a good many of the regular congregation are from African or Caribbean backgrounds. Members feel the church has a 'loving and friendly atmosphere' and would like it to be known that 'all are welcome'.

Services: Sunday 11am; Wednesday 7.30pm Testimonial meeting □ Facilities: amplification □ Children: Sunday school 11am □ Wheelchair: level access at side entrance □ Other details: Reading Room (open Tues & Fri 11.30am–2.30pm, Sat 10.30am–12.30pm) □ Visiting: open service times only

Ninth Church of Christ, Scientist, London

Marsham Street, SW1 □ Telephone: 222 3740 □ Bus: 11, 88, 507 □ Tube: St James Park □ Parking: on street □ Contact: clerk □ Available: telephone church for appointment □ Other staff: Librarian (222 6047)

Ninth Church, at the Great Smith Street end of Marsham Street, stands just a few hundred yards away from Dean's Yard and Westminster Abbey. The church, in a modified Byzantine style, is a major work of Sir Herbert Baker. Built in 1928, this red brick edifice has a large circular auditorium 100 feet in diameter with seating for up to 1,000. The modest exterior of the church conceals a surprising interior. From the lobby, steps lead up to the entrance of the auditorium which has a sloping floor and above, a domed ceiling with a circular sky light. Surrounding the dome is an inscription taken from the Book of Revelation (ch 21, v 3–4).

The services are conducted on the basis of the King James Version of The Bible and The Christian Science Textbook by Mary Baker Eddy. At the Wednesday Testimony meetings, experiences of healing are related by members of the congregation.

Services: Sunday 11am; Wednesday 7pm Testimonial meeting □ Facilities: amplification □ Children: creche; Sunday school (up to 20 years) □ Wheelchair: several steps (no ramp) □ Other details: Reading Room (open daily 12noon–2pm, until 6.30pm Wed; closed Saturday) □ Visiting: open service times only

Eleventh Church of Christ, Scientist, London

1 Nutford Place, W1 □ Telephone: 723 4572 □ Bus: 6, 7, 8, 15, 15a, 16, 16a, 36, 36a □ Tube: Marble Arch □ Parking: on street □ Clerk: Margaret Robinson □ Available: telephone church for appointment □ Other staff: Librarian (486 0759)

Eleventh Church was founded in 1922 by a group of 65 members from First Church, London, and 20 or so other Christian Scientists. There followed the familiar story of worshipping in hired premises and temporary buildings until the permanent church was completed in 1927. It was dedicated, free from debt, a year later and now attracts a large and lively congregation, which is mixed both socially and ethnically.

The building stands on the corner of Nutford Place and Seymour Place, just off the Edgware Road. It has a large lobby on the ground floor, where the ushers and members of the congregation have an opportunity to exchange greetings before entering the auditorium. As is common in Christian Science churches, the auditorium, which can seat some 800 people, has a sloping floor. It can be reached by means of a lift, just by the side entrance.

Services: Sunday 11am & 7pm; Wednesday 7pm Testimonial meeting □ *Facilities: amplification, deaf loop* □ *Children: Sunday school 11am* □ *Wheelchair: lift to auditorium* □ *Other details: Reading Room, 80 Baker Street (open Mon–Sat 9.30am–7.30pm, except Wed 9.30–6.30pm, Sundays & holidays 2.30pm–6.30pm)* □ *Visiting: open service times only*

The Church of England

The origins of the Church of England lie with Henry VIII and the English Reformation. By passing the Act of Supremacy in 1534 Henry made himself the Head of the Church in England and Wales although he was by no means a supporter of Luther and other critics of Rome. The Church was shaped by subsequent monarchs and ecclesiastics, its theological position and its character being charted by the Thirty-nine Articles (1563), the King James Authorised Version of the Bible (1611) and, perhaps most significantly, the Book of Common Prayer (1662), the cadences of which are closely associated with Anglican worship. Still the Church defied too strict a definition—it was, and is, a 'broad Church', encompassing a wide range of approaches to worship and shades of theological opinion. As such it has always been open to the influence of forces emanating from within its ranks.

One such force is the Evangelical or 'low' church tradition. Though the great Revival is regarded as a 19th century phenomenon, spurred on by the Islington Conference where Evangelical churchmen have met since 1827, its ideals had been exemplified by Wesley in the century before. Broadly speaking, these 'low' churchmen uphold the sole authority of Scripture and place emphasis on the atoning death of Christ. 'Low' church services would not be out of place in many nonconformist churches; they are characterised by minimal use of trappings, vestments and sacramental formalities, and an emphasis on preaching or, in some churches, various experimental 'worship aids' such as drama and discussion. The other side of the coin is the 'high' or Catholic side of Anglicanism. This was revitalised by the Oxford Movement in 1838–45 which sought to remind the Church that its authority lay in the Apostolic Succession of its priests, and that it should never lose sight of its identity as a divine institution. In the Church's similarities with Rome, rather than its differences, lie its strengths. Thus 'high' worship is carried out with great respect for the liturgy and the sacraments, and it tends to be 'Mass' rather than 'Communion' which is celebrated, complete with servers, incense and priests in vestments. Both traditions are strong in London and indeed the full range of Anglican worship can be found here.

The different styles of worship is reflected to some degree in the liturgical alternatives available to Anglican clergy. As mentioned, the 1662 Book of Common Prayer was the unrivalled text until this century, but between 1965 and 1980 there appeared three alternative procedures—Series 1, Series 2 and Series 3—which were intended as evolutionary stages in the production of the definitive Alternative Service Book (ASB) of 1980. This contains both Rite B which retains much of the flavour of the old liturgy, and Rite A which is a modern language alternative. Many churches find that the use of different texts for different occasions and specific services is the ideal arrangement, and there are no hard and fast rules about aligning texts with churchmanship.

The architectural variety found amongst the churches also warrants some explanation. Few of the old churches in the City survived the Great Fire of 1666, and on to the stage stepped Sir Christopher Wren leaving us a splendid legacy of neo-Baroque, neo-Renaissance churches, culminating in St Paul's Cathedral, that are ultimately in a style all his own. In his wake came Hawksmoor and Gibbs adding their own innovations and touches. Elsewhere, the churches give an indication of when the area was developed. Thus we have the Georgian edifices of Paddington and St John's Wood, and in Kensington and Chelsea the Gothic Revival structures of the Victorian church-building boom, when Pugin, Butterfield and Comper rose to fame. There are sufficient exceptions to these general principles to avoid the risk of monotony.

The London Anglican churches have been learning to come to terms with their changing environment for many years. In the City, what were once parish churches to a sizeable local population have become Guild churches and they hold services to suit workers rather than residents—many are closed on Sunday. Other inner-city churches have reacted to the circumstances outlined in the 'Faith in the City' report and other publications, in a variety of ways. While there are many family-based parish churches, others cater more for an eclectic, transitory congregation. Many run active welfare programmes directly addressing such problems as homelessness and unemployment, and have utilised their space and facilities to great effect.

In the following chapter we have divided the Anglican entries into more manageable geographical chunks, based upon the Church's own system of Deaneries. Well-known churches not included, as they are either no longer used for regular public worship or are not expected to be so used in the near future, are All Hallows London Wall, and St Stephen Wallbrook.

Church of England: City

All-Hallows-by-the-Tower

Byward Street, EC3 □ Bus: 15, 42 □ Tube: Tower Hill □ Parking: only after 6pm □ Vicar: Rev Peter Delaney □ Address: as church □ Telephone: 481 2928 □ Available: at church most days □ Other staff: Kate Ricketts, Deaconess

All Hallows is amongst the oldest of all the city churches and, all around, glimpses of its long history can be seen, from Roman and Saxon relics to medieval walls and a 17th century crypt. One should not feel, however, that this is simply an interesting museum piece: through the energy of the present staff and willing volunteers, the ethos and atmosphere of the church is thoroughly modern. The diversity of activities, from home study groups to receptions in the aisles, is aimed at putting the church at the centre of a modern community.

The original All Hallows was built in 675 AD, 400 years before the Tower of London, and the present church has remnants and fragments from all the major periods of its history—there are Roman tiles and pipes, a Saxon arch in fine condition and remnants of two Saxon crosses found embedded in a Norman column after the bomb damage of 1940. The church escaped damage in the Great Fire but had to be rebuilt, a happy blend of the ancient and the neo-Perpendicular, after the Second World War. A guide for all this and more can usually be found if one visits the church. The parish records are among the most complete sets in existence and as such are important and fascinating historical documents. They are available for research by prior arrangement.

All Hallows refuses to rest on its history however and strives to be an accessible and contemporary place of worship. Services, following the ASB, attract a congregation of all ages and denominations—even family pets are welcome. As most worshippers travel some distance, tea and biscuits are provided afterwards in a friendly atmosphere.

On weekdays the church focuses on establishing links with the business community. The Eucharist is celebrated at various times to fit in with as many busy work schedules as possible. The Tuesday morning service is followed by breakfast.

The church runs an extensive range of other activities including discussion suppers, afternoon drama workshops, and a cultural exchange programme with the USA for young people. Art exhibitions, music recitals and an annual full scale dramatic production are also held at the church, which is always willing to experiment with new ideas.

In the midst of all this, the small 17th century chapel is always kept as a quiet place for private prayer.

Services: Sunday 11am Sung Eucharist; 1st Sunday 4pm Evensong; Weekday HC, Mon 12.15, Tue 8.30am, Wed 12.35pm, Thu 6.15pm, Fri 1.10pm □ Facilities: amplification □ Wheelchair: ramp available, toilets for disabled □ Visiting: open weekdays 9am–6pm, weekends 10am–4pm

St Andrew, Holborn

Holborn Circus, EC4 □ Bus: 8, 17, 18, 22, 25, 45, 46, 171, 243, 259 □ Tube: Chancery Lane □ Parking: very difficult □ Vicar: The Ven Rev Roger ED Sharpley □ Address: St Andrew's Vicarage, 5 St Andrew's Street, EC4 □ Telephone: 353 3544 □ Available: at services or generally at the Vicarage

St Andrew's is a Wren rebuilding of the medieval church on the site; its parish was a large one and St Andrew's was to become his largest parish church in London.

After the Blitz little more than the tower and walls were left but the restoration work has been sympathetic and has found some of the harmony of the Wren church, which was getting lost amid the clutter of later additions and 'improvements'. The church was reconsecrated in 1961.

The stone tower now stands over a little garden where there are two figures of charity children (like 18th century Dr Barnado's collecting boxes!) at the west entrance to the church. Inside, at the west end of the gallery, is the tomb of Thomas Coram, the founder of the Foundlings Hospital in Coram Fields, which is now a museum. This is the place where Handel's Messiah received its first public performance as a charity venture and St Andrew's has inherited the beautiful old Renatus Harris organ on which Handel used to play. The white marble font and the pulpit also come from the chapel of the former hospital, and other furnishings have been recently acquired in similar fashion.

The church, with its many interesting historical associations, attracts many visitors, among whom quite a number stop for private prayer. Services, following ASB Rite A, are held only on weekdays, by virtue of the Guild status conferred on St Andrew's in 1954. This reflects the fact that the old residential neighbourhood has been completely replaced by offices.

Services: Tuesday 1.05pm Holy Communion; Wednesday 8.15am Holy Communion; Thursday 1.05pm Holy Communion □ Wheelchair: level access via the back entrance, by the Vicarage □ Visiting: open 8.15am–5.30pm Monday to Friday (times vary in winter)

St Andrew-by-the-Wardrobe

Queen Victoria Street, EC4 □ Bus: 45, 59, 63, 76, 109, 141, 184 □ Tube: Blackfriars □ Parking: 'impossible' □ Rector: Rev John Paul □ Address: St Andrew's House, St Andrew's Hill, EC4 □ Telephone: 248 7546 □ Available: by telephone any reasonable time

St Andrew-by-the-Wardrobe, built on the site of an earlier church of the same name, owes its curious title to the fact that the Great Wardrobe of ceremonial gowns and robes of state used by the monarch was housed nearby, after being moved from the Tower of London. The Great Wardrobe was destroyed during the Great Fire, as was the original St Andrew's. The name was retained, however, when Sir Christopher Wren rebuilt the church.

The church suffered again in December 1940, when it was burnt out by a fire bomb. Reconstruction was completed in 1961, but the church retains much of its original character, largely due to the fact that many of the furnishings of the present interior are from other churches and are contemporary with Wren. The pulpit and font, for example, are from St Matthew's, Friday Street, which was also a Wren church, demolished in 1884. The organ was originally built in 1769, and came to the church in 1961. Other features include a sanctuary chair dated 1687, 16th century figures of St Andrew and St Ann and, by way of contrast, four modern windows by Carl Edwards.

The whole interior is spacious and light, with fine plasterwork on the ceiling, two 18th century chandeliers and much warm wooden panelling. The West Gallery, where the organ is sited, has very good acoustics and is used by choirs during musical events. The side galleries, with chairs used for extra seating at large services, contains many bookcases. These are the libraries of the Friends of Friendless Churches, the Ecclesiological Society and the Ancient Monuments Society.

A small private chapel, dedicated to St Ann, situated next to the main church, is open all the time for private prayer.

The church caters primarily for the weekday office workers since there is virtually no residential population in the parish. Services are held during the week at lunchtimes (except Monday), usually said Holy Communion, using the Book of Common Prayer. There are no regular Anglican services on Sunday; instead, the Syrian Orthodox liturgy is read at 10am. The Worshipful Society of Apothecaries uses the church for its Masters Day service, and it is the venue for Christmas Carol services organised by local firms and other bodies.

The present incumbent is Fr John Paul, who is also rector of St James, Garlickhythe. Since there is no church community (congregations are composed of weekday workers who attend their own churches at weekends) there is little in the way of community activities. There is an advanced Sunday school for adults on Sunday afternoons in the west gallery, which is at a high level and somewhat like extra-mural study, and a Thursday lunchtime Bible study group which meets at Father Paul's house. On the more secular side, the church often plays host to concerts and other musical events, as announced.

Services: Tuesday 12.30pm Holy Communion; Wednesday 1pm Holy Communion; Thursday 12.30pm Holy Communion; Friday 1pm Holy Communion □ Wheelchair: several steps, help required □ Visiting: open office hours Monday to Friday; tours available by arrangement

St Bartholomew the Great

West Smithfield, EC1 □ Bus: 8, 18, 22, 25, 46, 221, 243, 259, 277, 279, 501 □ Tube/BR: Barbican, St Pauls, Farringdon, Holborn Viaduct □ Parking: difficult □ Rector: Rev Arthur Brown □ Contact: The Verger □ Address: Church House, Cloth Fair, EC1 □ Telephone: 606 1575 (office) □ Available: most times

The Priory Church of St Bartholomew the Great, founded in 1123, is the oldest parish church in the City of London and, consequently, is of great architectural and historical interest. Rahere, a jester at the court of Henry I, was the founder of both the church and the nearby hospital. Both are dedicated to St Bartholomew in thanksgiving for Rahere's safe recovery from malaria and in response to a vision he had of the Saint. Today, after entering through a Tudor-style gatehouse, one can still see Rahere's magnificent Norman drum columns.

The church has had a chequered history, the most dramatic and destructive period of which was the Dissolution of the Monasteries under Henry VIII. Only the quire escaped entirely, but one side of the original square cloisters also survived. This was restored and re-opened in 1928—it had been used as a stable and been left with seven feet of earth covering the floor. Other parts of the church have been taken over for various other purposes. The 14th century Lady Chapel was converted into a house, and later a printing press where Benjamin Franklin once worked; parts of the triforium became a nonconformist school; and a blacksmith had his forge on the site of the north transept, as evidenced to this day by the blackened walls.

Notable features in this fascinating church include the pre-Reformation octagonal font, the 15th century monument to Rahere, and, one of many interesting juxtapositions of styles, a 13th century coffin together with a

Interior, St Bartholomew the Great, EC1

contemporary sculpture of the Resurrection in a window bay along the north aisle. The red-brick tower dates from 1622–8.

The church nowadays has a fine musical tradition established by a former rector, Prebendary N E Wallbank. There are two fully choral services each Sunday in the style of cathedral worship, which follow the Book of Common Prayer and are attended by about 150 people. The Priory Festival Choir is a society associated with the church which gives excellent concerts during the year and there are many other musical events. The church is also very popular for weddings.

Services: Sunday 9am Holy Communion, 11am Choral Eucharist or Choral Matins, 6.30pm Choral Evensong; Wednesday 12.30pm Holy Communion; Friday 11am Holy Communion □ Wheelchair: 1 step, easy access □ Visiting: open during day; visitors' book; guide books, leaflets etc available

St Bartholomew the Less

St Bartholomew's Hospital, West Smithfield, EC1 □ Bus: 8, 18, 22, 25, 46, 221, 243, 259, 277, 279, 501 □ Tube/BR: St Pauls, Farringdon, Barbican, Holborn Viaduct □ Parking: NCP, meters and some street parking □ Anglican Chaplain: Rev Michael Whawell □ Asst Anglican Chaplain: Rev Veja Goshai □ Catholic Chaplain: Rev C J Smith □ Free Church Chaplains: Rev Dr Gibbons, Rev D Langley □ Jewish Rabbi: Rev S Amias □ Available: most times on request by telephone/bleep system

Most of the activity of St Bartholomew the Less is associated with its role as the chapel of Bart's hospital. It became a parish church at the time of the Reformation, its parish, uniquely, being the hospital itself. The church is approached through the main gates of the hospital, and is tucked away on the left.

The Anglican staff comprises the Chaplain and Assistant Hospitaller, who arrange services and ward visits. They try to do all that a parish priest does for his parishioners. Of the other chaplains it is the Roman Catholic priest who makes the most use of the chapel, though needless to say they all try to be available day and night, offering pastoral care. Staff and students attend Matins as well as patients and their relations and friends. The 1662 Prayer Book is used at the Sunday morning Communion, while the evening service is said as the service of Communion for the sick. Both Matins and the Services of Holy Communion are kept reasonably short for the benefit of those who are not feeling too strong. The weekday services follow Series One.

The church, which is architecturally interesting (though not to the extent of its neighbour St Bartholomew the Great) has many historical connections and is worth a visit on its own merit. Office workers, and porters and others from Smithfield market, often drop in for private prayer.

Services: Sunday 8am and 5pm Holy Communion, 10.30 Matins; Weekday HC Tue 5.30pm, Wed 12.20pm, Fri 1.10pm (Roman Catholic Mass Sunday 4pm) □ Wheelchair: easy access □ Visiting: open 8am–10pm daily

St Benet, Paul's Wharf

Queen Victoria Street, EC4 □ Bus: 76, 184 □ Tube/BR: Blackfriars □ Parking: very difficult □ Vicar: Rev A Pryse Hawkins □ Telephone: 723 3104 □ Available: at services

This small and rather homely church, serving the Welsh-speaking Anglicans of London, was built by Sir Christopher Wren after the Great Fire. Finished in 1683, it is of singular interest in that it has remained largely unaltered through the years, and that Wren never repeated the Dutch style of the exterior, with its red and blue bricks and white stone dressings. The tower is topped with a delightful combination of dome and spire.

The interior boasts many original fittings; Grinling Gibbons and his craftsmen had a workshop in the courtyard and the church is thought to contain much of their work. The various Arms, including those of the House of Hanover, bear witness to the church's long association with the College of Arms across the road, members of which still have their own marked seats.

In 1879 the church was saved from demolition, and granted in perpetuity to Welsh-speaking Anglicans by Queen Victoria. Apart from some special services, worship must be conducted in Welsh. Although the Welsh community in London is not so large now and more dispersed, people travel to worship here and the congregations usually number around 20. Services are in the 'high' tradition, and the Book of Common Prayer is used. Amongst the special events held here are a service celebrating the Restoration of the Monarch (last Sunday in May), and, of course, St David's Day (March 1st). The church is involved in the City Arts Festival.

Services: Sunday 11am, 3.30pm (in Welsh) □ Wheelchair: no access—many steps □ Visiting: open only at service times or by prior arrangement with vicar

St Botolph-without-Aldersgate

Aldersdate Street, EC3 □ Telephone: 623 6970 □ Bus: 4, 141, 279a □ Tube: St Pauls □ Parking: difficult except weekends □ Priest-in-Charge: Rev Hereward Cooke □ Address: 19 Geraldine Rd, SW18 □ Telephone: 870 1873 □ Available: by telephone, anytime

Close to St Paul's Cathedral and opposite the church of St Anne and St Agnes, is St Botolph-without-Aldersgate, one of the three City churches dedicated to the patron saint of travellers.

The church, designed by Nathaniel Wright, was built in 1789–91 on the site of an earlier St Botolph's. While pleasant, the exterior of the church is unremarkable, with its tower so positioned that it is not prominent. The interior of the church is excellent however, and able to seat around 350 people in wooden pews. The sanctuary area is particularly fine, with its colourful plasterwork, elegant carved reredos and, above the altar, a window which is actually a painting on glass, the only one of its kind left in London. Created in 1788 by the artist John Pearson, this painting depicts Christ's Agony in the Garden of Gethsemane.

St Botolph's is a Guild church in the parish of St Edmund the King, and the priest-in-charge is Rev Hereward Cooke. One of the vital purposes of the church's ministry is the development of the role of the laity. The church has one regular weekly service, at Thursday lunchtime; most of these are informal, and are usually taken entirely by licensed lay readers and other members of the laity. These thirty minute services consist of a hymn, a Bible reading and prayers, while the focal point is an informal talk concerning aspects of Christian faith. Often there may be a series of talks on a particular aspect of faith, such as prayer. Congregations for these services are made up largely of local workers and retired people, and a number of visitors; whilst the numbers are small, attendance is growing.

Two Livery companies, the Plaisterers and the Ironmongers, have connections with the church, as does the Post Office, which had its headquarters next door until 1984. The churchyard is still known as Postmen's Park, and provides a pleasant spot where local office workers often eat their lunch during the summer months. St Botolph's was in danger of closure in the early 1980s, but the Friends of St Botolph's, formed in 1982, managed to prevent this. The friends are growing in numbers; they organise social events and publish their own newsletter *St Botolph's Alive!*

Services: 1st Sunday 1.05pm Holy Communion; Thursday 1.05 informal service □ Wheelchair: 3 steps □ Visiting: open 10.30am–3pm Monday–Wednesday & Friday, 12.30–2pm Thursday

St Botolph-without-Aldgate

Aldgate, EC3 □ Telephone: 283 1950/1670 (office) □ Bus: 5, 10, 15, 15a, 22a, 25, 40, 42, 44, 47a, 56, 67, 78, 225, 253 □ Tube: Aldgate □ Parking: very difficult □ Rector: Rev Malcolm A Johnson □ Address: St Botolph's Vestry, Aldgate, EC3 □ Telephone: 981 1401 □ Available: telephone for appointment

St Botolph-without-Aldgate sits on a roundabout on the eastern edge of the City of London. A church is said to have been on this site for over 1,000 years and the present-day church is the third to have been built here since Saxon times. Consecrated in 1744, restored in 1891 and 1966, St Botolph is an oblong, brick-built structure, with a square tower surmounted by a spire, built to the plans of George Dance the Elder. It stands north to south, contrary to usual practice. The interior houses many unusual artefacts including a Baroque oak panel depicting King David playing on his harp, and a highly-coloured east window based on Peter-Paul Ruben's well-known painting of Christ's Descent from the Cross. The church has associations with many famous names including Chaucer, Edmund Spenser, Daniel Defoe, and Jeremy Bentham who was baptised in 1747 in the little white font still to be found in the baptistry.

For all the interesting history, the rector and his team 'value their past but do not live in it', and St Botolph's has addressed itself to the realities of its present position. For example, the resident population of the parish today is very small and includes many Jewish people—thus, the Council for Christian–Jewish Understanding is based here. Also, the church invites those who work in the area to lunchtime music recitals (often on the church's fine organ, thought to be the oldest in Britain) as well as lectures, exhibitions, and most importantly, the Eucharist. The Sunday congregation, usually 40–50 strong, tends to comprise people who have travelled here specially, along with a number of tourists who may happen to join them in worship. Services are 'high', dignified and relaxed, following Rite A and with a good deal of lay participation.

St Botolph himself came to be associated with travelling—a Saxon St Christopher—and today this church bearing his name extends an invitation to travelling, homeless and rootless people to the Day Centre in the crypt. Staffed by seven social workers and around a hundred volunteers the crypt centre has expanded to provide not only food and shelter, but education, counselling, resettlement, perhaps even work. The project is most successful but is always in need of financial support in order to continue and to expand.

Another organisation based at St Botolph's until mid-1988 was the Gay Christian Movement, which sees its task as two-fold as indicated by their motto: 'Offering Gay Liberation to the Church and Christ to the Gay Community'. The GCM runs a counselling referral service on 587 1235, offering comfort and advice to people who, all too often, are made to feel isolated and despised. Although Gay people are particularly welcome to services here (which have included special services for AIDS sufferers), the GCM is at pains to avoid St Botolph's being regarded as a 'ghetto church'. Many other churches are equally welcoming, including St James Piccadilly, St Alban the Martyr, St Martin-in-the-Fields and St Mary the Virgin, Somers Town (qv).

Services: Sunday 10.30am Sung Eucharist; Weekday Eucharist Mon & Wed 1.05pm, Tue 5.45pm, Thu 12.10pm, Fri 1.20pm; Weekdays 4.30pm Evening Prayer □ Wheelchair: ramp □ Visiting: open 10am–4pm daily; visitors' book; leaflets and guidebooks available

St Botolph-without-Bishopsgate

Bishopsgate, EC2 □ Bus: 5, 6, 8, 8a, 22, 22a, 35, 47, 48, 78, 149, 243a, 263a □ Tube/BR: Liverpool Street □ Parking: difficult □ Rector: Rev Alan J Tanner □ Address: St Botolph's Vestry, EC2 □ Telephone: 588 1053 □ Available: telephone for appointment

The present St Botolph's, designed by James Gold and consecrated in 1728, is the fourth to be built on the site. During the building of this church, the foundations of the original, which may have been erected by the Saxon Bishop Erkenwald, were uncovered. The interior has galleries on three sides supported by Corinthian columns on oak plinths standing between the Victorian pews. A small pleasant garden lies on the north side.

The church serves the City commuters and visitors, having no real residential community. There are few church-based groups or activities, but on Friday at 1pm there is a fellowship lunch in the adjacent hall to which all are welcome. These feature discussions and guest speakers. Also, St Botolph's is the venue for occasional music recitals, and local companies and schools hold carol services here. Services are 'high' and follow Rite B; there is an adult mixed voice choir at the Sung Eucharist.

The rector also has charge of the nearby All Hallows, London Wall, and endeavours to be available to see anyone seeking spiritual help or counsel at any time.

Services: Tuesday 1.10pm Holy Communion; Wednesday 1.10pm Sung Eucharist; Thursday 12.10pm Holy Communion; 1st Sunday 11am Sung Eucharist (Confessions and Anointing of the Sick on request or by arrangement) □ Wheelchair: difficult access, several steps □ Other details: hall (available for hire) □ Visiting: usually open during the day

St Bride

Fleet Street, EC4 □ Bus: any along Fleet Street □ Tube/BR: Blackfriars, St Pauls, Chancery Lane □ Parking: NCP, meters □ Rector: Rev Canon John Oates □ Address: Rectory, Fleet Street, EC4 □ Telephone: 353 1301 □ Available: 24 hours □ Other staff: Lay Assistant Mark Upton

There is a story that goes as follows: back in the early 1700s, a pastry chef named William Rich had the task of designing a wedding cake for an important family, and he was struggling to find the inspiration to do something special. Then, as he looked out of the window, he saw the steeple of St Bride's, which Sir Christopher Wren had just completed. He made the connection between the name of the church and weddings, and went off to make a tiered cake based on the pattern of the steeple; the kind, he would no doubt be gratified to know, which is still being made today.

St Bride (Bridie or Bridget) is, like St Patrick, a patron saint of Ireland, and this dedication suggests that there was a Celtic community worshipping on this site even before St Augustine's mission to the south of England, in around 600 AD. Indeed, the bomb which ravaged the sixth church on the site in December 1940 led to the discovery, not only of parts of the earlier churches, but of Roman remains dating back to the second century. In the crypt there is a Roman pavement, two chapels, and a fascinating exhibition of archaeological finds among the various strata of the building.

As Fleet Street's parish church and the 'Church of the Media world-wide', St Bride's is not interested in denominationalism. You can buy the newspapers of all the major churches as well as the *Church Times*. Letters come from people who are not even Christians but would like help with a problem. Canon John Oates, the rector, holds seventeen chaplaincies, including the Press Association and the Association of Journalists. In the crypt there is an exhibition of the church's links with the Press, which is practically a history of printing in this country. Caxton's apprentice, Wynkin de Worde, was buried here. It was he who made a commercial proposition of the printing press.

Of the three Sunday services two are fully choral, enabling one to experience the spendid acoustic of this beautifully restored Wren interior. In certain respects the church has been improved; new vistas have been opened up as Wren intended them, where they had been hidden for centuries by the organ. Recitals are held three times a week, including an organ recital on Wednesdays, and there are regular lectures and tours of the church organised by the Friends of St Bride's.

High Altar, St Dunstan-in-the-West, EC4

Services: Sunday 8.30am Holy Communion, 11am Choral Matins/Eucharist, 6.30pm Choral Evensong; Weekdays 8.30pm Holy Communion (1.15pm Thursday), 5.15pm Evening Prayer □ Facilities: amplification □ Children: creche/Sunday school □ Wheelchair: level access □ Other details: church used for concerts, drama, etc; hall (available for donation) □ Visiting: open 8.30am–5.30pm daily; leaflets and postcards available; tours and parties catered for by arrangement, including access to tower

St Clement, Eastcheap

Clement's Lane, EC4 □ Bus: 43, 133 □ Tube: Monument □ Parking: 'impossible' □ Rector: Rev Prebendary Dr Hugh Fearn □ Address: 7 Bishop Street, N1 □ Telephone: 226 6992, 283 8154 (office) □ Available: telephone for appointment

Within the City's square mile, St Clement's Eastcheap is the smallest of the 45 churches, and also has the smallest parish, with only 16 residents. A walk around the parish boundaries can be accomplished in five minutes. Attendance at the two weekly services reflects the small size of the parish, despite the large number of office workers in the area during the week. ASB Rite B and the 1662 Book of Common Prayer are used at the Wednesday and Friday services respectively, and sermons are given by Prebendary Hugh Fearn. The nature of City life, compounded by the parish's size, precludes church activities outside the services.

The Vestry, which occupies part of the churchyard behind the church, is used as an office by Citicare, a Community Programme run by the Manpower Services Commission. This scheme provides graduates with placements in business.

Although the original medieval building on the site was one of the first churches to be destroyed by the Great Fire, which started in nearby Pudding Lane, it was one of the last to be replaced by Wren. The present building was constructed between 1683 and 1687. Inside, oak was used for the wall panelling, pews and pulpit. The reredos is by Sir Ninian Comper.

In December 1985 the font cover, and intricate piece enclosing a dove holding an olive branch, was stolen. The theft was reported in antique trade papers, and the thief was arrested when attempting to sell it. Unfortunately, the cover has since been locked away and can no longer be displayed safely in its rightful position.

Services: Wednesday 12.15pm Sung Eucharist; Friday 12.30pm Litany □ Wheelchair: 4 steps into the church □ Visiting: open between 9am and 5pm Monday to Friday; history booklet available

St Dunstan-in-the-West

184 Fleet Street, EC4 □ Telephone: 405 1929 □ Bus: 4, 6, 9, 11, 15, 15a, 17, 45, 63, 76 □ Tube/BR: Blackfriars □ Parking: very difficult □ Priest-in-Charge: Rev A T John Salter □ Address: 87 Richmond Ave, N1 □ Telephone: 607 2865 □ Available: every day except Monday

In common with many other City churches with a declining number of parishioners, St Dunstan's was converted from a parish church to one having the new Guild status following the Act of Parliament of 1952. Parish responsibilities were transferred to St Bride's (qv). As a Guild church, St Dunstan's is exempt from holding Sunday services, while the special ministry it offers is that of forging links between Anglicanism and overseas Churches.

The building, designed by John Shaw in 1833 complete with Gothic lantern tower, lies on the north side of Fleet Street. Its unusual octagonal shape is most appropriate to the church's ecumenical role for it allows several altars to be housed in positions of equal prominence.

Furthest from the entrance and on the right is the altar of the Lutherans and other continental Protestants, with its open copy of the Scriptures. On the left is an altar for the Old Catholic Church, next to an icon of the ancient Assyrian Church who worship in Aramaic and to whose safety Nestorius fled after the Council of Ephesus. At the front lies the chapel used by the Romanian Orthodox congregation (qv), opposite the altar dedicated for use by the Oriental Orthodox group of Churches.

The focus of Anglican worship here is the High Altar, which along with the reredos is of carved oak in a Late Gothic style. The Anglican services are on Tuesdays and Saints' Days, and follow Rite B. People attend from the nearby Law Courts and offices. Some belong to the breakfast study group which has met here for over 20 years, but it is largely a mobile congregation. Hundreds of visitors pass through the church daily.

Services: Tuesday & Saints' Days 12.30pm Holy Communion; Friday (once a month) 12.30pm Old Catholics' service □ Wheelchair: no access □ Visiting: open 8.30am–2pm or 2pm–6pm (alternate weeks) and all day Tuesday

St Edmund the King

Lombard Street, EC3 □ Telephone: 623 6970 □ Bus: 6, 8, 9, 11, 15a, 21, 22, 25, 43, 76, 133, 149, 501 □ Tube: Bank, Monument □ Parking: 'impossible' □ Parish Priest: Rev Hereward Cooke □ Address: 19 Geraldine Road, SW18 □ Telephone: 870 1873 □ Available: anytime by telephone

St Edmund the King stands on Lombard Street in the financial heart of the City of London; its elegant, highly decorated octagonal steeple, complete with its attractive clock suspended upon it from a bracket, forms a handsome landmark.

There has been a church on the site since at least 1170. The present building was erected by Sir Christopher Wren between 1670–76, with the steeple and spire added in 1706. It was one of the few City churches to be bombed in the First World War; fragments of the bomb are preserved in a glass case in the west wall. Further damage was sustained in the Second World War, damaged caused in this case by incendiaries. The church was later restored by Rodney Tatchell in 1957, with extensions to the vestry, including the addition of offices.

Inside, the church is small but has a spacious feel due to the high ceiling. The fittings are in dark wood, much of it carved, including the panelling, the pulpit and the elaborate rail around the font. Particularly impressive is the large and ornate reredos with its six gilded panels.

The congregation which attends the one weekly service—Holy Communion on Thursday at 12.30pm—is small, and consists largely of office workers and retired people, together with tourists, whose numbers increase in the summer months.

Many organisations use the church during the week, since it has a hall which is available for hire at a nominal fee for groups of up to 50 people. Most of the lettings are to charitable agencies, such as Alcoholics Anonymous, who meet here five times a week. Other regular users include Weight Watchers and a keep-fit group. There is also a weekly choir practice, and a prayer group organised by the congregation.

St Edmund the King is officially a parish church, although the local population is virtually nil. The parish priest is Rev Hereward Cooke, who has his office at the church; since the parish is large, Rev Cooke also has responsibility for two other local churches, St Mary Woolnoth and St Botolph-without-Aldersgate. Part of his ministry at St Edmund is to try to relate to the world of commerce, and to try to bring Christian insights to bear on the commercial life of the City. To this end, the church publishes a newsletter called *Lombard Street*.

Services: Thursday 12.30pm Holy Communion □ Wheelchair: ramps available □ Other facilities: hall (available for hire) □ Visiting: open 8.30am–5pm Monday to Friday

St Ethelburga the Virgin

Bishopsgate, EC4 □ Telephone: 588 3596 □ Bus: 5, 6, 8, 22, 35, 47, 48, 55, 67, 78, 149, 243a □ Tube/BR: Liverpool Street □ Parking: very difficult □ Priest-in-Charge: Rev Malcolm Johnson □ Address: c/o St Botolph's Vestry, Aldgate, EC3 □ Telephone: 283 1670/1950 □ Available: telephone for appointment

When St Ethelburga's was built in 1430 it was the tallest building in the area: now the medieval church is scarcely noticeable, hemmed in on all sides by tall office blocks. The church is unique in its dedication to St Ethelburga, the first abbess of the Benedictine abbey at Barking, and sister of St Erkenwald, who became Bishop of London in 675.

Extensive renovation of the interior was carried out in 1912, including the addition of stone flooring, the screen and the West Gallery, which houses a small organ. Of all the windows in the church, only the West Window contains original tracery. In three of the others, explorer Henry Hudson is depicted. One shows Hudson and his crew taking Communion at St Ethelburga's; the others depict scenes from their adventures in the Americas. Along with a fourth window, they were the work of the late Leonard Walker.

Set behind the altar in the sanctuary is a mural by Hans Feibusch, completed in 1962. There are other paintings of note, and the church treasures are on display. The parish chest which held the treasures for 300 years is now used as a receptacle for alms.

Existing as a Guild church since 1954, when the City's parish boundaries were redrawn, St Ethelburga's has a programme of weekday services which uphold the Catholic tradition of the Church of England. All services are according to the Book of Common Prayer. Associations with the Anglican Society, which uses St Ethelburga's for their meetings, and with the Oxford Movement (St Ethelburga's is its London home) tie in with this tradition.

After Rev Malcolm Johnson of St Botolph-without-Aldgate became priest-in-charge, the Wednesday Sung Evensong and study group were transferred to St Botolph's.

Services: Tuesday 12.10pm Sung Eucharist; Thursday 1.10pm Said Eucharist; 1st Wednesday 6pm Sung Evensong □ Wheelchair: level access □ Visiting: open only for services and activities

St Giles, Cripplegate

Fore Street, EC2 □ Bus: 9, 11, 21, 43, 76, 141 □ Tube/BR: Barbican, Moorgate □ Parking: meters □ Rector: Rev David Rhodes □ Address: 4 The Postern, Wood Street, EC2 □ Telephone: 606 3630 □ Available: most times □ Other clergy: Rev Paul Lewis (253 4720)

The centre of the Barbican complex, surrounded by modern blocks of flats and concrete towers, is the unlikely setting of one of London's oldest surviving churches—St Giles, Cripplegate. This church serves over half the residents of the City, and is also the parish church of South Islington.

Records show of a church being on the site as early as 1010, although the present church was originally built in the 14th century and has been added to and restored many times since. The church is almost haunted with history; Oliver Cromwell was married here, John Milton buried here, and Lancelot Andrewes, the great Anglican divine, was once vicar. During the Great Plague, 8,000 people in the parish died, and on 18th August 1665, there were 151 funerals for victims of the disease. The church is also one of only six in the City to survive the Great Fire of London; it was not so lucky in World War II, when it was burnt out during the Blitz. It was derelict for some years until the interior was completely restored, and it reopened in 1960.

Today, the church interior is light and spacious, with most of the fittings replaced. The style of the interior is still basically Early English and the whole is done out in pale colours. The east and west windows are stained glass, and were designed in the 1950s. There are many memorials and monuments.

The church itself has many links with City institutions, including City livery companies and many local business houses. It is also the civic church of the ward of Cripplegate. It also works closely with educational charities and with helping the aged and disabled (as befitting its patron saint).

There is a full complement of Sunday services using either ASB Rite A or the 1662 Prayer Book. The congregation is made up largely of local residents, most of whom are in the professional and executive class, as well as policemen, students and nurses from Bart's Hospital. Most of the older people in the area have weekend homes, and do not attend every week. Activities of the congregation include Bible study and discussion groups. There are no children of school age in the congregation, but there are youth clubs and similar activities at St Luke's, Old Street.

On most weekdays there are lunchtime services and often concerts and recitals, well supported by the commuters who work in the area. The church is also used for exhibitions.

Services: Sunday 8am & 10am Holy Communion, 6pm Evensong; Monday 8am Morning Prayer; Weekday HC Tue & Thu 8am, Wed & Fri 12.40pm □ Facilities: amplification, large print hymnbooks □ Wheelchair: level access □ Other details: hall (available for hire; contact Mr Freeman on 628 6155) □ Visiting: open 10am–5pm daily

St Helen, Bishopsgate

Great St Helens, Bishopsgate, EC3 □ Telephone: 283 2231 □ Bus: 5, 6, 8, 22, 35, 47, 48, 78 □ Tube/BR: Liverpool Street, Aldgate □ Parking: meters □ Rector: Rev Prebendary Dick Lucas □ Address: c/o church □ Available: ring for appointment □ Other clergy: Rev Hugh Palmer

St Helen's is is the major evangelical church in the city. The famous Tuesday lunchtime services, provided expressly for City workers and taking up topical business issues, attract up to 550 people. The message of these services is that the Bible 'is indispensible to those who wish to lead a balanced life'—a pertinent point for those who work in the up-and-down world of high finance.

Sunday services are also well attended, with around 300 in the morning and 500 mainly young people for the less formal evening service, when the singing is led by a choir. The central point of all services here is 'the teaching of the Word of God'. Another indication of the Bible-based outlook of the church is the impressive array of courses, lectures and meetings, including 'Read, Mark, Learn', a two year study course held at St Andrew Undershaft. This former church is now used as St Helen's church hall.

Other activities include World Prayer Groups which focus on the problems of a particular region, and forums where nurses discuss the ethical issues of their profession. Newcomers to the church are always welcome and the informal and friendly atmosphere of the 'After Eight' coffee bar enhances that welcome.

For all the modern approach, St Helen's is in fact one of the oldest churches in the City, possibly of Saxon foundation. The curious double nave interior stems from the establishment in 1212 of a Benedictine Nunnery; the nuns' chapel was added to St Helen's church separated only by an arcade screen. The 15th century 'squint' through which the nuns looked still survives in their (northern) nave. The many other features, especially the profusion of Elizabethan and Jacobean monuments have led to the church being called the 'Westminster Abbey of the City' and are too numerous to mention here. Suffice it to say that whether to see a pre-Great Fire interior, or hear a thoroughly modern sermon, St Helen's is well worth a visit.

Services: Sunday 10.15am and 7pm; Tuesday 12.25pm and 1.05pm □ Facilities: amplification, deaf loop □ Children: Sunday school and creche, 10.15am □ Wheelchair: deep steps, no ramp □ Other details: St Andrew Undershaft is used as church hall □ Visiting: open 9.30am–1pm and 6–10pm Sunday, 9am–5pm Monday to Friday; bookstall; St Andrew Undershaft open for coffee 10.15–11.45am Monday and Thursday

St James, Garlickhythe

Garlick Hill, EC4 □ Telephone: 236 1719 (Vestry) □ Bus: 6, 9, 11, 15, 15a, 17, 76, 95, 149, 184, 513 □ Tube: Mansion House □ Parking: 'impossible' □ Rector: Rev John Paul □ Address: St Andrew's House, St Andrew's Hill, EC4 □ Telephone: 248 7546 □ Available: most times (by telephone)

Designed by Sir Christopher Wren, St James Garlickhythe stands near Southwark Bridge; its 125-foot steeple is a landmark, topped by an impressive spire. A church has been on this site since William the Conqueror's time, and St James' boasts the oldest church registers in England, dating back to 1535; these survived the destruction of the original church during the Great Fire and the earlier ones are now deposited in the Guildhall Library. The present building was completed in 1682 and added to many times, particularly during the Victorian era. Damaged during the Second World War, it was closed for restoration between 1954 and 1963. It has been further restored recently.

Very few people live in the neighbourhood, and most of the fifty-strong congregation travel from outside, with a very comprehensive mix of ethnic groups and ages, although there are few children. There is a Sunday service on the first week of the month, with a regular weekday service on Tuesday lunchtime. Many City workers come to this service. The church has a strong musical tradition: Sunday services have a professional choir and many concerts are held here. The congregation meets after services, and visitors are immediately made welcome.

The rector, Fr John Paul, is also rector at St Andrew-by-the-Wardrobe, and has been with both churches since July 1986. In addition to looking after the two churches, he has a lot of pastoral work, including individual counselling for employees of large corporations such as British Telecom. Many people who work in the City prefer to come to the City churches for help with their problems since it affords them a certain anonymity that they would not get at their own parish churches.

Services: 1st Sunday 10.30am Holy Communion; Tuesday 1.15pm Holy Communion □ Facilities: amplification □ Wheelchair: difficult, 2 steps at entrance □ Visiting: open at service times and during office hours

St Katharine Cree

Leadenhall Street, EC3 □ Bus: 15a, 25 □ Tube: Aldgate □ Parking: difficult □ Priest-in-Charge: Rev Hugh Rom □ Address: Church Office, Leadenhall Street, EC3 □ Telephone: 283 5733 □ Available: 9am–5pm Monday to Friday

St Katharine Cree (the 'Cree' is a remnant of 'Christchurch' in the original name) is one of the most unusual and interesting churches in the City, dating as it does from the period after Inigo Jones but before Wren. The third church on the site, it has a tower dating from 1504 while the rest was built around 1630, when the Gothic style was beginning to give way to the Classical, and is thus something of a hybrid. The windows are of various shapes and sizes, and include a Catherine Wheel window in a square frame, while the interior boasts arcades with Corinthian columns below a clerestory of late Gothic design. Nowadays, an interesting architectural counterpoint is provided by the famous Lloyd's building by Richard Rogers, just across the road.

Like other City churches that are no longer feasible as parish churches, St Katharine Cree has a specific ministry and as Guild church to Commerce, Finance and Industry it promotes awareness of economic and financial issues through lectures and seminars. Otherwise, the church is open during the week for private prayer, and the Eucharist is celebrated (ASB Rite A) each Thursday lunchtime, followed by an informal gathering. A board inviting passers-by to the service is placed in the porch, and there is a regular congregation of between 12 and 15 people who work nearby. An important feature of the service is the music of the Father Smith organ, dating from 1686.

The church has put its facilities to good use by providing office space for several Christian organisations. The aisles have been boxed in to create the offices, one of which is used by the priest-in-charge and his assistant. Rev Hugh Rom has described his work as being a 'Ministry of Availability' and he keeps City-type hours to suit the needs of those who use the church.

An interesting tradition upheld at St Katharine Cree is the annual 'Lion Sermon' preached on 1st October. These sermons were endowed by a parishioner, Sir John Gayer, in gratitude for his safe deliverance from an encounter with a lion in the Levant in 1643. Also once a year, on the Sunday following 17 June, there is a special service for all who died on the troopship SS Lancastria that day in 1940. A wooden tablet commemorating the 4,000 dead, and a modern stained glass window depicting the ship, can be found on the south wall.

Services: Thursday 1.05pm Holy Eucharist □ Wheelchair: several steps up to church □ Other details: large room used for church & City functions □ Visiting: open 9am–5pm Monday to Friday

St Lawrence Jewry

Gresham Street, EC2 □ Bus: 6, 8, 9, 11, 15a, 21, 22, 25, 43, 76, 133, 149, 501 □ Tube: Bank, St Pauls □ Parking: some spaces available □ Vicar: Rev Canon David Burgess □ Address: The Vicarage, St Lawrence Jewry, EC2 □ Telephone: 600 9478 □ Available: by appointment

One of Wren's magnificent City churches, St Lawrence Jewry was built in 1677 to replace its predecessor, destroyed in the Great Fire. (This earlier church was built in 1136 on the edge of the one-time Jewish trading area, hence the name). The new church, sited next to the Guildhall, became not the local parish church but the Guild church of the Corporation of the City of London. The 175-foot steeple is a landmark to all those who approach the church along Gresham Street, and the exterior, with its Corinthian colonnade along the east side, is very impressive.

The interior is a modern reconstruction, carried out by Cecil Brown in the 1950s (the church, like so many others in the City, was gutted by fire-bombs during the Second World War). Spacious and attractive, it is styled in sympathy with Wren's original embellishments and there is a wealth of stained glass. The Commonwealth Chapel, so called to remind us of the part that the City of London played in the Commonwealth's development, has service standards and several national flags of Commonwealth countries hanging from its walls. At the west end of the church is another small chapel, the Tower Chapel, which is regularly used for private prayer.

As the official church of the Corporation of London, mayoral services are held here five times a year. It is also the church of several Livery companies, including the Loriners, the Haberdashers and the Girdlers (the latter company having held services at St Lawrence since 1180). Lunchtime services following the Book of

Common Prayer. With no resident congregation in the area, there are few activities outside services.

The church has a fine organ, built by Noel Mander in 1957 to replace the one destroyed in the bombing. There are organ recitals every Tuesday lunchtime at 1pm. Also in the church is a grand piano which used to be owned by Sir Thomas Beecham; this is also used for lunchtime recitals, at 1pm every Monday. Leaflets are available informing visitors about the history of the church, the organ and bells, and also the stained glass windows.

Services: 1st Sunday 9.15am Holy Communion; Wednesday 8.30am Holy Communion; Friday 12.15 and 1.15pm Holy Communion □ Facilities: amplification, deaf loop □ Wheelchair: level access □ Visiting: open 7.45am–5pm Monday to Friday, from Easter to the Lord Mayor's Show

St Luke's Church Centre

Roscoe Street, EC1 □ Bus: 5, 55 □ Tube/BR: Moorgate, Old Street □ Parking: on street □ Priest-in-Charge: Rev Paul Lewis □ Address: as church □ Tel: 253 4720 □ Avaible: most times, though sometimes at St Giles Cripplegate

The Church Centre is a small, square modern building on the corner of the street. There is a stained glass window, and the porch has church announcements, but otherwise it fits quite unobtrusively into the pattern of this neighbourhood: small office buildings and blocks of flats. Most unusually for the City, this is a residential area, and indeed working-class. St Luke's serves the Peabody Estate, and also the Golden Lane Estate, which was the City of London's model estate until the Barbican was built. In Whitecross Street there is a market which dates back to Elizabethan times.

The former parish of St Luke's was divided between St Clement's, King Square (north of Old Street), and St Giles, Cripplegate (south of Old Street). St Luke's official status now is Mission Chapel to St Giles.

The congregation is small but growing. Once a week Mass is said in a flat on the sixteenth floor of a tower block; it is easier for some of the old folk there to attend. There is a thriving mothers and toddlers group, and an active under-25's group, which organises visits to the theatre with follow-up discussion meetings. Many local organisations, including a ballet group, use the church during the week. The sanctuary can be closed off behind folding doors.

Services: Sunday 11.15am Eucharist; Monday 10.15am House Mass; Wednesday 10am Eucharist □ Other details: hall □ Visiting: by arrangement

St Magnus the Martyr

Lower Thames Street, EC3 □ Bus: 3a, 10, 15, 21, 35, 40, 43, 44, 47, 48, 70a, 133, 501, 513 □ Tube/BR: Monument, London Bridge □ Parking: some courtyard space on Sundays □ Rector: Rev Michael J Woodgate □ Address: The Rectory, as church □ Telephone: 626 4481 □ Available: most times

St Magnus the Martyr, by the Monument, is one of the finest Wren churches in the City of London and one of the best-preserved. It was built in 1676 after the destruction of the medieval building in the Great Fire. In the early 1920s it underwent a major interior renovation, some Wren features obscured in the 19th century being restored, and some work by Martin Travers being added, including two altars, some statues and a rood over the High Altar, all of which have enhanced the beauty and dignity of the church and its worship.

St Magnus upholds the Catholic tradition of the Church of England in both worship (using BCP and Roman Rite) and teaching, but it seeks to minister to all Christians, especially those who work in the City of London. It is particularly concerned with the promotion of the spiritual life, and an increasing number of people from both the City and beyond come for spiritual direction. The Eucharist is celebrated on working days (except Monday) at lunchtime, and on Sundays there is a solemn celebration at 11 am. The Sunday congregation is small but devoted and hard-working, providing the necessary support for the weekday ministry to City workers. A Wednesday lunchtime Bible Study and discussion brings together Christians of different traditions. Candidates for preparation for the Sacraments are specially welcome, as are any who simply want to learn more of the Christian faith. A devotional guild under its medieval title of 'The Fraternity of Our Lady de Salve Regina' was revived in the 1920s and now meets almost daily to pray for the needs of the Church and the world.

Many visitors from both home and abroad visit the church each year. Coffee is served after most services and functions, and those who bring packed lunches are welcome to eat them in the crypt. Occasional concerts and recitals are given, and from time to time, exhibitions are arranged to highlight features of the church and its rich history going back a thousand years while linking them with the church's present ministry. Newcomers to services and visitors for whatever reason are made to feel most welcome.

St Magnus is the Ward church for the Bridge Ward in the City of London and also the church of three livery companies: the Fishmongers, the Plumbers and the Coopers. More recently it has become the London spiritual home for the young crew of a sailing barge which moors from time to time at the wharf beside the church, and which is run by the St Paul's Trust to give youngsters experience of life on the water.

Services: Sunday 11am Solemn Eucharist; Tue, Thur 12.15pm Eucharist (said); Wed, Fri 1.15pm Eucharist (said); Principal Feast Days 12.15pm Solemn Eucharist; Sat (occasional) 11am Eucharist (said); Thursday 1.30pm Benediction □ Wheelchair: level access, except crypt □ Visiting: open 9am–4pm Tuesday to Friday, 9.30am–1pm Sunday, and often 9.30–1pm Saturday; bookstall; trail for children; tours by arrangement

St Margaret, Lothbury

Lothbury, EC2 □ Bus: 9, 11, 43, 76 □ Tube: Bank □ Parking: 'impossible' □ Rector: Rev Chandos Morgan □ Address: The Rector's Lodgings at church □ Telephone: 606 8330 □ Available: most times at the church

Situated on Lothbury, a relatively quiet street behind the Bank of England, St Margaret's contains many furnishings collected from City churches either closed down or destroyed in the 18th and 19th centuries. The church was built between 1686 and 1690 by Christopher Wren in a Classical style, and as it originally contained few furnishings the additions were easily accommodated. The main addition is the rood screen from All Hallows, Upper Thames Street. It runs the full width of the church. The south aisle was made into a chapel in 1891 by the erection of a screen designed by G F Bodley and incorporating altar rails from St Olave's, Jewry. Bodley also arranged the furnishings added to the church. This chapel is now used for the lunchtime Communion services.

The life of the church is now geared totally to those people working in the area and with the services for the Stock Exchange Christian Association and the London Banks' Christian Union it retains the historical links with the major industries of the area. As with many City churches there are no weekend services. Holy Communion is celebrated on Wednesdays (using ASB Rite B) and Thursday (using the 1662 Prayer Book) allowing people working nearby to attend. Food is available. There is an organ recital every Wednesday at 1.10pm.

Rev Chandos Morgan has been at St Margaret's since 1983 and has quickly adapted his ideas to the requirements of a City church. He spends time visiting the surrounding businesses and Livery companies, both of which use the church for their commemorative and Christmas services.

Services: Morning Prayer Monday to Friday 9.15am; Holy Communion Wednesday 12.10pm, Thursday 1.10pm (also Stock Exchange Christian Association Wednesday 1–2pm; and London Banks' Christian Union, Friday 12–12.40pm and 1–1.45pm) □ Wheelchair: 1 small step □ Visiting: open from 7.45am to 5.30pm Monday to Friday; leaflets etc are available in the entrance hall

St Margaret Pattens

Eastcheap, EC3 □ Bus: 8a, 10, 15, 21, 35, 40, 43, 44, 47, 48, 70a, 133, 501, 513 □ Tube: Monument □ Parking: on street □ Priest-in-Charge: Rev Canon Eric Jarvis □ Address: St Margaret's Office, 8 Hart Street, EC3 □ Telephone: 488 4318 □ Available: ring for appointment

A church dedicated to St Margaret of Antioch has existed on this site, set back from the corner of Eastcheap and Rood Lane, for over 900 years. The present building was designed by Wren and was completed in 1687. The 199-foot-high spire was completed in 1703, and is the third highest in the City. The offices built into the north gallery, while partly detracting from the charm of the interior, have enabled the church to accommodate the Christian Study Centre, incluing the College of Preachers, which is St Margaret's attached speciality as a Guild church.

Inside the church a number of interesting items can be seen. An hourglass, dated 1750, beside the pulpit was used to time the sermons. At the west end of the nave are two canopied pews used by the church wardens, elaborately carved and the only examples of their kind in London. Wren was said to have occupied one during services.

The non-residential nature of this City parish results in only one weekly service being held, attended by 10 to 15 local office workers. The service consists of a Eucharist, with the Book of Common Prayer and the Alternative Service Book as texts. Two special services are held each year; for the Worshipful Company of Patten Makers, on Ascension Day and for the Worshipful Company of Basket Makers, held in the autumn.

Services: check with church □ Wheelchair: several deep steps to main entrance □ Other details: lecture room upstairs in converted gallery □ Visiting: open during the day, Monday to Friday

St Martin, Ludgate

Ludgate Hill, EC4 □ Bus: 4, 6, 9, 11, 15, 15a, 17, 76, 141, 502, 513 □ Tube/BR: Blackfriars, St Pauls □ Parking: very difficult □ Priest-in-Charge: Rev Gordon Watkins □ Address: St Martin's Vestry, Ludgate Hill, EC4 □ Telephone: 248 6054 □ Available: daytime

This is a Guild church with no Sunday services. Instead there is Holy Communion on Thursdays, usually consisting of a hymn and a short address, using the Book of Common Prayer. Rev Watkins describes his approach as 'central' churchmanship. The rest of the week he leaves for people to enjoy private prayer, except Wednesday lunchtimes, when music recitals are held. These are of a high standard, with a professional choir.

St Martin, Ludgate, is a Wren original. It survived the War with virtually no bomb damage. Entering the church one can pick up a guide-board which explains some of the history and points of interest. The first church on the site is said to have been built by Cadwallader, a Celtic king, who is supposedly buried in the crypt. A later church, facing north-south, was about twice the size of the present one, but was lost in the Great Fire. In his rebuilding, Wren designed the spire with the specific intention of having it set off the dome of St Paul's on the skyline. The interior is supported by four central pillars, which govern the overall square design.

Services: Thursday 1.15pm Holy Communion □ Wheelchair: 7 steps and no place for a ramp □ Visiting: open 10.30am–3.30pm; guide-boards available in English, French and German

St Mary Abchurch

Abchurch Lane, EC4 □ Telephone 626 0306 □ Bus: 6, 8a, 9, 10, 11, 15, 15a, 17, 21, 35, 40, 43, 47, 48, 70a, 76, 95, 133, 199, 501, 513 □ Tube/BR: Monument, Bank, Cannon Street □ Parking: very difficult □ Priest-in-Charge: Chancellor Rev E Garth Moore □ Address: 1 Raymond Buildings, Grays Inn, WC1 □ Telephone: 242 3734 □ Available: telephone for appointment

Abchurch Lane is a narrow thoroughfare connecting King William Street and Cannon Street, a totally unremarkable lane were it not for the unexpected pleasure of St Mary Abchurch, with its own paved forecourt, hidden halfway along.

The brick exterior, with its small steeple, is in the typical style of its architect, Sir Christopher Wren, who built the church between 1681 and 1685 to replace the earlier building, consumed in the Great Fire. The real beauties of the church lie inside; of particular significance is the domed ceiling—nearly forty feet across and unbuttressed—a rare feature in Wren's smaller churches. Lit by small oval windows, the smooth surface of the dome was painted in 1708 by William Snow to depict the worship of Heaven. Surrounded by angels and cherubs, it has at its apex the Divine Name—written in Hebrew—radiating rays of light.

All of the woodwork is in dark wood. The chief glory here is the reredos, an exceptionally fine piece of carving, and quite unique; it is the only authenticated work of Grinling Gibbons in any of the City's churches (St Paul's excepted) and is also his largest piece. The High Altar is a small, ornate Communion table.

In common with many other City churches, the lack of a resident population in the area has led to the church being changed in status from a Parish to a Guild church. Many Guild churches have a speciality; at St Mary, this is a Ministry of Healing. Special services for this are held every second Monday of the month at 5.45 pm (except during August and September), attracting people from all over London, representing not only all ages, social groups and races but also many denominations as well. Counselling takes place at any time.

The priest-in-charge, the Worshipful Chancellor Rev E Garth Moore DCL, is both a Fellow of Corpus Christi College in Cambridge (dividing his duties between the college and the church) and also an ecclesiastical judge, presiding over Church courts around the country. Occasionally, courts are held in St Mary Abchurch.

There are only two regular services each week, Holy Communion on Wednesday and Thursday, both said. The Book of Common Prayer is used. Those who attend are mainly office workers or visitors.

Having no regular congregation, the church holds few activities of its own, but it is used by the Fruiterers' Guild for their special services. The church contained the offices of the Church's Fellowship for Physical and Spiritual Studies, who also hold meetings after the Healing Ministry, and the premises are used by the Anglican Society for the Welfare of Animals.

Services: Wednesday 12.30pm Holy Communion; Thursday 1.00pm Holy Communion; Roman Catholic services twice a month; every second Monday in month (except August and September) 5.45pm Ministry of Healing □ Wheelchair: small flight of steps on entering the church □ Other details: Rectory room; the church can be made available for events □ Visiting: open Monday, Wednesday and Thursday from 11am to 4pm most weeks—check by phone; small guide leaflet available

St Mary Aldermary

Bow Lane, EC2 □ Telephone: 248 4906 □ Bus: 6, 9, 11, 15, 17, 76, 95 □ Tube: Mansion House □ Parking: very difficult □ Priest-in-Charge: Rev Victor Stock □ Address: The Rector's Lodgings, St Mary-le-Bow, Eastcheap, EC2 □ Telephone: 248 5139 □ Available: most times at St Mary-le-Bow

St Mary Aldermary is a Guild church in the parish of St Mary-le-Bow, and is situated on Bow Lane, near the junction of Queen Victoria Street and Cannon Street. This site has led to the church being dominated by the surrounding buildings to the point where it is now partially hidden. Services are held at lunch times from Tuesday to Friday. They are all Mass services, which include the singing of hymns and are attended by up to a dozen people that work in the area. The church does not have a hall or kitchen but worshippers meet in the Vestry with packed meals after the services.

The history of St Mary Aldermary goes back to 1080 when the church was used as the burial place for many Lord Mayors of London. In 1510 the Lord Mayor of the time made funds available for the building of a new church, completed in 1518.

This church was destroyed in the Great Fire of London, after which it was replaced by a Gothic church, similar in design to its predecessor and built by Wren in 1682. Inside the elaborate Gothic influence is evident with much carved stone, stained glass and Wren's own version of fan-vaulting that covers the entire ceiling.

Services: Weekday Mass Tue & Thu 1.15pm, Wed & Fri 12.15pm, Holy Days 12.15pm & 1.15pm; Friday 1.15pm Benediction; Confession after every service □ Wheelchair: 1 small step □ Visiting: open for services, staying open until 3.30pm

St Mary-at-Hill

Lovat Lane, EC3 □ Bus: 10, 15, 40, 44 □ Tube: Monument □ Parking: very difficult □ Rector: Rev Dr B A C Kirk-Duncan □ Address: 8 St Mary-at-Hill, EC3 □ Telephone: 626 4184 □ Available: telephone for appointment

Hidden away amongst narrow cobbled alleys and passages, between Eastcheap and old Billingsgate Market lies St Mary-at-Hill. This Wren church is rated by Sir John Betjeman as having one of the least spoiled interiors in the City. Although much of what we see is Victorian, it is the work of the woodcarver William Gibbs Rogers who had a respect for and a sensitivity towards 17th century craftsmanship seldom found amongst his contemporaries. The complete set of box pews and sword rests are only some of the features that make the church worth visiting.

St Mary-at-Hill is also well known for its music. The fine 1835 organ is used for weekly recitals, and for a monthly performance of a Bach Cantata together with an ensemble of young musicians. These musicians, who may be professionals or students from the Royal Academy of Music, give their time and skills voluntarily, and the performances are sponsored by local companies. There is also a choir which can be heard at Tuesday lunchtime. About a dozen people attend these Communion services which are traditional Anglican in form, using the 1662 Prayer Book.

St Mary-at-Hill has associations with many City firms and Livery companies, and the Billingsgate Ward Club continue to regard the church as their local church although the famous fish market has moved away. The Rev Dr Kirk-Duncan is particularly involved with their Billingsgate Christian Mission, which helps the elderly of the parish and operates a free dispensary run by volunteer doctors and nurses.

The interior of St Mary-at-Hill was badly damaged by fire on 10th May 1988.

Service: Wednesday 1.15pm Holy Communion □ Wheelchair: no access □ Visiting: open 9am–5pm Monday to Friday

St Mary-le-Bow (Bow Church)

Cheapside, EC2 □ Bus: 8, 22, 25 □ Tube: Bank □ Parking: difficult except weekends □ Rector: Rev Victor Stock □ Address: Rector's Lodgings, St Mary-le-Bow, EC2 □ Telephone: 248 5139 □ Available: most times at church

St Mary-le-Bow is a church famed for its steeple—one of Wren's most splendid creations—and for Bow Bells. The Great Bell of Bow features in *Oranges and Lemons* of course, and one has to be born within earshot of these bells to be a true Cockney.

The church's recent fortunes have improved considerably since the arrival of a new rector in September 1986. By the simple expedient of extending the hours the church is open and arranging the times of service to suit the needs of people who work in the area, Rev Victor Stock has seen attendance grow enormously. Thus Morning and Evening Prayers (the latter also known here as 'Going Home Prayers') are held before and after people are at work, respectively, and the Eucharist is also celebrated outside working hours; there is a popular informal discussion session on Tuesday at 1.10pm. For the most part services are kept brief. The nearest thing to a traditional Sunday service is the Thursday evening Parish Communion, featuring a sermon and music.

The church itself was gutted in 1941 and the present interior is largely the work of Laurence King during the 1950s. There is no division, save a modern rood by John Hayward, between the nave and chancel. Ths stained glass is also by Hayward, though many of the windows are clear affording much light. Other rooms include the crypt and the Court of Arches, both underground, which contain Roman and Norman architectural remains.

Although there are no congregational activities, the church is regularly used by Livery companies and City institutions for special services. There are also exhibitions of paintings here and every Thursday lunchtime there is a music recital.

Services: Thursday 5.30pm Evening Prayer & Parish Communion; Tuesday & Friday 8.30pm Eucharist; Wednesday 12.30pm Eucharist; Monday–Friday 8.15am Morning Prayer; Monday–Wednesday 5.45pm Evening Prayer □ Children: creche at foot of tower □ Wheelchair: 4 shallow steps to nave; no access to crypt chapel □ Other details: meeting room □ Visiting: open 7.30am–7pm Monday–Friday

St Mary Woolnoth

Lombard Street, EC3 □ Telephone: 626 9701 □ Bus: 6, 8, 9, 11, 15a, 43 □ Tube: Bank □ Parking: 'impossible' □ Priest-in-Charge: Rev Hereward Cooke □ Address: 19 Geraldine Road, SW18 □ Telephone: 870 1873 □ Available: anytime by phone

The Guild church of St Mary Woolnoth is not difficult to find, occupying as it does a commanding position near the Bank of England. Indeed, anyone coming to the church by tube will discover that Bank Station is directly beneath the church, the crypt having been sold in the late 19th century and the dead re-interred at Ilford. Two of the station's exits are in the church's walls.

The exterior of this remarkable church is bold and imposing, with its twin turreted tower supported by Corinthian columns. It is the only City church designed by Nicholas Hawksmoor, Wren's famous pupil. Built on the site of earlier churches of the same name, Hawksmoor's church was completed in 1727. The interior is unusual, being square in shape, possibly influenced by Roman architecture; the central lantern, with its four semi-circular windows, is supported by four groups of three massive Corinthian columns. The gallery was taken down in the 19th century, but the carved wooden fronts were thought to be quite fine, and were mounted straight onto the walls, where they now form a frieze around the interior.

Nowadays, there are few services, and none on Sundays, since the local residential population is almost non-existent. The congregation of the weekly Holy Communion service on Tuesday is made up largely of local office workers and retired people.

Two choirs are attached to the church, and, as well as singing at services, give three concerts each during the year. The Woolnoth Society, a group formed by members of American banks, also meet at St Mary's, and hold their own carol service. The presence of so many American firms in the area means that there is a large Thanksgiving Day service which is well attended.

Services: Tuesday 1.10pm Holy Communion □ Wheelchair: very difficult □ Visiting: open 8.30am–5pm during the week

St Michael

Cornhill, EC3 □ Bus: 8, 22, 25 □ Tube: St Paul's □ Parking: very difficult except Sunday □ Rector: Rev David Burton Evans □ Address: St Michael's Vestry, Cornhill, EC3 □ Telephone: 626 8841 □ Available: at church Sunday morning and 9.30am–4pm Monday to Friday

Although only three people, all of whom are caretakers, now reside in the parish, St Michael's has retained its status as a parish church. Earliest records of the church date from 1055, though the present Classical structure was designed by Wren and built on to an old tower which survived the Great Fire. When this tower had to be largely demolished in 1715, it was replaced by the pinnacled and arguably incongruous Gothic affair we see today; it is commonly attributed to Hawksmoor who was still working in Wren's office at that time.

The interior was heavily Victorianised, though much of the consequent gloominess has now been relieved with the installation of clear glass. Most features are by George Gilbert Scott, though the excellent work of William Gibbs Rogers (qv St Mary-at-Hill) is much in evidence. Note also the huge carved pelican of piety at the west end; authoritative commentators seem unable to agree whether it is of marble or wood.

Sunday services are based on the Book of Common Prayer and alternate between choral Matins and choral Eucharist with masses by composers as diverse as Palestrina, Mozart, Vaughan Williams, Langlais and Michael Berkeley. This fine long-standing musical tradition draws many people to the services and the church has its own professional-standard choir. Other musical events at the church include organ recitals on Mondays and the Cornhill Festival of Music, held every 18 months, which is a prestigious event of international repute. A composers competition is also organised. Choirs from all over the world travel here to perform.

St Michael's is host to many memorial and special services; for example the Stock Exchange and for Lloyds of London. It is also the venue for the annual City New Year Service, held on the second Tuesday in January. The Patrons of the Living are the Drapers' Company who hold their services here as well as the Merchant Taylors' Company, the Woolmen, Master Mariners and the Guild of Air Pilots and Air Navigators who all hold their services here and regard it as 'their church'.

The former graveyard is now an attractive garden to the south of the church building much frequented by City workers in summer as a peaceful spot in which to meet and eat their lunches.

Services: Sunday 11am Choral Eucharist; Wed and Fri 1.10pm Holy Communion □ Wheelchair: 4 steps □ Visiting: open 10am–1.30pm Sunday and 8am–5pm Monday to Friday; small selection of books available

St Michael Paternoster Royal

College Hill, EC4 □ Telephone: 248 5202 (office) □ Bus: 6, 9, 11, 15, 15a, 17, 76, 95, 149, 184, 513 □ Tube/BR: Cannon Street □ Parking: NCP opposite □ Chaplain: Rev Canon Bill Down □ Address: 6 Hartsbourne Avenue, Bushey Heath, Watford □ Telephone: 950 3178 □ Available: at church office 8am–6pm weekdays □ Other clergy: Revv Glyn Jones, Moses Wu

Dick Whittington, four-times Lord Mayor of London and famous figure of popular legend, was a great benefactor. One of his good works was to rebuild his parish church, St Michael Paternoster Royal and it was here, in 1423, that he was buried. That particular building was destroyed in the Great Fire, but it was rebuilt between 1686–94 by Sir Christopher Wren. Gutted by fire bombs in 1944, the church was refurbished by Elidir Davies in the 1960s.

The church exterior remains much as Wren designed it; it has the advantage of being fronted by a small, landscaped area which affords visitors splendid views of the church, with its elegant tower prominent. The reconstructed interior is also fine and is sympathetic with the character of the church. Its dark wooden panelling has been restored, as has the original ironwork and all of the old church's wall monuments have been cleaned and put back. An impressive modern feature is the stained glass by John Hayward including, at the rear of the church, a window depicting Dick Whittington (complete with cat).

St Michael ceased to be a parish church a long time ago and was designated as a Guild church in 1954, although recently this has changed again and the church is now a chapel under the Bishop of London's jurisdiction. The church's main function is as the headquarters of the Missions to Seamen, and the incumbent, the Rev Canon Bill Down, is the General Secretary of the organisation. The Missions to Seamen runs 90 seamen's clubs worldwide, and cares for all seafarers of all races and all creeds, offering help, counselling and welcome in over 300 ports through its network of chaplains. Canon Down travels 100,000 miles a year over a three-month period visiting the various places run by the Missions to Seamen.

The church itself has no regular congregation, since there are few services and no resident population in the area to speak of. The 9.30am weekday services are mainly attended by staff, and the Thursday Holy Communion services at 12.30pm have a congregation of up to 20 made up largely of local office workers. On Sundays, the church is given over to Chinese Anglicans, and there are no English language services then. On special occasions, such as Livery company services, the church is filled.

Services: Daily 9.30am Morning Prayer; Thursday 12.30pm Holy Communion; Sunday 11am Anglican Chinese language service □ Facilities: amplification □ Wheelchair: 3 steps; ramp available if required □ Other details: hall may be available on written request □ Visiting: open 8am–6pm Monday to Friday

St Olave

Hart Street, EC3 □ Bus: 15, 42, 47a, 56, 78 □ Tube/BR:Tower Hill, Fenchurch Street □ Parking: on street □ Rector: Rev Canon Eric Jarvis □ Address: St Olave's Rectory, 8 Hart Street, Mark Lane, EC3 □ Telephone: 488 4318 □ Available: most times at church or Rectory

'. . . there is attraction of repulsion for me in St Ghastly Grim and, having often contemplated it in the daylight and the dark, I once felt drawn to it in a thunderstorm at midnight. "Why not?" I said, in self-excuse. "I have been to the Colosseum by the light of the moon; is it worse to go and see St Ghastly Grim by the light of lightning?" ' This is how Charles Dickens talks of the principal gateway into the St Olave's graveyard in *The Uncommercial Traveller*. Since 1658 this gate has stood, strong and iron-spiked, adorned with skulls and crossbones, and it presents the visitor with a grand, if macabre, contemplation before entering what is really a delightful medieval church.

The present building was constructed about 1450 and is one of the eight remaining churches of the City which survived the Great Fire of 1666. It is a low-roofed church of ragstone with a south-west tower, and is said to have been constructed by two fellmongers (ie skinners). The dedication is to a sainted King of Norway who once helped Ethelred the Unrede repulse the Danes by pulling down London Bridge.

This connection with Norway has always been continued, and today one will even find the national flag inside the church. In fact, during the post-war restoration work King Haakon VI of Norway laid a dedication stone, next to which is a fragment of the stone of Trondheim Cathedral where the saint is buried.

The parish is very small today, with few residents. Communion is therefore held on only one Sunday each month. However, every Wednesday and Friday at 1.05pm there are music recitals which attract many local office workers and others. Two other churches used at one time to be connected with St Olave's: All Hallows, Staining and St Catherine Coleman. The former was taken down in

St Ghastly Grim, St Olave, EC3

1870—only the 70 ft high tower remains (in Mark Lane). It is over 400 years old and is a good example of Perpendicular architecture. The latter used to stand in Fenchurch Street, but was finally pulled down in 1925.

Services: Thursday 8.15am Holy Communion; 1st Sunday 11am Holy Communion; Monday–Friday Morning and Evening Prayer (HC as announced) □ Wheelchair: steep steps, very difficult □ Other details: hall □ Visiting: generally open during the week, usually closed at weekends

St Paul's Cathedral

St Paul's Churchyard, EC4 □ Bus: 4, 6, 8, 9, 11, 15, 15a, 17, 22, 25, 141, 501, 502, 513 □ Tube/BR: St Paul's, Blackfriars, Mansion House □ Parking: NCP Car Park in Ave Maria Lane, Corporation coach park SE side (no street parking) □ Dean: Very Rev T Eric Evans □ Address: 9 Amen Court, EC4 □ Telephone: 236 2827 □ Other clergy: 4 Residential Canons; many other staff □ Enquiries: (Chapter House) 248 2705, Virgers (and Lost Property) 248 4619

St Paul's has an ecumenical outlook. One is welcome to worship here regardless of denomination. There is no regular congregation as such, at any time most of the people will be visitors, but there are regular attenders, and a Congregational Fellowship meets several times a year to bring worshippers and supporters of the church together. Then there are the Friends of St Paul's who help visitors and give out information on the cathedral's activities.

There is no individual incumbent (although of course this is the church of the Bishop of London, whose 'cathedra' or throne is in the Choir). In time-honoured fashion the cathedral is governed by the Dean and Chapter, that is, the four Residentiary Canons. There is also the College of Minor Canons, and the Prebendaries, and all have seats in the Choir. As well as clergy some 130 people are involved in running the cathedral.

One immediately associates St Paul's with its special services, particularly those associated with royalty such as Jubilee and Thanksgiving services. The wedding of the Prince of Wales and Lady Diana Spencer in 1981 focused the attention of the world as the royal carriages drove up Ludgate Hill to the Great West Entrance. The cathedral stands as the apex of the achievement of the English architectural Renaissance and is the masterpiece of Sir Christopher Wren.

Here we can only assure the visitor that the Whispering Gallery is well worth paying to see, but you do have to be fit to climb up. Those with a good head for heights can ascend to the top of the magnificent dome, from where there is a panorama of the whole of central London. Directly below the dome, on the ground floor, is a memorial to Churchill, and directly below this in the crypt, the striking tomb of Admiral Lord Nelson. To see all the beautiful furnishings of the cathedral would take several hours.

Four services are held here each day. Every Sunday over 1,000 people come to the two main services. The form of worship steers a middle course, avoiding both high ceremonial and over-simplicity. Sunday Mattins and Evensong are from the Book of Common Prayer, as is the Sunday 11.30am Choral Communion except on the 3rd and 5th Sundays of the month when it is taken from the ASB. At other services the choice of the form is left to the individual celebrant. The musical

Worshippers, St Paul's Cathedral, EC4

tradition *is* 'high', and there is the choir of 12 men and 38 boys (resident in St Paul's own Choir School).

Today, as ever, St Paul's plays a major role in the religious life of the metropolis. However it cannot avoid being a great monument and most people who come here are sightseers pure and simple. At present there is no admission charge, though one does have to pay to get into certain, restricted access, parts of the cathedral.

Services: Sunday 8am Holy Communion, 10.30am Choral Mattins, 11.30am Choral Communion, 3.15pm Choral Evensong, July 11am Choral Communion; Weekdays 7.30am Said Mattins, 8am Holy Communion, 10am Choral Mattins (Saturdays only), 12.30pm Holy Communion (Mon–Thur & Sat), 5pm Choral Evensong □ Facilities: amplification □ Wheelchair: level access entrance available but notification needed □ Other details: lecture room (for audio-visual presentations etc), crypt chapel (occasional lectures), library, etc □ Visiting: open from early morning until 6pm daily; shop, open 9am–4.45pm; fees charged for admission to ambulatory, galleries, crypt and treasury; conducted tours at 11am, 2pm and 2.30pm weekdays (fee charged; group rates available); entrance to all parts may be restricted during special services

The Chapel of St Peter-ad-Vincula

HM Tower of London, EC3 □ Bus: 15, 42, 47a □ Tube: Tower Hill □ Parking: very difficult □ Chaplain: Rev John Llewellyn □ Address: Chaplain's House, HM Tower of London, EC3 □ Telephone: 709 0765 Ex 246 □ Available: at service times

The small chapel of St Peter-ad-Vincula sits within the walls of the Tower of London next to the Jewel House. A chapel is mentioned in 1210 but the present building dates from around 1520, which nonetheless makes is something of a rarity as an example of Tudor architecture in London. The original plain design has been augmented over the centuries, and today the chapel is a happy blend of ancient and modern.

The most noteworthy tomb is the magnificent 15th century monument to John Holland, Duke of Exeter. The unusual font, which can be dated from around 1490, is a fine example of Tudor work; it has survived due to the foresight of a chaplain who concealed it during the Puritan purges, and it was re-discovered just over 100 years ago in an empty tomb! The organ is a rare piece, the first Schmidt instrument in the country, while an interesting modern addition is the silver cross by the altar, the staff of which was carved in 1970 from a 900 year-old oak roof bean from the White Tower.

Apart from the fabric of the chapel however, it is its very position which makes it so evocative of the history of the realm. A list at the entrance records the burial of many prominent people, amongst whom are Sir Thomas More, Queen Anne Boleyn, John Fisher and Lady Jane Grey. To visit during the week, one must pay to enter the Tower grounds and join a guided tour which terminates at the chapel.

The chapel is not merely a museum piece however, for there are two services each Sunday. The first is mostly attended by residents and staff of the Tower, while the 11 am service attracts a good number of both regulars from all over London and tourists. admission to worship is, of course, free but this does not enable one to have a free tour of the Tower. The services are traditional, using the

1662 Prayer Book, and there is a notably fine choir. Details of services are published in *The Times* and *The Daily Telegraph*.

Services: Sunday 9.15am Holy Communion (said), 11am Sung Matins with sermon (No services during August) □ Wheelchair: no access □ Visiting: open 9.30am to 4pm (5pm during summer) weekdays as part of guided tour of Tower (fee charged); free entrance for services

St Peter-upon-Cornhill

Cornhill, EC3 □ Bus: 15a, 25, 35, 47, 48 □ Tube: Bank, Monument □ Parking: 'impossible' □ Priest-in-Charge: Rev John Cross □ Address: The Vestry, St Peter-upon-Cornhill, EC3 □ Telephone: 626 9483 □ Available: contact secretary, 8am–4pm Monday to Friday (except August)

The Cornhill door to this church is all too easily missed, squashed as it is between office buildings. The best entrance is along a small alleyway at the side of the church, and through a small churchyard with two large plane trees. A good view of the attractive steeple can be gained from this churchyard.

The church is on the itinerary of the City Heritage Walk and the visit may well include a short talk, not only on the history of St Peter's but also on the present work, for this is one of the more active City churches. For example, while the Thursday lunchtime Holy Communion (a traditional though shortened form of service during the 1662 Book of Common Prayer) is attended by usually fewer than ten worshippers, a Praise Group meeting at lunchtime on Mondays with guitar accompaniment and sometimes a talk or discussion, attracts between 50 and 60. Various prayer groups also meet during the week, and as the mid-day timing suggests, these, like the services, are geared to people working in the city. Indeed, much attention is given in talks, discussions and prayer groups to the role of the Church today and its relevance to the world of the City. Close links have been established with many local companies, and the church works alongside personnel departments and voluntary groups.

Built by Wren in 1677–81, the church came through the Blitz largely unscathed, and has many handsome fittings. Of particular interest is the chancel screen, designed by Wren himself, reputedly with the help of his sixteen year old daughter. It is one of only two by Wren and the only one in its original setting. It is the church of the Royal Tank Regiment and several other regiments. Also linked to the church is the British Sailors' Society, an interdenominational society of which the rector of St Peter's is usually a director.

Regular organ recitals are given on the instrument declared by Mendelssohn to be 'the finest in London', and the church is also the venue each December for the medieval mystery plays presented by the St Peter Players. This is an amateur dramatic group composed of people from various walks of life, and their popular week-long run of performances raises much needed money for the upkeep of the church.

Services: Monday 1.10pm Praise Group meeting; Thursday 12.30pm Holy Communion; Wed and Fri 1.10pm Prayer Group □ Facilities: amplification □ Wheelchair: 2 steps to church □ Visiting: contact secretary or verger for details.

St Sepulchre-without-Newgate (Church of the Holy Sepulchre)

Holborn Viaduct, EC1 □ Bus: 4, 8, 22, 25, 279 □ Tube/BR: St Paul's, Farringdon, Holborn Viaduct □ Rector: Rev Arthur Brown □ Administrator: Andrew Pearmain □ Telephone: 248 1660 □ Available: most times

The Church of the Holy Sepulchre has many associations with music. Sydney Nicholson founded the School of English Church Music here and the ashes of Sir Henry Wood are interred in the North Chapel. The latter became Assistant Organist here at the precocious age of 14, and today, along with many other famous musicians, he is commemorated in the North Chapel on the many embroidered kneelers inscribed with musical motifs. Indeed, nearly every item of furniture in this chapel is in memory of a deceased musician. St Sepulchre is also the church where the famous City of London Choir originated.

The Musicians' Benevolent Fund organise an annual festival of St Cecilia with glorious music sung by representatives of the choirs of St Paul's Cathedral, Westminster Abbey, Westminster Cathedral, and the Chapel Royal. Also on Fridays every week there is a music recital at the church during lunchtime beginning at 1.10pm. The church houses a fine Renatus Harris organ built in 1677.

The church sits opposite the Old Bailey and within its tower are the original 'Bells of Old Bailey' celebrated in the nursery rhyme. These ten surviving bells have been restored after war damage and with the addition of two new bells are now rung at least once per month. There is also an interesting hand bell inside the church which was rung at midnight by the sexton in Newgate Prison before an execution.

The church was founded in 1137 but suffered greatly from the Great Fire. Very little of the medieval building remains—the fan-vaulted porch being the only substantial remains and also a 15th century piscina on the south wall which shows some blackening by the fire. St Sepulchre was restored, however, by Wren, and his font and some of his pews are still in use.

The church does not have a sizeable congregation. It mainly functions nowadays as a venue for music recitals and the interested visitor. It has no Sunday services as these take place in the nearby church, St Bartholomew the Great, and it closes altogether during February.

Services: Tuesday 8.15am Holy Communion, 1.10 Choral Service; Thursday 9am Holy Communion □ Wheelchair: awkward doors, but access possible □ Visiting: open 9am–4pm Monday to Friday; closed during February

St Vedast-alias-Foster

Foster Lane, EC2 □ Bus: 8, 15, 25 □ Tube: St Paul's □ Parking: difficult except weekends □ Rector: Rev Raymond Avent □ Address: The Rectory, Foster Lane, EC2 □ Telephone: 606 3998 □ Available: telephone for appointment □ Other staff: Christine Brown, Verger

There has been a church of St Vedast here since 1249 for, though this French saint is almost unknown in Britain, there was a Norman French colony settled here at the time the first church was built. His name has been subject to many corruptions, such as Vastes, Fastre, Faister and—its most English variant—Foster. Hence the unusual name of this church.

The Wren-designed church we see today was completed in 1673, apart from the particularly graceful spire which was added in 1697. The church was bombed during the Blitz but was faithfully restored in 1962, and it was fortunate enough to receive various pieces of Wren period furniture such as the organ case, reredos and pulpit. Modern features include the east windows by Brian Thomas and the introduction of 'collegiate' style seating, whereby members of the congregation face each other across the nave.

Of the congregation, a good proportion come because they appreciate the traditional nature of the services, which are Catholic in form. Unusually, the 1928 Prayer Book (never approved by Parliament) is used on Sundays. The main service is the Sunday Sung Mass, which is announced by a sweet peal of bells and followed by wine in the Parish Room. There is a daily Low Mass at lunchtime, coffee and toast are provided after the Saturday Mass, and there is a monthly parish lunch to which all who come contribute. The Week of Prayer for Christian Unity held in January is shared with the nearby Lutheran Church of St Anne and St Agnes on the Sunday of that week.

The Parish Room and church itself are available for use by various organisations currently including the Pewterers, Saddlers, Weavers, the Ecclesiological Society, bell ringers, prayer groups, Alcoholics Anonymous, and the London Group who are concerned with relating Christian beliefs to commercial life. The church has a small garden which is open to the public.

Services: Sunday 11am Sung Mass; Weekdays 12.15pm Low Mass; Saturday 8.30am Low Mass; Confession 12.45pm Wednesday or by appointment □ Children: creche at foot of tower □ Wheelchair: 2 steps; wide aisles □ Other details: Parish room □ Visiting: open 8am–6pm Monday–Friday, 8.30–9.30am Saturday, 8am–12noon Sunday; bookstall

Temple Church

Inner Temple Lane, EC4 □ Bus: 4, 6, 11, 15, 15a, 171, 502, 513 □ Tube: Temple □ Parking: difficult except Sundays □ Master: Rev Canon Joseph Robinson □ Address: The Master's House, Temple, EC4 □ Telephone: 353 8559 □ Available: telephone for appointment □ Other clergy: W D Kennedy-Bell, Reader

Reached through a narrow passageway off Fleet Street and situated within the Inns of Court, the Temple Church is one of the most fascinating churches in London, and is certainly one of the oldest. It was founded in 1185 by the Order of Knights Templar and later used by the rival Order of Knights Hospitallers, before acquiring its present status in 1608. This status itself is unusual for the Temple Church has no parish, but is the private chapel of the Inner and Middle Temples. As such, it is outside the jurisdiction of the Bishop of London and has a master rather than a rector, who acts as a chaplain to the lawyers of the Inns of Court.

However, it is the building itself, though much restored, that is perhaps most remarkable, both inside and out. The original church, modelled on the Church of the Holy Sepulchre in Jerusalem, is round, and is one of the finest examples of the Transitional style when the Romanesque was giving way to the lighter Gothic. The triforium arcading in the Round Church exemplifies this style having semi-circular arches which intersect to create pointed arches. The floor has several effigies of knights set into it, and around the wall are stone heads with faces contorted into grotesque and often humorous expressions.

The Round Church constitutes the nave, but contains no pews. All the seating, arranged collegiate fashion, is in the enlarged choir area, built in true Gothic and added in 1240. This is rich in stained glass and has many interesting features. It was 'beautified' by Wren and subsequently by Victorians who swept away all his work. Thus the reredos, carved by William Emmett, escaped the terrible damage the church suffered during the Blitz and was restored to its original home in 1953.

Although the church is deemed a private chapel, the public is most welcome to attend the services on Sundays. The main Sunday service is the 11.15 Choral Morning Prayer, in the cathedral style. The music is provided by a professional choir of men and boys which is quite famous and has made several recordings. Between 100 and 150 people attend this service, the number almost doubling during summer and at special festivals. The congregation is predominantly adult, most of whom travel some distance to attend. In summer, many tourists and visitors join them.

Services: Sunday 8.30am Holy Communion, 11.15am Morning Prayer (choral), 12.30pm (Greater Festivals and 1st Sunday of the month) Holy Communion; occasional weekday services as announced (No services during August and September) □ *Facilities: amplification* □ *Wheelchair: 1 step at the entrance* □ *Visiting: usually open 10am–4pm daily; often closed August and September*

Church of England : Westminster

All Saints

Margaret Street, W1 □ *Bus: 8, 25, 53, 73* □ *Tube: Oxford Circus* □ *Parking: on street* □ *Vicar: Rev David Hutt* □ *Address: Vicarage, 7 Margaret Street, W1* □ *Telephone: 636 1788/9961* □ *Available: most times* □ *Other clergy: Rev Gerald Reddington*

Since its consecration in 1859, All Saints' has been at the centre of both fame and controversy. The startling interior of dark brick, with contrasting tiles and inlaid marble covering almost every inch of the wall space, has been described as embodying many things, from beautiful mystery to tasteless extravagance.

The church was designed by William Butterfield to exemplify the ideals of the Oxford Movement, principally that the attention of all the worshippers whould be directed towards the single altar which itself is not hidden by a screen. Having satisfied this demand, it seems Butterfield's imagination ran riot, creating the lavishly decorated interior that has been described as 'frozen turmoil'. The west window, a riot of blues, reds and greens depicting the Tree of Jesse, is particularly impressive in the pervading gloom of the rest of the church.

There are countless other features of this church, not least the handsome spire, and it is no surprise to learn it has been called the 'Cathedral of Anglo-Catholicism'. The liturgical tradition has continued unaltered and, along with the excellent quality of the music, this goes a long way towards explaining why a church with such a small, sparsely-populated parish attracts such large congregations. The church employs a professional choir which, accompanied by the splendid Harrison organ, lends a cathedral-like flavour to services. A further attraction, it is felt, is that regular confessional times are regarded as an important part of the church's role, alongside daily canonical worship and the ready availability of skilled pastoral help and counsel.

Given the church's location in a business area there is little obvious call for a community programme, but the incumbent, Fr Hutt, is keen to develop outreach groups to teach and help local people. The old choir school dining room has been converted to community use, while the church itself continues to be a place dedicated to God available to all, whether for the purpose of prayer, worship, or whatever.

Services: Sunday 8am Low Mass, 10.20am Morning Prayer, 11am High Mass, 5.15pm Low Mass, 6pm Evensong & Benediction; Weekdays 6.45am Morning Prayer, 7.30am Mass, 1pm Mass (except Sat), 5.45pm Evening Prayer, 6.30pm Mass. Confessions at 12.30pm, 3.30pm and 6pm except Sunday □ Wheelchair: ramp □ Other details: community room □ Visiting: open daily from 6.40am (Sun 7.30am) to 7pm; visitors book; Sunday gift shop

All Souls, Langham Place

2 All Souls Place, W1 □ Telephone: 580 4357 □ Bus: 3, 53, 137 (& Oxford St buses) □ Tube: Oxford Circus □ Parking: limited on-street space □ Rector: Rev Richard T Bewes □ Address: 12 Weymouth Street, W1 □ Telephone: 580 6029 □ Available: by telephone (try church first) □ Other staff: five other clergy and full administration staff; Director of Administration Rob Cook (580 3522)

Visiting All Souls, Langham Place, you are encouraged to feel at home right away. On entering you first encounter the volunteer staff at the Welcome Desk; then, armed with information, you discover just what an impressive church this is. It is a Georgian building, designed by Nash, and is his only surviving church on mainland Britain. It was built in the celebratory mood following the battle of Waterloo. The chancel, though, is modern, and its wooden floor can be raised and lowered hydraulically. In 1974 there was a major restoration of the interior. The floor was excavated some fifteen feet, and here the Waldegrave Hall has been constructed. There is also the Well, a small seating area, and a refectory.

This is the country's most famous evangelical church, and it has an international reputation. The services vary in style: traditional, with organ and choir, or (increasingly) informal, with a music group. Once a month an orchestra us used. There is a full clergy, under the rector, Richard Bewes. The service text is varied (BCP and Series 3), but straightforward English is preferred, not least so it can be understood by the many visitors from overseas. The church operates a tape library of past sermons, which is available to the general public.

Just across the street are the offices of BBC Radio, and since 1935 their Daily Service has often been broadcast from All Souls. For the main parish Sunday service the church is packed, with a congregation of around a thousand drawn from anywhere up to twenty miles away. One Sunday each month is an

All Souls, Langham Place, W1

'Invitation Sunday' when all are welcome to hear the basic message of the Gospels. Those who have only recently made a commitment to church worship are encouraged to join a 'Beginners' Group', to discover more about Christianity. Also, nothing if not even-handed, All Souls runs a group called 'Agnostics Anonymous' for those who want to come along and argue their doubts with others.

A community centre in Cleveland Street serves the poorer east side of the parish with additional Sunday services as well as facilities for youth clubs. It also acts as a family centre and as a day centre for the elderly. The main activity though, outside Sunday services, is the fortnightly prayer gathering in the Waldegrave Hall. This is regarded as an essential part of the life of the church, and about three hundred people turn up. On alternate Tuesdays there are the 'Fellowship Groups', about eighty of them, each with ten or so members, which meet in homes all over London. The All Souls International Fellowship runs a number of activities specially aimed at those who come from overseas. Also, the church supports an organisation called 20/20, which runs social activities for those in their twenties (many of whom are unattached and new to London). More information on all these and many more activities are available from the Welcome Desk.

Services: Sunday 9.30am Communion, 11am Morning Service, 6.30pm Evening Service; Thursday 1.05pm Lunchtime Service. The church is often host to the BBC daily service, to which members of the public are invited to attend, (please be quiet during these services). Many special services; contact the church for details □ Facilities: amplification, deaf loop, large print ASBs □ Children: creche at Sunday morning services; Sunday school □ Wheelchair: lift outside main entrance on left—ring bell for assistance □ Other details: church hall, two meeting rooms, refectory, Clubhouse, Tape Library (sermons, etc), Book Centre, etc □ Visiting: open 9am–10pm Sunday, 9am–6pm most other days; the Welcome Desk is open to give help and information to all visitors, and also sells guide books, etc

The Church of the Annunciation

Bryanston Street, W1 □ Bus: any to Marble Arch □ Tube: Marble Arch □ Parking: difficult except Sunday □ Vicar: Rev Michael Burgess □ Address: 4 Wyndham Place, W1 □ Telephone: 262 4329 □ Available: most times

When first built in 1914, the Church of the Annunciation must have been quite a landmark and, although it is all but hidden by modern office blocks and hotels, it remains a fine building, well worth seeking out. Built in an Edwardian Gothic style, it occupies the site of the old Quebec Chapel. Nearby was a riding school for soldiers whose barracks stood on the site of the present Marks & Spencer; the church still contains many military references, including images of the warrior saints, George and Michael.

Stained glass is also much in evidence, some of it by Bewsey. The two east windows are impressive, though the finest work is in the baptistry. The Stations of the Cross are by Beule of Ghent. In all, the church provides a rich setting for worship in the 'high' Anglican tradition with full ceremonial . Service details are published in *The Times*.

Upstairs at the church is a small gallery. This is let cheaply to young artists, enabling them to display their work in an attractive and central location.

Services: Sunday 11am Solemn Mass, 6pm Low Mass, 6.30pm Benediction; for weekday services, see The Times. □ *Children: Parish school services* □ *Wheelchair: level access* □ *Other details: music room, crypt, gallery upstairs* □ *Visiting: open as far as grille 8am–7pm daily; remainder for services only*

Chapel Royal

St James's Palace, St James Street, SW1

The Queen's Chapel

Marlborough House, Marlborough Road, SW1 □ *Bus: 9, 14, 22, 25, 38, 55* □ *Tube: Green Park* □ *Parking: on street, difficult* □ *Sub-Dean: Canon Anthony Caesar* □ *Address: as Chapel Royal* □ *Telephone: 930 6609* □ *Available: most days*

Strictly speaking, the Chapel Royal is not a building but a body of clergy and choristers who serve the spiritual needs of the Sovereign. Dating back to the 11th century, 'the Chappell' would accompany the Monarch of the day on all his travels, including Henry V's invasion of France. It was Queen Anne who moved the choral foundation of the Chapel Royal to St James's Palace, and since 1938, the Chapel has also used the Queen's Chapel.

Of the original Tudor building which stood on the site of St James's Palace, only the chapel and gatehouse remain. Part of the ceiling of the chapel, attributed to Holbein, commemorates the marriage of Henry VIII and Anne of Cleves, and is richly decorated with Royal Heraldry, cyphers and names of the Cleve family estates. The many Royal marriages that have taken place here include Queen Victoria's marriage to Prince Albert in 1840.

Queen's Chapel, designed in the Palladian style by Inigo Jones, was built for Roman Catholic worship in 1623–7. It was built for the bride of Charles I, Henrietta Maria, who brought her Catholic clergy with her from France. Wren refurnished the chapel later for another Queen, Catherine of Braganza, wife of Charles II. Up until 1936, several European congregations, including German and Danish Lutherans, were given permission to worship at the Queen's Chapel.

The fine tradition of church music of the Chapel Royal is maintained at the services in both chapels. The great organists and musicians of the past, including Purcell and Handel, set an example in style that was copied by the cathedrals of England. Further, the services feature, in cathedral tradition, a choir of 'six Gentlemen and ten Children' who still wear the ancient scarlet and gold state coats.

From the first Sunday in October to Good Friday, services are held at the Chapel Royal, St James's Palace. From Easter Sunday to the last Sunday in July, services move to the Queen's Chapel. Both chapels are closed during August and September. Between 75 and 100 people attend services, including Palace staff and their families. The Book of Common Prayer is used and visitors are welcome.

Services: Sunday 8.30am Holy Communion, 11.15am Sung Eucharist on 1st Sunday and Festivals, Sung Morning Prayer on other Sundays; Saints' Days 12.30pm Holy Communion □ *Wheelchair: Chapel Royal, several steps down; Queen's Chapel, one small step* □ *Visiting: service times only until further notice*

Christchurch, Mayfair

Down Street, W1 □ Bus: 2, 2b, 14, 16, 19, 22, 25, 30, 36, 36b, 38, 52, 52a, 55, 73, 74, 137 □ Tube: Green Park, Hyde Park Corner □ Parking: very difficult □ Priest-in-Charge: Rev David Prior □ Address: 4 Chester Square, SW1 □ Telephone: 730 8889 (Office) □ Available: all enquiries, phone above number

Tucked away on Down Street near Green Park, this small Victorian Gothic Church does not look as grand or smart as its Mayfair address may suggest. Christchurch is now part of the work of St Michael's, Chester Square (qv). The single weekly service now held here, usually led by Rev David Prior (Vicar of St Michael's), is at Wednesday lunchtime and is aimed at business people working in the area. The objectives are two-fold: firstly, to run a teaching series for those who are already Christians; and secondly, to be an evangelistic force in the Mayfair area. The short meetings usually include a talk and are followed by coffee and sandwiches.

Services: Wednesday 1.05–1.35pm □ Wheelchair: several steps at main door □ Visiting: open at service times only

Parish of Christchurch St Marylebone 1, St Mark

255 Old Marylebone Road, NW1 □ Bus: 6, 7, 8, 16a, 18, 27 □ Tube: Edgware Road □ Parking: on street □ Rector: Rev Dennis C King □ Address: as church □ Tel: 723 7544 □ Available: ring for appointment □ Other clergy: Rev Nicholas Smith

Designed by Bloomfield and completed in 1870, this red brick Victorian church, the daughter church of St Mary's in Bryanston Square, was originally built for the use of servants and the lower class of the parish. Now, since the amalgamation of several small parishes in the area whose churches were destroyed during the war, St Mark's and St Paul's, Rossmore Road, are together the churches of the parish of Christchurch, run by a parish team. Rev Dennis King is both parish Rector and the Vicar of St Mark's.

After spending several years in America and Jamaica, Fr King was appointed to St Marks in 1984. When he arrived the church was in need of repair. The paintwork was peeling away from the walls, buckets were placed in the nave to catch dripping rainwater and the electric system was liable to explode at any moment. Several thousand pounds had been collected, but only with the leasing of St Mark's hall to a gymnasium and the parish school to a video company were enough funds finally raised for the work to begin.

The interior of the church has now been repaired with complete rewiring, re-painting, and a new heating system installed. The white walls, blue pillars and the solitary stained glass window create a peaceful atmosphere. This is despite its position on the busy Old Marylebone Road, close to the junction of the Edgware Road.

Although St Mark's shares the social activities organised at St Paul's, there is one room available in the Vicarage for meetings and social groups of up to 30 people. The regular activities include a discussion group after the Wednesday service and an AA meeting on Friday evenings.

The numbers attending services at St Mark's have been small since the renovation of St Paul's, but the remaining congregation is committed and enthusiastic. As both churches use the same liturgy (ASB Rite A), worshippers choose their church largely according to convenience of locality and service times, although St Mark's does attract the more elderly parishioners.

Services: Sunday 8am, 10am (with choir); Tuesday 8am; Wednesday 12.30pm Eucharist followed by discussion; Thursday 11am; Friday 1.20pm; Saturday 9.30am (except in summer) □ *Facilities: large print texts* □ *Wheelchair: 1 small step* □ *Visiting: open for services only*

Parish of Christchurch St Marylebone 2, St Paul's Church Centre

9 Rossmore Road, NW1 □ *Bus: 2, 2b, 13, 74, 113, 159* □ *Tube: Baker Street, Marylebone* □ *Parking: on street* □ *Vicar: Rev Jack Maple* □ *Address: as church* □ *Telephone: 262 9442* □ *Available: ring for appointment*

After lying empty and derelict for seven years, St Paul's Centre is now a good example of the transformation which inner city churches can undergo to meet both community and congregational needs. Its role as a place of worship has been supplemented, but not superceded, buy a broader role as a community centre. Fr Jack Maple recognised in 1983 that the parish lacked the facilities and space it required to be a community in the true sense of the word, and as his idea of a church is that 'it should be seen serving the local community not just in worship', the work began.

By using funds from previously sold church property, several appeals and help from the GLC, over £180,000 was raised for conversion costs. Architect Quentin Pickard combined the original chancel and nave into one large hall, which can be converted from a place of worship into a dance hall in just a few minutes. For the Sunday morning service, a wooden altar from the chapel is placed under the original reredos—a Pre-Raphaelite painting of the risen Christ, Mary, St Paul and angels. Services are informal; organ music, for instance, is replaced by guitar and flute. By Sunday afternoon the altar is placed back in the chapel and the chairs put back in storage, ready for the activities that take place throughout the week. Activities range from a morning playgroup each weekday to ballroom dancing and volleyball.

Smaller rooms have been built underneath what was once the gallery. The rooms consist of a small chapel with seating for 20, a reception office and seating area, a meeting room with seating for up to 30 people, a kitchen, storeroom and toilets. New offices are to be built next year in the gallery. The office is manned during the week by a specially appointed member of staff who can give information on the centre's programmes.

In all, St Paul's is a successful, modern church centre. Its design, worship and secular activities demonstrate an awareness of the realities of inner-city life.

Services: Sunday 9.30am; Thursday 7.30pm in chapel, followed by prayer group □ *Facilities: large print texts* □ *Children: creche; Sunday school* □ *Wheelchair: easy access; toilets for disabled* □ *Other details: hall, meeting rooms* □ *Visiting: open every day*

Grosvenor Chapel

South Audley Street, W1 □ Bus: any along Oxford Street □ Tube: Marble Arch, Bond Street □ Parking: difficult except Sunday □ Priest-in-Charge: Rev Dr Anthony Marks □ Address: Liddon House, 24 South Audley Street, W1 □ Telephone: 499 1684 □ Available: most times

Fr Marks describes worship at Grosvenor Chapel as 'a very Anglican version of the Catholic religion that is both liberal and thoughtful'. The forms are recognisably Catholic, but the modern ASB Rite A language is used and—unusually for 'high' Anglicanism—Fr Marks delivers a substantial and challenging sermon at the main Communion service (11 am Sunday) when between 40 and 80 people attend. There is a professional choir and the standard of the music is very high.

Most of the congregation, some of whom may also come during the week, have made a conscious decision to embrace this style of worship, irrespective of how far they have to travel. They are of mixed ages, but are generally educated and independently minded, perhaps even slightly eccentric; it is worth noting that the most famous regular worshippers of recent times were Sir John Betjeman and the novelist Rose Macauley.

Grosvenor Chapel was built as a private estate chapel in 1730 and has been a Chapel of Ease to St George's, Hanover Square since 1831. The West End grew up around it, and the once local congregation moved away. During the Second World War, the chapel was used for worship by the US Armed Forces, and the Visitors' Book gives evidence of the many Americans, particularly ex-servicemen, who visit while in London. It is appropriate that the building, described as 'somewhat Colonial-looking' by Pevsner, should have been the model for so many churches overseas, especially in North America. The well-proportioned facade, surmounted by a short copper spire, is in what we are assured was once yellow brick.

The interior is dominated by the dramatic chancel screen and rood installed by Sir Ninian Comper in 1913. The rood is supported by massive white Ionic columns, and it is probable that Comper planned to extend these columns along the nave and to house his new High Altar under an extravagant baldacchino. Mercifully, all this proved to be impracticable, and the remainder of the chapel is as plain and dignified as an 18th century chapel should be. There is no amplification as it is felt to be quite unnecessary and potentially damaging to the special character and intimacy of divine worship. Intimacy is certainly a feature of the weekday services held in the screened-off chancel—it seats only six.

Because of its central location, the chapel is often used for memorial services. Marriages are few and Fr Marks is anxious to prevent the chapel becoming merely a fashionable West End venue for weddings. There are free music recitals every Tuesday lunchtime, and an occasional programme of lectures on theological or spiritual issues also takes place here.

Services: Sunday 8.15am Holy Communion, 10am Morning Prayer, 11am Sung Eucharist and sermon; Weekdays 12.30pm Holy Communion (plus 6.30pm Wed, 8am Thur) □ Wheelchair: 2 steps; help required □ Other details: Liddon House Retreat Centre □ Visiting: open 8am–6pm weekdays, Saturday mornings and Sunday service times only.

Guards Chapel (The Royal Military Chapel)

Wellington Barracks, off Birdcage Walk, SW1 □ Telephone: 930 4466 (Office) □ Bus: 10, 11, 24, 29, 70, 507 □ Tube: St James Park □ Parking: on street □ Padre: Rev JN Thomas □ Address & Telephone: c/o church office □ Available: daily except Mondays □ Other staff: Chapel Keeper, and secretary

The public entrance to the Guards Chapel is off Birdcage Walk, via a narrow cloister containing the Rolls of Honour of each regiment of the Household Division and the Book of Remembrance for those killed in the bombing of the original chapel in 1944. The cloister leads into the narthex at the rear, and as you enter, the Cenotaph of the Division, on the south wall, is directly in view. This short walk to the chapel quickly sets the atmosphere: this is both a church devoted to the worship of God and a monument to the many who have died defending their country.

All around are memorials to the seven regiments of the Division—from the upper walls and the narthex hang Regimental Standards and colours, many bearing the scars of battle and dating back as far as the American War of Independence. At the rear are a simple memorial to those killed in the Falklands War and the torn standard of the Blues and Royals, picked off the street nearby after an IRA bomb killed four of their number. Along the south wall are the Regimental Chapels, with the furnishings designed in consultation with the regiment concerned. Behind each altar is a list of actions in which each regiment was involved.

The original chapel, built in 1838, was destroyed by a bomb in 1944, except for the font and the sanctuary. Not only has the font been reinstalled, but the sanctuary itself, a colourful example of Victorian mosaic, was incorporated into the modern design and now stands out elegantly framed by the clean lines of the new chapel. Equally the new chapel's light and plain simplicity provides a counterpoint to the sombre war memorials.

The congregation, as one might expect, is largely made up of members of the Division, both past and present, but the very traditional format combined with a fine professional choir and Household Division band attract many overseas visitors and members of the public. Interdenominational services are also held when the padre invites Methodist or Roman Catholic ministers to preach. Many memorial services are held, while the padre is also kept very busy with marriages.

Services: 1st Sunday of month 11am Sung Eucharist; other Sundays 11am Choral Matins, 12 noon Holy Communion □ Facilities: amplification, deaf loop □ Wheelchair: access by ramp—separate door on right of main west portico by arrangement □ Visiting: open 10am–3pm Tuesday to Friday; guidebook available

Holy Trinity with All Saints

Prince Consort Road, SW7 □ Telephone: 584 9253 □ Bus: 9, 33, 49, 52, 52a, 73 □ Tube: South Kensington □ Parking: difficult on weekdays □ Priest-in-Charge: Rev Dr Martin Israel □ Address: Flat 2, 26 Tregunter Road, SW10 □ Available: whenever in

Holy Trinity was built in 1903 by G F Bodley, the last church he designed, and arguably his masterpiece. Baroque in style, its small facade belies the beauty of the church's interior. Inside it is most impressive, almost a miniature cathedral, with its magnificent stained glass windows and furnishings, including the altar, the brass eagle lectern, large pulpit, and reredos (a memorial to the architect).

The worship is in the broad Anglican tradition, not on the Catholic side (there are no vestments or incense), but not properly described as evangelical either. Services are based on the Book of Common Prayer. The church has a very fine musical tradition, and has a small professional choir. There is also an excellent organ; the organist-in-charge is a Professor of Music at the Royal College of Music. When taking the service, Dr Israel has no assistants, but members of the congregation help by reading the First and Second Lessons, and also the Epistle. Sunday congregations number around fifty and comprise mainly middle-aged to elderly people, though some are in their twenties and thirties and there are students from the numerous colleges in the area.

The church is used from time to time for concerts by the Royal College of Music; the church acts as host for these concerts in return for having the organ serviced regularly.

Services: Sunday 8.30am, 11am Choral Morning Prayer, followed by Holy Communion (except 1st Sunday: Choral Eucharist); Friday 11.45am Holy Communion □ Facilities: amplification □ Wheelchair: level access via west door □ Other details: hall □ Visiting: open 20 minutes before services

King's College Chapel

King's College, Strand, WC2 □ Bus: any along Strand □ Tube: Aldwych, Temple □ Parking: some space in college grounds □ Dean: Rev Canon RJA Askew □ Address: Room 7c, King's College □ Chaplains: Rev Chris Moody (CE), Rev Bob Styles (RC), Rev Kevin Swain (Free Church), Rev Alexander Fostiropoulos (Orthodox) □ Address: Room 6b, King's College □ Telephone: 836 5454 □ Available: term time

Although listed in the Church of England Diocese Book, King's College Chapel is a genuinely inter-denominational place of worship. Anglican Communion and Roman Catholic Mass are celebrated regularly, and each Thursday there is either a Free Church or informal student-led service, as well as Orthodox Vespers, sung in basso profundo by Fr Fostiropoulos.

Students are most welcome to any service regardless of denomination. Indeed the various chaplains work closely together, and the chapel services are seen as only a part, though a vital one, of the whole range of Christian activities and groups based at the College. These include the Joint Christian Forum, which organises talks and debates, and the 'City Limits' scheme. This scheme enables students to break out of the college 'bubble' by becoming involved with the real lives of Londoners, especially the homeless, ill and under-privileged.

The chapel itself is a richly decorated room designed by George Gilbert Scott and opened in 1864 to replace the original chapel which was rather austere. The plan is that of a Roman basilica, the semi-circular apse here being decorated with a mosaic of Christ in Majesty. Interesting recent features include two icons painted by a Russian woman who learnt the traditional skills from a community of nuns, and the extraordinary silver cross which incorporates a working mantrap; the idea is that Christ, here signified by a palm leaf, keeps apart the jaws of evil and death, allowing man to go free.

Important aspects of many services are the organ and the chapel choir, called the King's Singers, but not to be confused with the professional group of singers drawn from ex-schools of King's College, Cambridge. The chapel has had a choir since 1843 but only since the last war have members been recruited from the student body. The Advent Choir service, which features the choir to good advantage, is particularly well-attended.

Services: Monday 9.30am Morning Prayer, 1.10am RC Mass, 5.30pm Choral Evensong; Tuesday 9.30am Morning Prayer; Wednesday 9.30am Morning Prayer, 1.10pm College Communion Service; Thursday 9.30am Morning Prayer, 1.10pm Student-led or Free Church service, 5.30pm Orthodox Vespers; Friday 9am Holy Communion, 1.10pm RC Mass □ Facilities: amplification □ Wheelchair: easy access □ Visiting: open 9am–7pm during term; visitors not encouraged

The Queen's Chapel of the Savoy

Savoy Hill, The Strand, WC2 □ Telephone: 836 7221 □ Bus: any bus to the Strand □ Tube/BR: Embankment, Aldwych, Charing Cross □ Parking: difficult □ Chaplain: Rev John Williams □ Address: 18 Coombe Lane West, Kingston-Upon-Thames □ Telephone: 942 1196 □ Available: by arrangement

Tucked behind the Savoy Hotel, this is the Chapel of HM the Queen, and as such enjoys a unique status. It is not one of the Chapels Royal; it has a 'precinct', but no parish; and it is not under the jurisdiction of any bishop. The Queen is both spiritual and temporal 'lord' of the chapel.

There are no residents in the five-acre precinct but the chapel has a regular congregation of 40 or 50, with perhaps another 30 tourists attracted by the royal associations. The services are fully in 1662 tradition 'untouched by modern revision' and are enhanced by a cathedral-standard choir of men and boys. People should not be daunted by the grand status of the chapel—it is open throughout the week for private prayer and all are welcome to services.

The chapel has a long and distinguished history dating back to the reign of Henry VII. This is some degree reflected by the chapel's array of heraldry, including coats of arms, enamelled emblems and plaques. The ceiling, a magnificent affair made to resemble the one destroyed by fire in 1864, depicts the shields of all the monarchs associated with the chapel up to the time of Queen Victoria.

During the refurbishment following the fire, the fine reredos was installed. It extends the whole width of the chapel and contains at its centre a small 14th century icon of the Madonna and Child in Florentine style. Among the surviving Victorian windows is one commemorating Richard D'Oyly Carte, whose name is synonymous with the Savoy operas of Gilbert and Sullivan.

Services: Sunday 11.15am Matins, 12.30pm Holy Communion; Wednesday 12.30pm Holy Communion □ Wheelchair: no access □ Visiting: open 11.30am–3.30pm on Tuesday, Wednesday and Thursday

St Anne, Soho

Chapel of St Anne's Clergy House, 57 Dean Street, W1 □ Bus: 14, 22, 38, 55 □ Tube: Leicester Square, Oxford Street □ Parking: NCP Gerrard St nearby □ Priest-in-Charge: Rev Fred Stevens □ Address: c/o church □ Telephone: 437 5006 □ Available: most times

The steeple of St Anne's, with its curiously bulbous top carrying four clock faces, is a well known landmark of Soho and is all that remains of a church that suffered serious bomb damage in the Second World War and was eventually pulled down in 1953. This steeple was not part of the original 17th century church however, but was erected in 1803, the work of one Samuel Pepys Cockerell. At the moment, the site of the church is used as a car park, but there are advanced plans for redevelopment which include a new underground car park, community rooms, flats and a local museum, as well as a new church. All this is scheduled for completion in 1989.

In the meantime, services will continue to be held at the clergy house in a small, dignified chapel panelled in dark wood. Around twenty people attend each Sunday for a simple Rite A service with hymns. One other room on the premises is used for the social gatherings of the small congregation, while the ground floor and basement are given over to a hostel for the young homeless of the area. Called 'Centrepoint', the hostel was started by the church in the 1960s, but is now an independent charity.

The priest-in-charge, Rev Fred Stevens, sees his task at the moment as 'building up the Anglican worship in the Soho area until we can take off in 1989'. Certainly the new buildings will enable St Anne's better to serve the needs of Soho and will ensure a strengthened church presence in the area.

Services: Sunday 10am Holy Communion with hymns & address; Tuesday 1.05pm Holy Communion; Wednesday 8am Holy Communion □ Wheelchair: no access; long flight of stairs to chapel □ Visiting: open for services only

St Barnabas

St Barnabas Street, SW1 □ Bus: 11, 39, 137 □ Tube: Sloane Square □ Parking: difficult □ Priest-in-Charge: Rev Oystein J Holth □ Address: The Clergy House, St Barnabas St, SW1 □ Telephone: 730 5054 □ Available: most times

Reputedly the first church built to embody the ideals of the Oxford Movement, St Barnabas, situated just off the Pimlico Road, still upholds this tradition of worship. The church, adjoining a primary school and vicarage built in the same rough stone, was completed in 1850 to a rambling Early English style design by Thomas Cundy, Junior.

The building was paid for by Fr Bennett, the then vicar of St Paul's, Knightsbridge, who donated his entire private fortune. Subsequent gifts and bequests have made for a very interesting interior: dominated by Bodley's carved rood screen, it contains examples of many well-known designers' work. The reredos (1893) is by Bodley and Garner, the Lady Chapel was decorated by Sir Ninian Comper in 1900 and the baptistry added by Fred Hunt in 1902.

As the Archdeaconry of Westminster has more churches than are required to minister to the area, the future of St Barnabas has been in some doubt, though it is now hoped that the church will be restored to full parish status under a new incumbent. Since 1975 it has been under the pastoral care of Rev Oystein Holth, who also acts as an industrial chaplain.

Services: Sunday 9.30am Sung Mass; Weekdays 6.30pm Sung Mass; Major festivals 7.30pm Sung Mass □ Children: school service on Fridays □ Wheelchair: several steps □ Visiting: open at service times only

St Clement Danes

Strand, WC2 □ Bus: any along Strand □ Tube: Aldwych, Temple □ Parking: on street □ Padre: Rev Michael Stokes □ Address: c/o church □ Telephone: 242 8282 □ Available: 8am–5pm daily

The name of St Clement's is forever associated with the old nursery rhyme 'Oranges and Lemons'. According to legend, in the middle ages, when the old city walls were still in existence and St Clement's stood outside the gate at Temple Bar, merchant mariners trading with the City were able to avoid the customs duties by unloading their cargoes near the church which stood on the Strand, or shoreline, of the river, and taking goods through the churchyard. Some of the fruit might have gone to the churchwardens in appreciation of their co-operation.

Today's church is a post-war restoration of the 1682 building by Sir Christopher Wren. The steeple, by Wren's pupil Gibbs, survived the Blitz intact, but following the bombings the church stood sadly empty until 1958, when it was reconsecrated. It is now the Central Church of the Royal Air Force. Inside, there are pews which open like a telescope to allow space for the numerous and well-attended special services. Squadron and Unit badges, hand-worked in slate, are set into the floor.

Regular Sunday services are led by a chaplain who is a serving Padre of the Royal Air Force, posted here for two or three years. The congregation is steady at around the 80 mark, mostly retired Royal Air Force personnel and their families. Some regular worshippers, though, actually have no RAF connection.

St Clement Danes' former parish has been amalgamated with that of St Mary-le-Strand. Parochial responsibilities have been transferred there. Very few people, in any case, are resident nearby. Australia House continues to use St Clement's as its local church, but one does regret the passing of the annual service held by the London flower ladies, at which the dignified dark oak panelling must have been cheered by a multitude of blooms. Of course, the frequent special and commemorative services that are held by the RAF add their own special touch.

Many British and other Commonwealth visitors enter the church each day with a special purpose. All Royal Air Force personnel who have ever lost their lives while still on active service are commemorated in the Books of Remembrance kept at the church. The series of books are shown in glass cases and a page is turned each day. Copies of the books may be consulted. The church has American associations too. The organ was a gift from the USAF and there is an American shrine beneath the north gallery, with its own Book of Remembrance.

Services: Sunday 8.30am Holy Communion, 11am Mattins (except 1st Sunday), 12.15pm Holy Communion (except 1st Sunday), 3.30pm Evensong; 1st Sunday 11am Choral Eucharist; Weekdays (except Mon) 12.30pm Holy Communion □ Wheelchair: easy access □ Visiting: open 8am–5pm daily; bookstall

St Cyprian

Glenworth Street, Clarence Gate, NW1 □ Bus: 2, 3, 53 □ Tube: Baker Street, Marylebone □ Parking: difficult except Sunday □ Vicar: Rev Peter Harding □ Address: 16 Clarence Gate Mansions, NW1 □ Telephone: 402 6979 □ Available: most times □ Other clergy: Rev Derek White (402 5468)

The story of St Cyprian's begins with the tireless dedication of one man, the founder, Rev Charles Gutch. A member of the Oxford Movement, he had been attached to two London churches before applying, in 1864, to set up a new parish amongst the poor of Marylebone, in what was described at the time as 'a neglected and heathen part of London'.

Fr Gutch began with a mission church in two rented houses; he started Sunday schools, various clubs and addressed himself to the needs of the poor, the sick and the homeless. He met with great success, and his only regret was that he never lived to see the building of a large, permanent church. St Cyprian's, designed by Sir Ninian Comper, was consecrated in 1903, a long, lofty church with stately pillars. A huge altar was installed but most of the interior decoration was left to succeeding generations of worshippers, who have created a fine example in the manner of a medieval West Country church.

The parish has changed greatly since Fr Gutch's day, for it is now characterised by luxury mansion blocks, with some bedsits and hotels. Though the present day worshippers are much better off than their predecessors, the Catholic tradition of worship has not changed. An excellent choir sing at the Sunday High Mass from a wide repertoire, including Byrd, Faure and Mozart. The service is followed by coffee. There are few activities based at the church as most members are very busy, but Fr Peter Harding describes the congregation as very friendly, creating a happy atmosphere at the church.

Services: Sunday 8am Low Mass, 10.30am Mattins, 11am High Mass & Sermon; Weekday Mass : check porch notices □ Children: Sunday school 11am □ Wheelchair: 2 steps, help required □ Visiting: open as much as possible

St Gabriel

Warwick Square, SW1 □ Telephone: 834 2136(office) □ Bus: 24 □ Tube/BR: Victoria, Pimlico □ Parking: on street □ Vicar: Rev D W Skeoch □ Address: 30 Warwick Square, SW1 □ Telephone: 834 9589 □ Available: telephone office for appointment

During the 19th century, the residential areas of Belgravia and Pimlico were developed on what were formerly market gardens and swampy wastes. St Gabriel's, set in a tree-lined square among the tall town houses typical of the area, was one of many churches built around this time in the new suburbs. It was consecrated on May 12 1852 by Bishop Blomfield, known as the 'Churchbuilder'. The Marquis of Westminster contributed the site, and funds were raised among the future parishioners. The church was designed by Thomas Cundy, surveyor of the London estates of Earl of Grosvenor.

The church is in a very good state of repair, and its attractive interior is kept spotless by the parishioners. Notable features include a Kempe window in the sanctuary which narrowly escaped bomb damage during the war, an art nouveau altar rail, and an imposing brass pulpit of granite columns. There are many bas-reliefs and paintings donated by mourners in memory of loved ones.

The Walkers organ was re-built in 1970 and equipped with a moveable console which allows the whole church to be filled with sound. In 1967 a nave altar was installed, but the High Altar is still used for Wednesday evening services. The number of communicants is rising, and Sunday attendance is around 100. Services are described as being 'middle to high Anglo-Catholic': incense is used at festivals and the Stations of the Cross are done together with local Catholics. Indeed a positive attitude towards ecumenism is fostered here, and there are also links with the local Methodist church.

Under the auspices of the next-door Warwick Arts Trust, the church is used as venue for concerts, some of which have been broadcast on Radio London. Parish activities include outings and care for the elderly. There are study groups, and a longstanding scout and cub pack use the Parish Hall.

Services: Sunday 8.15am Eucharist, 9.15am Morning Prayer, 10.30am Sung Eucharist and sermon, 6pm Eucharist, (also Sung Eucharist: 5pm in winter; 6pm in summer); Mon, Tue, Thur 7.30am Morning Prayer, 8am Mass, 6pm Evening Prayer; Wednesday 9am Morning Prayer, 6pm Evening Prayer, 7pm Mass; Saturday 9.30am Morning Prayer, 12.30pm, 6.30pm Mass, 6pm Evening Prayer □ Facilities: Braille texts available □ Children: creche; school Mass 9.30am Wednesday □ Wheelchair: easy access □ Other details: various halls for hire □ Visiting: open for services or by arrangement

St George, Hanover Square

Hanover Square, W1 □ Telephone: 629 0874 □ Bus: 3, 6, 12, 13, 15, 15a, 53, 88, 159 □ Tube: Oxford Circus □ Parking: extremely difficult □ Rector: Rev William Atkins □ Address: 2a Mill Street, W1 □ Telephone: 629 0874 □ Other staff: R J Smith, verger

This is a grand church, by a pupil of Wren, with an elaborate but effective bell-tower and a large Classical portico which must have been thought innovative in 1725. The two obelisks are 18th century lamp standards.

The church stands near the Old Bond Street end of Mayfair, and serves Mayfair as part of its parish. Its attendance includes residents of Peabody Trust dwellings, as well as people from wealthy suburbs like Hampstead and Blackheath. Inside it is opulent, with a number of splendid features. Rev Atkins has produced an up-to-date guidebook in which he remarks that 'a parishioner from two centuries ago, if he could return today, would not find much to startle or dismay him'.

St George, Hanover Square, W1

Here we have space to mention only a few, such as the organ, the same one which the composer Handel heard here each Sunday for 35 years; and the east window. This is a Tree of Jesse from a Carmelite church in Antwerp, Belgium. The glass dates from about 1525. The excellent state of the interior brings to light the wealth of the patronage over the years. This is also witnessed by the panels listing all the church wardens from 1724, a plethora of noblemen amongst them.

The church has long been a fashionable venue for society weddings. Among those married here were Disraeli, George Eliot, Marconi, and Theodore Roosevelt; there are many other equally famous names, and the church records have had to be moved to Westminster Archives because of the huge amount of public interest they provoked.

Present congregations range between 70–80, which shows a healthy increase over the days before Rev Atkins arrived in 1955, when the average attendance was only eight. There is also a lunchtime service now on Fridays. Services are perhaps 'high' but accessible rather than aloof, with good choral music and an attentive congregation.

Services: Sunday 8.30am Holy Communion, 11am Holy Communion; Friday 11am Holy Communion □ Wheelchair: a few steps □ Visiting: open 8am–5pm weekdays; postcards/guidebcok/yearbook available; guided tours by arrangement

St Giles-in-the-Fields

St Giles High Street, WC2 □ Telephone: 240 2532 □ Bus: 1, 7, 8, 22, 24, 25, 29, 38, 55, 73 □ Tube: Tottenham Court Road □ Parking: on street □ Rector: Rev Gordon C Taylor □ Address: 15a Gower Street, WC1 □ Available: at home or through Verger at church □ Other clergy: Rev P Galloway

St Giles-in-the-Fields has one of the best known steeples in London and, because of this and the prominent position afforded by the large churchyard to the south, the church escapes being totally overshadowed by nearby Centre Point. Designed by Henry Flitcroft (who was preferred to the more famous Hawksmoor) and completed in 1734, St Giles is one of the best preserved and most handsome Georgian churches.

Services at St Giles have also been described as Georgian, and certainly, under the long-serving rector, Rev Gordon Taylor, the church has remained a bulwark of traditional Anglican worship, neither 'high' nor 'low'. Only the King James Bible and the 1662 Prayer Book are used, and one can still hear sung Psalms at the choral Matins and Evensong. Sermons, delivered from a 17th century pulpit without the aid of amplification, are thoughtful and topical, as befits a church which also houses a pulpit which was regularly used by both John and Charles Wesley.

The church's history is steeped in human suffering. St Giles started in 1101 as the chapel of a leper hospital, and a 1620s building on the site (by now a parish church) was rendered unusable by damp caused by excessive burials, including many Plague victims buried in the churchyard. Condemned prisoners passed the church on their way from Newgate to Tyburn, and received their last drink of ale here ('St Giles' Bowl'). Also, soon after Flitcroft's church came to be built, the parish contained some of the most notorious and appalling slums in England.

Courtyard, St James, Piccadilly, W1

The bombings of the Second World War and extensive redevelopment have altered the parish beyond recognition, and today there is no church hall or parish school. However, since 1971 St Giles has been the venue for an Annual Bible School, run in October and November, when over 1,500 people come to hear free lectures given by leading New Testament scholars. The church also has a strong lunchtime ministry to workers in the area on Wednesday and Thursdays, with lunchtime organ recitals on Mondays.

Services: Sunday 8am Holy Communion, 11am Morning Prayer, 12 noon Holy Communion, 6.30pm Evensong; Wednesday 1pm Holy Communion; Thursday 1.25pm Preaching service □ Wheelchair: easy access; one small step □ Visiting: open 9am–4pm daily

St James, Piccadilly

Piccadilly, W1 □ Telephone: 734 4511 □ Bus: 9, 15, 19, 22 □ Tube: Piccadilly □ Parking: meters on street □ Rector: Rev Donald Reeves □ Address: St James Rectory, 197 Piccadilly, W1 □ Available: by appointment □ Other staff: Deaconess Sheena Barnes; curates

Entering St James', Piccadilly, one cannot help but notice the number of people about. They may be seeking help or advice, browsing through the literature by the door, looking round the weekend market, heading towards the Wren Cafe, consulting the staff of the Centre for Health and Healing, or simply enjoying the atmosphere and beauty of this famous church. Truly, St James' runs an extensive programme and strives to make itself relevant both to local people and a wider international community. The Welcome Desk will help anyone through the maze of activities.

Services attract large multi-racial congregations of up to 200, and owe much to the personality and radical approach of the rector, Rev Donald Reeves. The current state of involvement and outreach at St James' is largely due to his enthusiasm and dedication. Worship here is in a broad-based modern style with a good deal of congregational contribution. Further, the Interfaith project has established firm links with Buddhist, Hindu, Jewish and Moslem groups in Central London, particularly with the monks of Peace Pagoda in Battersea Park (qv).

The services are also enhanced by the fine choir and musicians who benefit from the excellent acoustics. The church is used for a variety of other musical events, from the annual festival of Baroque music to rock concerts to raise money for anti-drug campaigns. The latter is indicative of St James' special commitment to reaching young people.

The church was devastated by bombing in the Second World War but was rebuilt between 1947–54, with a new spire, to the designs of Sir Albert Richardson. The interior is wide and filled with pews under a handsome panelled ceiling of white and gold, and features a splendid reredos and font by Grinling Gibbons which escaped wartime damage.

The full range of events at St James', including lectures, seminars, exhibitions, therapy, yoga and workshops is too large and ever-changing to list here, but visitors can find information at the church. An appeal to restore the fabric of the church, Wren's personal favourite of all the churches he designed, is currently underway, alongside fund-raising to set up numerous new projects designed to reach, help or teach more people. In all, St James' is an unparalleled example of how a West End church can address itself to the widest possible range of people, concerns and activities.

Services: Sunday 8.30am Holy Communion, 11am Eucharist, 6pm Evening Prayer; Weekdays 8.30am Holy Communion (Tue–Fri), 1.05pm Holy Communion (Tue), 5.45pm Evening Prayer (Tue, Wed, Fri); Saturday 11pm Compline □ Facilities: amplification □ Children: various groups □ Wheelchair: easy access, toilet for disabled □ Other details; cafe, various halls and rooms used continuously, bookstall □ Visiting: open all day, every day; often events in the evening

St James, Sussex Gardens

Sussex Gardens, W2 □ Bus: 12, 88 □ Tube: Lancaster Gate □ Parking: small car park □ Vicar: Rev David Perkins □ Address: The Vicarage, Sussex Gardens, W2 □ Telephone: 723 8119 □ Available: most times

St James' is the Civic church of Paddington, an area of transient population now with over two hundred hotels in the parish. The congregation includes teachers and professional people, mainly single, as well as the homeless families sent to the hotels here by the London borough councils of Brent and Tower Hamlets, and of course short-stay visitors from home and abroad. The whole parish is leafletted annually, as part of the church's mission, but although, under the care of Rev David Perkins, there is a focus on evangelism, services are neither 'high' nor 'low' in the formal sense. St James' is proud of its professional choir, which gives regular concerts here. Other, often well-known, ensembles have performed here, always to a good-sized audience.

It is a Gothic Revival church, built in 1843 and later redesigned and enlarged. The architect of the new-style building, who re-oriented the church, was Street, the designer of the Law Courts on the Strand. The rededication took place in 1882. The original tower and spire are still there, and it is still definitely Gothic with vaulting and stained glass, but the church is now of cathedral proportions, able to seat over 1,000.

The stained glass in the baptistry is especially interesting in that, under the portrait of St James, is a series of scenes of life in old Paddington. Next to the chancel is the war memorial chapel, where one can come for private prayer; it is also used for the weekly meetings of a meditation group.

The church, with its three halls, is the centre for much social activity, including lots of children's parties. It is also host to the Korean community, who hold services here once a month.

Services: Sunday 8am Eucharist, 10.30am Sung Eucharist, 6.30pm Choral Evensong, (once a month 1.30pm service in Korean) □ Facilities: amplification, large print books □ Children: creche and Junior Church in the hall during the 10.30am service □ Wheelchair: some steps but help is always available; toilet for disabled □ Other details: large and small halls □ Visiting: open for services and activities only

St John the Evangelist

Hyde Park Crescent, W2 □ Bus: 7, 12, 15, 27, 88 □ Tube/BR: Lancaster Gate, Paddington □ Parking: car park □ Vicar: Rev Thaddeus Birchard □ Address: The Vicarage, 18 Somers Crescent, W2 □ Telephone: 262 1732 □ Available: most times □ Other clergy: Rev Bob Callaghan (724 1888)

The original designs for St John's were for a church of grand proportions able to seat 1500 people, and were drawn up by Samuel Pepys Cockerell. On his death a new architect, Charles Fowler, was commissioned to design a smaller and less expensive church. This was completed after three years of building and was consecrated on 26th January 1832 by the Bishop of London. The brick built church has a symmetrical west front which culminates in the twin towers at the end of the nave. The windows have the flattened arch of the Perpendicular style.

The interior is largely structurally unchanged from when it was built, except for the addition in 1907 of a nave altar surrounded by altar rails, but has changed in feel by the inclusion of modern paintings and artwork. Perhaps most striking of these is 'The Cross of a Hundred Crosses' by Michael Caddy, hanging in the Lady Chapel. Other features are the statue of the Virgin and Child and the altar in the Lady Chapel, both retrieved from the bombed St Michael's, and the reredos with its Old and New Testament scenes.

Rev Thaddeus Birchard has been vicar here since 1980 and has seen the size of his congregation grow to the extent that between 150 and 200 people now attend Sunday worship. Of the Sunday services, the Parish Eucharist is traditional in style, based on the ASB, while the Evening Service is more informal, indeed charismatic.

The church gives financial support to various charities, and is actively involved with a local housing project, providing shelter for the homeless, and has a student and family ministry.

Services: Sunday 8am Holy Communion, 10am Parish Eucharist, 6.30pm Evening Service; Daily 7am Morning Prayer (9am Sat), 6pm Evening Prayer; Weekday HC Mon 6.30pm, Thu 7.30pm, Fri 12.30pm, Sat 9.30am □ Facilities: amplification, deaf loop □ Children: Sunday school during 10am service □ Wheelchair: not difficult, only two steps—ramp available □ Other details: church hall □ Visiting: open all day, every day; books, etc, available

St John's Wood Church

St John's Wood, NW8 □ Telephone: 586 3864 (office) □ Bus: 2b, 13, 74, 113 □ Tube: St John's Wood □ Parking: forecourt car park □ Vicar: Rev John Slater □ Address: St John's House, St John's Wood, NW8 □ Telephone: 722 4378 □ Available: ring for appointment □ Assistant Curates: Revv Nicholas Barry (722 9188), Andrew Walker (722 4766)

This Georgian church was part of the elaborate plans instigated by the Prince Regent, for the district around the park that carries his name, and for the then largely underdeveloped area of St John's Wood. It was designed by Thomas Hardwick and consecrated in 1814, but commanded littie attention at the time with so much going on nearby. 'God's own Regency drawing-room', as one parishioner described the church, does evoke the era most convincingly with its wooden box-pews, rounded windows, and interior pillars painted white with subtle gold details.

If the interior of the church has not changed, St John's wood certainly has, not least in matters religious. Three synagogues have arisen, originally as a result of the 1930s influx of Jewish regugees from Europe; more recently, the splendid Central Mosque was built by the park. The church meets up with the Mosque and the Liberal Jewish Synagogue to form the St John's Wood Trialogue, an occasional discussion group designed to break down cultural barriers and lead to better understanding.

Indeed, although the vicar, Rev John Slater, eschews labels—'we are average Church of England, not trying to be anything in particular'—he regards his congregation as an intelligent, questioning lot given to discussion, with a deep interest in spirituality. The annual retreat, which has much emphasis on silent meditation, has been led by some most cerebral Christians.

The style of worship is diverse. The Parish Eucharist is informal with much lay participation, while the following Sung Eucharist features the organist and choir offering music from Byrd and Palestrina to Langlais and Duruflé. The emphasis on Sunday evening is on congregational hymn singing.

Other activities include the large youth club, run with the help of two ILEA youth workers, scout and cub packs, and Westminster Crossroads, a local support group for the physically handicapped. Mr Slater is involved with 'as much visiting as possible', as means of establishing trust and support in the community.

Services: Sunday 8am Holy Communion, 9am Morning Prayer (except 1st Sunday), 9.30am Parish Eucharist, 11am Sung Eucharist (Morning Prayer 1st Sunday), 6.30pm Evening Prayer (Choral Evensong 1st Sunday); Weekday Eucharist Mon 12 noon, Tue, Thu & Sat 6.30pm, Wed 7.30am, Fri 10am; Weekdays 6pm Evening Prayer □ Children: creche for 9.30am Sunday service □ Wheelchair: some shallow steps; ramp to church hall □ Other details: hall (shared with URC) □ Visiting: open at service times only

St Margaret, Westminster

Parliament Square, SW1 □ Bus: any to Parliament Square □ Tube: Westminster □ Parking: difficult except Sunday □ Rector: Rev Canon Donald Gray □ Telephone: 222 5791 □ Available: most times

It stands in the shadow of Westminster Abbey and its history is intimately linked with that of its great neighbour, but St Margaret's is also important in its own right. Since 1614 it has had strong links with the House of Commons just across the road, and it was here the House assembled in 1918 and in 1945 to give thanks for victory and peace.

It is likely that the first church on the site was built to serve the community which grew up around Westminster Abbey following its foundation in 1065. It became the parish church of Westminster serving an area roughly the same size as the whole of the City of Westminster today, and remained the only parish church until the fourteenth century. It came under the authority of the Abbey rather than that of the Bishop of London until 1840, and today, since 1972, it has once again been fully re-integrated with the Abbey, the parish boundaries having shrunk so that they barely cover the area of Parliament Square.

The present church is the third on the site, and dates from the 16th century. It is Perpendicular in style but much restored, though it retains some of the original features. The great attraction for the casual visitor is the east window which shows portraits of Henry VIII and Catherine of Aragon at the scene of the Crucifixion. There are several excellent monuments.

Over half a million visitors to London come to St Margaret's each year. They are attracted by the numerous historical associations. Caxton, Chaucer and Pepys worshipped here and there are many American connections. Sir Walter Raleigh was beheaded just outside the church and his body is buried in front of the altar. In recent years the church has been chosen for famous weddings including that of Sir Winston Churchill. There is a special leaflet detailing points of interest for American visitors.

St Margaret's holds many concerts and lectures and occasional services during the summer to reduce pressure on the Abbey. There are numerous memorial services for parliamentarians and other notables. Services are traditional, using the Book of Common Prayer, and there is an ecumenical approach which suits a church with so many visitors. A lunchtime Holy Communion is held on Wednesdays and there are special services for the opening of the parliamentary year and its terms.

There are extensive restorations in progress, and expected to continue for some years. It is hoped that a showpiece church will emerge. To help pay for the works, the Speaker of the House of Commons organised a regatta on the Thames in July 1986. The last three rectors have all been chaplains to the Speaker and carried out their pastoral role in Parliament with MPs and staff.

Services: Sunday 8.15am Holy Communion, 11am Choral Mattins (Sung Eucharist, 1st Sunday), 12.15pm Holy Communion; Wednesday 12.30pm Lunchtime service □ Facilities: amplification □ Wheelchair: some steps; ramp planned □ Visiting: open 9.30am–4.30pm (6.30pm in summer); bookstall

St Mark

Hamilton Terrace, NW8 □ Telephone: 624 4065 (office) □ Bus: 8, 16, 16a, 159, 176 □ Tube: Maida Vale, St John's Wood □ Parking: on street □ Vicar: Rev Donald Aird □ Address: 114 Hamilton Terrace, NW8 □ Telephone: 328 4373 □ Available: at office, Wed–Fri 10am–12noon

St Mark's, built in 1847 in an Early English style, is noted for its internal furnishings, especially those in the chancel with its fine frescoes and mosaics and marble tile floor, centring on the Lion of St Mark. The chancel ceiling is a splendid affair covered with florets and angels, and the east window representing the Te Deum with Christ enthroned is a good example of the work of Clayton and Bell.

The church originally had galleries around three sides and could seat 1,400. The size of the congregation nowadays is rather more modest, with between 40 and 50 people attending the most popular service, the Sunday Sung Eucharist. A professional choir directed by organist Alan Gibson is often invited to sing. Most

Interior, St Martin-in-the-Fields, WC2

worshippers are long-standing regulars though there is often a number of visitors in the congregation.

At the time of writing the church was still in the throes of extensive redevelopment work which includes the conversion of the nave into a community centre. A smaller, more appropriate worship area will remain, and the building will be available to serve the community in the widest number of ways.

Services: Sunday 8 am Holy Communion (in winter, 8.30am), 10.30am Sung Eucharist and Sermon (Matins on 1st Sunday of month); Tuesday 6pm Holy Communion; Thursday 11.30am Holy Communion □ Facilities: amplification □ Wheelchair: small ramp to side entrance opened on request □ Visiting: open at service times only

St Martin-in-the-Fields

Trafalgar Square, WC2 □ Bus: any to Trafalgar Square □ Tube/BR: Charing Cross □ Parking: on street □ Vicar: Rev Canon Geoffrey Brown □ Address: 5 St Martin's Place, WC2 □ Telephone: 930 0089/1862 □ Available: most times □ Other clergy: Revv Philip Chester, Stephen Roberts

This is the Royal parish church, by virtue of its position just across the square from Admiralty Arch, which is the formal entrance to Buckingham Palace, although the Royal Parks are of course now open to the public. George I served here as a church-warden, and this led the church to place the Royal Arms so prominently on the pediment of the elegant colonnaded porch. There is a Royal box, (and also an Admiralty box), above the the High Altar, but these days one is unlikely to come across any of the Royal Family at services here. Rather, many tourists are to be found worshipping with the regular congregation.

The first St Martin's was indeed surrounded by fields. The church was built in the 13th century and dedicated to the saint whose simple act of charity, the sharing of his cloak with a beggar, rewarded him with a vision of Christ. A second church was constructed in 1544, and in 1721 this was replaced with the present structure designed by Gibbs. The somewhat austere classical exterior, faced with round-arched windows between pilasters with Corinthian capitals, thus continuing the theme of the portico, is embellished with a wonderful steeple, topped with the famous pierced convace-sided spire. Inside, rococo plasterwork and the carved oak staircase and pulpit contribute to an atmosphere of dignity and reverence.

Services during the week are kept brief and are usually held in the side chapel. On Sunday, services are held throughout the day and include Holy Communion at 9.45am which is led by the Sunday Morning Choir and is the main service of the day. Tea and coffee are served afterwards in the crypt. A Chinese Anglican service is held later; bilingual prayerbooks are available (English/Cantonese). The Choral Evensong is led by the St Martin-in-the-Fields Consort of singers. Services are traditional here, central Anglican, neither 'high' nor 'low'.

Where St Martin's is truly innovative and original is not in the services, but in its charity work. Ever since the end of the First World War, when soldiers were returning from France, many homeless, destitute and sick, this church has been dedicated to caring. There is a soup kitchen in the crypt, a lifeline to the down-

and-outs who today more than ever continue to throng the Charing Cross arches. There is also a special mission to young visitors from overseas. From the end of 1987 the crypt will house a new Visitors Centre, a bookshop and a restaurant; other activities will be moved to the Social Service Centre. The club called 'The Centre' at 5 St Martin's Place, is a well-established, lively meeting place where Londoners and others can find evening classes, folk music, discussion groups and even discos.

Services: Sunday 8am, 9.45am Holy Communion, 11.30am Morning Prayer, 2.45pm Cantonese Service, 4.15pm Choral Evensong, 6.30pm Evening Prayer; Weekdays 8am Mattins, 8.15am Silent Prayer, 8.30am Holy Communion, 5.30pm Evensong, 5.45pm Silent Prayer, 6pm Prayers (except Thursday); Monday 6.30pm Prayers for healing, or healing service; Wednesday 1.05pm Holy Communion; Thursday 6pm Holy Communion; Friday 12.30pm Holy Communion; Saturday 9am Mattins, 9.15am Silent Prayer, 9.30am Holy Communion □ Facilities: amplification □ Children: creche 9.30–11am Sunday at 12 Adelaide St WC2 □ Wheelchair: ramp at side entrance □ Visiting: open 7am–7pm daily

St Mary

Bourne Street, SW1 □ Bus: 11, 19, 22, 137 □ Tube: Sloane Square □ Parking: on street □ Parish Priest: Rev John Gilling □ Address: The Presbytery, Graham Terrace, SW1 □ Tel: 730 2423 □ Available: most times □ Other clergy: Rev Nicholas Kavanagh

Built in the 1870s as a slum church, St Mary's was simple, cheap and red-brick. However, areas change, and since the War especially this small parish has turned into one of the most select neighbourhoods in London. But, even before this, the church was attracting wealthy supporters from Belgravia. It was not all a fashionable search for novelty either. By the turn of the century St Mary's had made her reputation as a 'high' church par excellence. The sanctuary was redesigned and fitted with the present splendidly baroque High Altar (by Martin Travers) in keeping with the new focus of the church. Travers also produced a fine statue of the Virgin as 'Our Lady of Peace' to mark the end of the First World War, which stands in the sanctuary. There are other chapels, and statues, all suitably Anglo-Catholic in tone.

As with the architecture and decoration, so with the music and the liturgy. Sunday services use the traditional prayerbook (though ASB Rite A is used during the week). Sunday High Mass is conducted by priests, acolytes, servers, all vested quite grandly, with full pomp and circumstance. It is accompanied by a choir, all professional, with Palestrina's setting of the Mass, and some lovely organ music. The acoustics are very good. The present incumbent describes the service as 'high-powered and beautiful'. It is attended by a congregation of about 90–140, with roughly the same number present for the earlier Parish Mass. High Mass is followed by a short sermon.

St Mary's describes itself as a good place to make friends, though one must say that in the past it has been criticised for being 'cosy and introverted'.

Outside services the church is not open, but one should in any case attend for worship to see St Mary's at its best. After morning worship refreshments are provided in the Undercroft.

Services: Sunday 9.45am Parish Mass, 11am High Mass, 6.15pm Evensong and Solemn Benediction, 9am and 7pm Low Mass; Weekdays Evensong 6pm, Two Low Masses: for times see the church notice board □ Children: Sunday school □ Wheelchair: easy access, 2 steps □ Other details: Undercroft □ Visiting: open for services and activities only.

St Mary, Bryanston Square

Wyndham Place, W1 □ Telephone: 723 0466 (office) □ Bus: 1, 2, 2b, 13, 18, 27, 113, 159, 176 □ Tube: Baker Street, Edgware Road □ Parking: difficult except Sunday □ Rector: Rev Iain MacKenzie □ Telephone: 935 2200 □ Available: most time □ Other staff: Mr John Keast, Verger (258 0168); Dr Brian Blackwood, Organist & Master of Choristers (262 3846) for details of Music Society

St Mary's was intended to provide a foil to Marble Arch which lies just under half a mile to the south, but the line of vision is now somewhat interrupted by the trees in Bryanston Square. The architect was Sir Robert Smirke, best known for the British Museum, and St Mary's elongated pepper-pot steeple, however unusual it may appear, is a common feature of his churches.

Consecrated in 1824, the church had very 'low' and evangelical beginnings, when 1,500 people would regularly flock to hear the substantial sermons of the early rectors, although records show there were only some 900 communicants a year. The churchmanship was broader by the turn of the century and is now described as 'central'. The 1662 Prayer Book and ASB Rite B are used alternately. The present rector, Rev Iain MacKenzie, has introduced Sung Eucharist (to replace a 'Holy Communion with hymns') and Choral Matins, both of which feature a mixed choir and the fine Harrison organ to good effect.

The congregation, usually numbering between 120 and 150, reflects the cosmopolitan nature of the parish. There are a good few West Indians and Africans, Embassy staff and their families, as well as Americans and others staying at the local hotels amongst the worshippers. A Children's Church (a title preferred to the uninviting 'Sunday School') has a regular attendance of around 50. The children later join their parents in the church during the 11am service. This togetherness of worship is regarded as highly important by Fr MacKenzie.

The church has excellent acoustics and a reputation for good music. The flourishing Music Society organises regular recitals and concerts, and puts on full scale choral productions for Easter and Christmas. St Mary's is used for special services by the Industrial Society and the Greater London Fund for the Blind, amongst others, and an annual festival is celebrated jointly with the Swedish Church in Harcourt Street (qv). Each Wednesday morning the children of the voluntary aided C of E school attend a service at the church.

The rector is also an annual lecturer at St Giles-in-the-Fields (qv). This theological expertise is further evidenced by his post as Examining Chaplain to the Bishop of London, advising the Bishop on theological matters.

Services: Sunday 8.30am Holy Communion, 11am Sung Eucharist or Choral Matins, 6.30pm Evensong; Wednesday & Saints' Days 1pm Holy Communion □ Children: Children's Church 11am Sunday in hall; school service 9.15am Wednesday in church □ Wheelchair: ramp provided if notified □ Other details: hall in various and almost constant use □ Visiting: open around service times

St Mary-le-Strand

Aldwych, WC2 □ Telephone: 836 3216/3205 □ Bus: any bus to the Strand or Charing Cross □ Tube: Aldwych, Temple □ Parking: difficult except Sundays □ Rector: Rev Edward Thompson □ Address: 3 Drake Court, Tilney Avenue, SE19 □ Available: most times □ Other clergy: Rev David Derrick (737 3809)

Visitors who emerge from Aldwych Underground station will have no difficulty in finding St Mary-le-Strand and its sister church St Clement Danes (qv); both churches occupy island sites in the middle of the Strand. Together, they form a united parish, although nowadays St Clement Danes has lost its status as a parish church and is the chapel of the Royal Air Force.

One of London's most beautiful small churches, its elegant Portland stone exterior and steeple forming an attractive landmark, St Mary-le-Strand was built in the early 18th century by James Gibbs. A Roman Catholic, he received his training in Rome and was much influenced by the Italianate style. The church's interior is very fine and surprisingly spacious. The most striking feature is the magnificent ceiling, full of detailed plasterwork laid out in lines of squares and lozenges. Above the altar are three stained-glass windows of deep blue.

Services are in the Catholic tradition, based on the Book of Common Prayer; there is incense on Sundays and at Sung Eucharist on Saints' Days. The Sunday congregation is largely elderly residents, students and people who come from a distance due to family associations with the church. The congregation is small, but increases considerably at special services. During the week, those attending are largely local businessmen and civil servants. An address or lecture is given each Friday lunchtime.

A third of Fr Thomas' working life is spent helping charities, several of which are attached to the parish. Each year, the church also provides a Christmas dinner for the residents of Bruce House hostel. St Mary-le-Strand is also the official church of the WRENs and their Association; they hold a monthly service at the church.

A major restoration of St Mary-le-Strand was begun in 1977, after being officially launched by Sir John Betjeman. Most of the work is now done, such as the dismantling and rebuilding of the steeple, and the cleaning and repair of the exterior stonework, although the work is expected to continue for some years. Recently pelican crossings have been set up, enabling people to reach the church across the busy Strand much more easily.

Services: Sunday 11am Holy Communion; Tuesday 1.05pm Holy Communion; Thursday 1.05pm Holy Communion □ Facilities: amplification; large print prayer book □ Wheelchair: difficult—several steps □ Visiting: open weekdays 9.30am–4pm; bookstall, etc

St Mary Magdalene

Rowington Close, W2 □ Bus: 18, 36, 36b □ Tube: Royal Oak, Westbourne Park □ Parking: not difficult □ Vicar: no incumbent at present

Founded by Dr Richard Temple West to exemplify the ideals of the Oxford Movement, the church still stands as the 'Victorian Gem' it was when built, between 1865 and 1878. The architect George Street had two problems with the site in that it was on a slope and was also an island between roads. The result is a novel design with entrances at different levels and an off-centre spire.

The lofty interior is full of decoration. Chancel and sanctuary have a painted ceiling, while the High Altar and reredos stand in an octagonal alcove which makes effective use of gold gilding. Throughout the rest of the church there are numerous mosaics, statues and alabaster panels. The extravagant crypt was Comper's first commision.

The present organ, the original having been damaged in a fire during construction, is the fourth replacement and was built by John Compton in 1933. No amplification is needed as the church is acoustically perfect for preaching and the performance of music. The church's Music Society gives a recital every other month.

At the end of the 1950s the residential area around the church was completely demolished, making way for the large block of flats that now dominates the area. As a result the community was dispersed; church attendance fell significantly and has not revived. Present congregations number around twelve for the Sunday morning Mass, and six in the evening, while perhaps only one or two worshippers can be expected during the week. For this reason the only service held in the main body of the church is the Sunday morning Mass; the others take place in the chapel downstairs.

Services: Sunday 10am Mass, 6pm Evening Prayer and Benediction; Monday–Friday except Wednesday 8am; Wednesday 8pm; Saturday 10am □ Wheelchair: difficult □ Visiting: apply at Clergy House for key

St Mary on Paddington Green

Paddington Green, W2 □ Telephone: 262 3787 □ Bus: 18, 36, 36b □ Tube: Edgware Road □ Parking: limited space □ Vicar: Rev Prebendary John Foster □ Address: 6 Park Place Villas, W2 □ Telephone: 723 1968 □ Available: any time

St Mary's on Paddington Green does indeed sit on a little patch of green, though its peace is somewhat disturbed by the traffic on the Westway which roars past just a hundred yards to the south. This cloud certainly yielded a silver lining however, for it was compensation from the Ministry of Transport for the loss of some of its churchyard that financed a thoroughgoing and award-winning scheme of restoration that was completed in 1973.

The restored church, a square yellow-brick affair, is now a splendid example of late Georgian architecture, free of later 'improvements'. The original pulpit, altar and font were restored and new fittings in period design, such as box pews, were added to complete the picture. The new organ is said to have a truly 18th century tone, and benefits from the church's excellent acoustics which make it a popular venue for concerts.

The congregation is a reflection of the variegated nature of the parish which encompasses the shops and bustle of the Edgware Road and the select charm of Little Venice. Services are High Church in form, and follow Rite B.

Services: Sunday 8am Holy Communion, 10am Sung Eucharist □ Children: Sunday school & drama group □ Wheelchair: easy access □ Other details: hall for hire □ Visiting: open for services or by arrangement

St Marylebone, NW1

St Marylebone

Marylebone Road, NW1 □ Telephone: 935 7315 (Vestry) □ Bus: 2, 13, 18, 30, 74, 113 □ Tube: Baker Street, Regents Park □ Parking: meters □ Rector: Rev Christopher Hamel Cooke □ Address: 21 Beaumont Street, W1 □ Telephone: 935 8965 □ Available: contact church office □ Other clergy: Revv David Head, Richard McLaren

This is a splendid church, unfortunately ignored by the tourist hordes mulling around Madame Tussaud's across the busy Marylebone Road. It has a long stately facade, topped with a balustrade in Renaissance manner, and a tower in two stages, the top part of which resembles a giant bell. There is an old churchyard, and indeed the church is redolent with historical associations. Robert Browning and Elizabeth Barrett married here in 1846, and Byron was baptised in the old church. Charles Dickens lived next door. St Marylebone is not, as some think, a corruption of St Mary le bon, ie good, but takes its name from the little river which runs through here (bourne = brook), now underground.

In the crypt here is a new Healing and Counselling Centre, a joint venture by the Church of England and the National Health Service. This comprises a NHS surgery run by doctors who are members of the British Holistic Medical Society. Acupuncture and osteopathy, and other complementary (sometimes known as alternative) therapies are also available. Together with this is the Christian Healing Centre, with its team of counsellors and befrienders. Other organisations including the Institute of Religion and Medicine have their headquarters here.

The congregation is a lively cross-section and people from all over north London. On Sundays around 120 attend, 90 during the week. Across the road from the church is the Royal Academy of Music, and together there is being installed a new organ, which will be one of the finest in London. The music is of a very high standard, with a professional choir of ten singers. A postgraduate course in sacred and liturgical music is shortly to be run at the church by the RAM in co-operation with the parish. Another venture is the Music Therapy Unit—a 'bridge' between the church itself and the Healing Centre. The crypt also boasts a social centre with cafe and lending library.

Services: Sunday 8am Holy Communion, 10am Young Families Eucharist, 11am Choral Eucharist, 6.30pm Evensong; Wednesday 1.10pm Holy Communion; Thursday 5.15pm Holy Communion; Healing services 6.30pm on 1st Sunday of month □ Facilities: amplification, Braille books □ Children: see Sunday 10am □ Wheelchair: ramp □ Other details: rooms (available for hire) □ Visiting: open everyday 9am–1pm

St Matthew

Great Peter Street, SW1 □ Bus: 88 □ Tube: St James Park, Westminster □ Parking: not too difficult □ Vicar: Rev Michael Hayes □ Address: 20 Great Peter Street, SW1 □ Telephone: 222 3704 □ Available: most days □ Other clergy: Rev Stuart Bates

Built by Sir George Gilbert Scott between the years 1849–51, St Matthew's is an Anglo-Catholic Revival church. The exterior features a short but massive tower on the south side, and a large porch in which booksales are sometimes held. The church is built of Kentish ragstone, somewhat like large cobblestones, and it stands less than half a mile from Westminster Abbey.

Inside the church was more spacious, but it suffered so badly from a fire in 1977 that the restorers had virtually to construct a new, smaller church within the shell of the old. There is also a Lady Chapel which stands upstairs from the main church. It managed to survive the fire intact and so preserves the design of Sir Ninian Comper, from earlier this century; the west window in particular is worthy of note.

The emphasis is on sacramental worship—all the sacraments are practised—and confession is available after every midday Mass. There is incense, as befits a church which follows the Catholic tradition within the Anglican Church, and the ASB Rite A is used in services.

Services: Sunday 8am Mass, 10am Solemn Mass; 6pm Evening Prayer, 6.30pm Mass; Weekdays 8am, 12.30pm Mass; Saturday 11.30am Mass; Confessions Monday to Friday 1pm □ Facilities: amplification □ Children: creche □ Wheelchair: easy access (except Lady Chapel); toilet for disabled □ Visiting: open most days

St Matthew, St Petersburgh Place

St Petersburgh Place, W2 □ Bus: 12, 88, (A2) □ Tube: Queensway, Bayswater □ Parking: on street □ Vicar: Rev Gareth Evans □ Address: 27 St Petersburgh Place, W2 □ Telephone: 229 2192 □ Available: most times

There isn't much that doesn't happen at St Matthew's. At any time one might find a student practising singing; a group of Ethiopians celebrating an Orthodox Mass in Amharic or Geez; a police surgery or a doctor talking with patients; a brass band giving a music recital; a pavement stall inviting passers-by to visit the church; a full-scale dramatic production or a film crew (the films *Minder* and *Plenty* feature the church); or, of course, an Anglican service.

The services themselves are varied and inventive. Rev Gareth Evans uses the traditional Authorised Bible and the 1662 Prayer Book, but he may conduct 'dialogue sermons' on themes such as 'Happiness' and invite a celebrity to read some poetry or play music. Along with its open door policy towards visitors, the church has an 'open theology' in order to attract worshippers from all walks of life wishing to celebrate a 'common-sense Christianity'. The congregation is a good cross-section of society, including a number of tourists from the nearby hotels.

The church is also involved with community issues. It offers counselling for drug-users, rape victims and prostitutes, as well as providing help for the elderly and sufferers from AIDS and domestic violence.

Even if one finds only the calm and quiet one expects from a parish church, one's visit will be worthwhile. There is a large consortium of old instruments, and the church is a centre for the study of harmoniums—indicative of the emphasis placed on music at St Matthew's. Although the Victorian Gothic church is similar to many others, it is light, attractive and well cared-for; it has a classic 19th century French escapement clock, and the spire is the second highest in London.

Services: Sunday 8.15am Communion, 11am Matins, 12.15pm Communion, 6pm Evensong; Wednesday 12.15 Communion; (Plus Ethiopian Orthodox Mass, Sunday 9.30am–2pm & monthly Quaker meeting 2.45pm) □ Facilities: amplification □ Children: Sunday school □ Wheelchair: level access □ Other details: hall □ Visiting: usually open 8am–1pm daily

St Michael, Chester Square

Chester Square, SW1 □ Telephone: 730 8889 (office) □ Bus: 2, 10, 11, 16, 19, 22, 29, 36, 38, 39, 52, 55, 70, 76 □ Tube/BR: Victoria □ Parking: meters □ Vicar: Rev David Prior □ Address: 4 Chester Square, SW1 □ All enquiries (for counselling, consultation & information) through the Parish Office

Near the hectic Victoria Coach Station is The Well, a coffee bar run by St Michael's and regarded as its 'presence on the street'. The venture indicates the church's concern to share the Christian gospel, as well as providing refreshments. The Well stocks Christian books, magazines and videos. In addition, staff are available to talk to anyone who asks, but the style is kept low-key. St Michael's House, next to The Well, is soon to be taken back into the life of the church. Situated ideally for its original purpose as a youth club, it will become a centre for varied ministry in the area, particularly among teenagers.

Over the last few years, an increasing interest has developed at St Michael's in the ministry of the Holy Spirit. There is a strong emphasis also on expository preaching, every-member ministry, and the centrality and uniqueness of Jesus Christ. The church recognises a call to serve the local community and is extending its ministry accordingly. While the main Sunday morning service at St Michael's is more traditional and formal (Series 3 at Holy Communion, 1662 Prayer Book at Morning Prayer), the evening worship is led by a folk-style group. This features informal worship, biblical exposition and sharing in Holy Communion on alternate Sundays.

Congregations at morning services number between 150 and 200, with up to 100 in the evenings. There are about 18 home groups, each with between 6 and 12 people, meeting for varied purposes but enabling people to know each other better and discuss matters in greater depth. Many members work at The Well on a voluntary basis.

The building itself, nestling in a dignified square, is one of many Victorian Gothic Kentish ragstone churches in the area; but don't let its appearance and Belgravia location mislead you—St Michael's parish is now a mixed environment and the congregation is drawn from a wide range of ages, nationalities and backgrounds. The church's interest lies not so much in the building's fabric (which is soon to be completely restored inside and outside), but in the worship and activities shared by its members.

Services: Sunday 8.15am Holy Communion, 11am Holy Communion (except 2nd & 4th Sundays, Morning Prayer), 7.30pm Evening Service; Thursday 11.30am Holy Communion □ Facilities: amplification □ Children: creche and Sunday school at 11am □ Wheelchair: easy access; some shallow steps □ Other details: The Well coffee bar, 1 Elizabeth St, SW1 open 10am–6pm weekdays □ Visiting: open at service times only

St Paul, Covent Garden

Bedford Street, WC2 □ Telephone: 836 5221 (Vestry) □ Bus: 1, 14, 19, 22, 24, 29, 38, 55, 176 □ Tube: Leicester Square, Covent Garden □ Parking: difficult □ Rector: V Rev David Elliott □ Address: 14 Burleigh Street, WC2 □ Telephone: 379 7488 □ Available: any reasonable time

St Paul's, the 'actors' church', is probably most famous around the world for events that didn't happen. It was here that Professor Higgins met Eliza Doolittle in Shaw's *Pygmalion*, and where they married in Alan Jay Lerner's *My Fair Lady*. The great Tuscan portico of the church, in the piazza, is a landmark, yet strangely enough this is not the entrance. To enter one has to head for Bedford Street, go through the gates, and down the path through the garden of ease. The coats of arms are those of the Duke of Bedford, who developed this area, formerly the convent garden of the monks of Westminster Abbey. His architect, who had trained in Italy, and returned around 1630, was Inigo Jones.

Inside, the church is rectangular in shape, with a classical altar surround complete with columns. At the rear of the church, below the organ gallery is a wooden screen panelled with black memorial plaques for famous stage and film personalities such as Ivor Novello, Boris Karloff, and Hattie Jacques. There is also a wreath carved by Grinling Gibbons, who is buried here. The north and south walls contain more of these memorials.

The church's theatrical associations date back to when it was built; Inigo Jones himself was also a stage designer. Many visitors come because of the links with the stage, and the church is used frequently for memorial services for well-known actors. Theatre people, who are not settled in any parish, often choose to be married in St Paul's. The Actors' Church Union have their administrative offices in the church and also hold their own services. In nearby premises is 'Radius', the religious drama group.

Despite the church's fame, the present Sunday congregation is small, only about 35 people a week, mainly students from nearby Kings' College and some retired parishioners. Visiting theatre people make up the rest. However, a lot goes on in Covent Garden, and some annual events—such as the Time Out street entertainers festival—do make use of the building, especially the portico. There have been regular concerts in the church, as well as song recitals, organ recitals, orchestral concerts, and even a performance of Mozart's *The Marriage of Figaro*. More are planned.

Services: Sunday 11am Eucharist; Wednesday 1.10pm Holy Communion; Thursday 8.30pm Holy Communion □ *Facilities: amplification* □ *Wheelchair: 4 steps into church* □ *Other details: small garden* □ *Visiting: open 8.30am–4.30pm most days*

St Paul, Knightsbridge

Wilton Place, SW1 □ *Telephone: 235 3460 (office)* □ *Bus: 9, 14, 19, 22, 30, 52, 52a, 73* □ *Tube: Knightsbridge, Hyde Park Corner* □ *Parking: difficult* □ *Vicar: Rev Christopher Courtauld* □ *Address: 32 Wilton Place, SW1* □ *Telephone: 235 1810* □ *Available: most times* □ *Other clergy: Rev Raymond Davis (235 3437)*

The yellow-brick Perpendicular exterior of this church, by Thomas Cundy Jr, is unremarkable, but inside there is a lavish array of treasures, many of which have been given by worshippers and friends. Much of the finest decoration, notably the chancel and rood screen, was done by G F Bodley. He established the dominant colours of olive and green and gold, together with the brick red of the carpet and the unusual iron pillars in the nave. Although the church has been redecorated several times, the rich interior retains its late-Victorian feel because all additions and alterations have been made with respect for Bodley's ideals.

Amongst the many notable features are the tiled wall panels by Daniel Bell, and the Stations of the Cross, which together with chancel wall paintings of eminent representatives of the Catholic tradition in Anglicanism, were painted by Gerald Moira. These give a vivid indication of the 'high' churchmanship of St Paul's, which was established by the very first incumbent, Rev W J E Bennett. During the Oxford Movement controversy, he was criticised by Bishop Blomfield for 'deviations from the ordinary forms of our Church', such as adopting the Eastward position, and placing the Host in the mouths of communicants rather than in their hands. These were sensitive issues—there were anti-Roman Catholic riots at this time—and Bennett was forced to leave, in 1851.

The 'high' tradition continued, however, though there have been significant developments by Fr Christopher Courtauld such that he now describes the church as being 'both Catholic and Evangelical'. He has encouraged a family atmosphere at services, and the church is geared towards welcoming visitors whether as tourists or worshippers. The reputation for musical excellence, established in the 1870s, continues at St Paul's, and the splendid choir can be heard at the sung solemn Eucharist (Sunday 11am). There are organ recitals and occasional concerts held here, and the church has been used as a venue for recordings and for BBC broadcasts. Perhaps because of the splendour both of the interior and the music, St Paul's is a popular church for weddings.

Fr Courtauld has encouraged people to become involved with the church, and there is an active parish life. The church hall is used for women's groups and for a mothers and toddlers group on Wednesday mornings. Other local groups use it for meetings and social gatherings. Unlike many city centre churches, the congregation at St Paul's has remained fairly constant over the years. It relies on donations to survive, but its future both as a tourist attraction and as a well-loved place of worship seems assured.

Services: Sunday 8am, 9am Holy Communion, 11am Solemn Eucharist, 6pm Evensong; Mon, Thur, Sat 8.30am Holy Communion; Tue, Fri 7.30am Holy Communion; Wednesday 12.30, 6.15pm Holy Communion; Confessions Friday and Saturday 6.20pm and by appointment □ Facilities: deaf loop □ Children: Sunday school; creche □ Wheelchair: 3 steps □ Other details: hall □ Visiting: open weekdays, and Saturday and Sunday mornings

St Paul, Portman Square

Robert Adam Street, W1 □ Telephone: 935 5941 (office) □ Bus: any along Oxford Street □ Tube: Marble Arch □ Parking: difficult except Sunday □ Priest-in-Charge: Rev Richard Bewes □ Address: c/o All Souls (qv) □ Other staff: Mrs E Blundell for details of conference facilities

The modern St Paul's is a large building in Robert Adam Street built to replace an 18th century church in nearby Portman Square. Looking much like an office block and containing several large rooms and a restaurant as well as a church, the building was specifically designed for its 'conference centre ministry', providing space and facilities for up to 70 Christian-based organisations during the course of the year.

As such the church is a lively place, and it has strong links with both All Souls, Langham Place and the London Institute for Contemporary Christianity in Henrietta Place. A joint leaflet is published, including details of the lunchtime 'Christian Profile' meetings at St Paul's. Part of the church's ministry to the local business community, these meetings often feature guest speakers and are attended by up to 100 people. St Paul's is also a parish church of course, and there is a Sunday service for a small congregation of local residents.

Entering the building and climbing the stairs to the church proper, one should not miss Albert Holden's celebrated picture of 'Christ the Guest', said to have been painted after Holden's sudden conversion while studying Holman Hunt's work of the same name in St Paul's Cathedral. The church has a curious ceiling designed like the roof of a tent, pegged down to the walls, symbolising the pilgrimage inherent in the Christian life. There are striking modern stained glass windows, an unusual circular communion rail and an award-winning ceramic tile mosaic decorating the sanctuary. Note also the small plaque in memory of Sir George Williams (d. 1905), the founder of the YMCA.

Services: Sunday 11am Morning Worship; Monday 8am Prayer & Breakfast; Wednesday 1.05–1.35pm Lunchtime service □ Facilities: amplification, deaf loop □ Wheelchair: no access □ Other details: conference rooms, restaurant, committee rooms □ Visiting: open during day, ring bell; bookstall

St Peter, Eaton Square

Eaton Square, SW1 □ Telephone: 235 3194 (Vestry) □ Bus: any to Victoria □ Tube/BR: Victoria □ Parking: difficult □ Parish Priest: Rev Desmond Tillyer □ Address: 24 Chester Square, SW1 □ Telephone: 730 4354 □ Available: any reasonable time □ Other clergy: Rev Alan Chidwick

Despite the terrible fire of 20 October 1987 that reduced this fine Georgian church to a burnt-out shell, worship has continued here (in side buildings to be precise) almost unabated. The vestries are being converted into a chapel and it is hoped eventually to return to worshipping in the restored main body of the church. The temporary arrangement can seat around 70 people, and the Primary School hall has been used for major festivals.

St Peter's continues its practice of worship firmly in the Anglican Catholic tradition, though this is manifested in a wide range of Sunday services. The day begins with a simple said Eucharist using the Book of Common Prayer, while the Solemn Mass at 11am has incense, servers and a professional choir. These traditional acts of worship are punctuated by Family Mass, a short informal ASB service with an emphasis on active involvement by the congregation, especially the children.

After most services, there is still an opportunity for the mixed congregation of local residents and visitors to get together and talk. The church strives to maintain a strong sense of community, and there are a number of groups for all ages.

Services: Sunday 8.15am Eucharist, 10am Family Mass, 11am Solemn Mass; Weekdays 12.30pm Mass; Wednesday 8am Mass, 1.10pm Teaching service followed by lunch □ Wheelchair: 2 steps to temporary chapel □ Visiting: open for services only and daily when verger on duty

St Peter, Elgin Avenue

61 Elgin Avenue, Paddington W9 □ Bus: 6, 18, 28, 31, 46, 86 □ Tube/BR: Westbourne Park, Warwick Avenue □ Parking: easy, on street □ Vicar: Rev John Cooper □ Address: St Peter's Vicarage, 59 Elgin Avenue, W9 □ Telephone: 289 2011 □ Available most times

The original St Peter's of 1860 was demolished in 1974 after it was discovered that Kentish ragstone disease had made it unsafe. The new building, by Biscow and Stanton who are better known for municipal architecture than for churches, is an entirely functional and economical modern design in brick with little interior decoration. A small bas relief of a saint on the east end is from the original church but looks rather lost on the expanse of plain brick.

At the rear of the church is a sliding partition wall behind which lies a social room and kitchens where functions and receptions are held, and where coffee is served after the service. The walls can also be slid back to provide extra room in the church.

The Sunday service follows the 'high' Anglican tradition and the congregation is steadily on the increase. In an area with such a transient population this is encouraging and is due largely to the outgoing attitude of the church towards the community. St Peter's is also a member of the Paddington Christian Council which unites various denominations in common work of both a religious and secular nature, such as the support of anti-nuclear lobbies and anti-apartheid groups. There is also a lively parish magazine which discusses modern problems of faith and life.

One of the church's main priorities is the improvement of housing for disadvantaged groups in the area. The church owns some property in the parish and runs a shared ownership scheme. The vicar is also involved with the Paddington Housing Association for the needy and the St Agnes House trust for single parent families. Attached to the church is a purpose built block of flats for OAPs with a resident warden. The vicar is on the board of trustees.

Services: Sunday 11am Sung Eucharist, 6.30pm Evening Prayer; Monday 8.30am Holy Communion (chapel of St Mary's Hospital, Harrow Road); Thursday 7.30pm Holy Communion □ Children: creche at Sunday services; Children's service Monday 10am □ Wheelchair: easy access; toilet for disabled □ Other details: hall (available for hire) □ Visiting: open for services; otherwise apply for keys at vicarage

St Saviour

Warwick Avenue, W9 □ Bus: 6, 47 □ Tube: Warwick Avenue □ Parking: space available □ Vicar: Rev Gary Bradley □ Address: 42 Warwick Avenue, W9 □ Telephone: 286 4962 □ Available: most times

The original Victorian church of St Saviour's had to be demolished (as did many similar churches in the area) due to Kentish ragstone disease weakening the structure. It was replaced in the 1970s by this compact brick church with a tall, tapering spire. Inside, the pews are arranged around the altar and this, combined with the small size and good lighting, makes for an intimate atmosphere. The interior is decorated quite plainly, the main feature being a modern statue of the

Madonna and Child by Jo Karin Jonzen (1985) on the north of the altar, and some exuberant stained glass by John Hayward (1984).

The character of the worship is also modern but with a solidly traditional base. Services are Catholic in structure though from early 1987 the more contemporary laguage of Rite A has been used, while the sermons aim to be exploratory and topical. A feature of the church's life is the series of the study groups held at the Vicarage each Monday evening when a wide range of Christian issues are discussed, and the doctrines of other churches, for example, may be explored. There is no fixed membership of these groups, and all are welcome. Fr Bradley will also hear confessions by arrangement, and regular retreats are organised.

The congregation is largely quite young and contains many members of the acting profession (Fr Bradley is himself a former actor), while there is a core of older worshippers who have seen both church and parish change over the years. Often, amongst the congregation are Baptists, Lutherans and Roman Catholics, attracted by the style of service or the 'open' atmosphere. Bringing people together in worship is recognised as an important role of the Church.

Other events based at St Saviour's and aimed at reaching out into the community include interdenominational scout and guide groups, a mums and toddlers group and Sunday lunches for the elderly and the housebound, who are collected and driven to the church by volunteers. The hall and rooms are available to community and welfare groups at subsidised rates. The church also has its own theatre which is available for use by local professional and amateur groups. Based at the church is the Westminster Bereavement Service which selects, trains and sustains volunteers who visit the recently bereaved facing difficulty in their grief. Bereavement therapy is an important factor in the ministry of this church.

Services: Sunday 8am Holy Communion, 10am Parish Communion; Mon–Fri 6.30pm Holy Communion; Thursday 10.30am Holy Communion □ Facilities: deaf loop; large print texts □ Children: Sunday school 10am; creche facilities for Parish Communion □ Wheelchair: lift □ Other details: hall for hire □ Visiting: open by arrangement with vicar, and 6pm–7pm daily

St Saviour, Pimlico

St George's Square, SW1

and St James The Less

Thorndike Street, SW1 □ Bus: any along Vauxhall Bridge Road (plus 24 for St Saviour's) □ Tube: Pimlico □ Parking: on street □ Vicar: Rev Ronald Rogers □ Address: 59 Aylesford Street, SW1 □ Telephone: 821 9865 □ Available: evenings

St Saviour's is a large Gothic Revival church built in 1864. With its church hall, it occupies the north end of St George's Square, near the junction with Lupus Street. This is an area of shops and schools, of council estates and Victorian terraces now converted into luxury flats. The congregation of St Saviour's is drawn from both these communities, though the core of the church-goers are traditionally-minded, long-term residents. The worshippers are involved in charity work and support the lectures and concerts held at the church, and it is hoped to develop more study groups and outreach work. Services at St Saviour's follow Rite A, except at the early Sunday morning Sung Eucharist, when the 1662 Prayer Book is used.

The Church of St James the Less is rather smaller. It was built in 1861 to an Italianate design by G E Street, who also built the Law Courts, and is a Grade I listed building. It forms a charming group with the church school. The congregation here is composed almost solely of residents of the surrounding Lillington Gardens estate; around 40 attend the Sunday Service, which follows Rite A. Membership is growing here, and there are fortnightly Bible study meetings.

The churches were united into one parish in 1972 under the pastoral re-organisation of that year. The parish has regular ecumencial contacts, including a joint Evensong each quarter with the local Methodist and Roman Catholic churches.

Services: St Saviour's: Sunday 8am and 10am Sung Eucharist, 6.30pm Evensong (2nd, 3rd and 4th Sunday; time may vary in winter); Weekdays 8am Holy Communion. St James the Less: Sunday 11am Sung Eucharist, 6.30pm Evensong (1st Sunday only; time may vary in winter) □ Wheelchair: ramp available at St Saviour's; few steps at St James the Less □ Other details: both churches have halls □ Visiting: both churches are open for services only

St Stephen, Paddington

Westbourne Park Road, W2 □ Bus: 7, 15, 28 □ Tube: Royal Oak □ Parking: on street □ Vicar: Rev T J Knights □ Address: 25 Talbot Road, W2 □ Telephone: 229 5731 □ Available: at all times

In spite of its red doors, St Stephen's (built in 1856 on an island site at the junction of Westbourne Park Road and Talbot Road) appears rather gloomy from the outside. As a result of war damage, it no longer has the spire than once gave height and proportion to the tower.

Once inside, a very different atmosphere is immediately apparent. This is a spacious church, much beautified in recent years and totally orientated to the worship of God. In front of the High Altar in its apse of 1901 now stands an impressive free-standing altar, installed in 1974, which is used on Sundays and major Feast Days. In the transepts are a beautiful Chapel of Our Lady and a more sombre Chapel of the Holy Souls. The nave is brought into unity by the fine set of Stations of the Cross.

As may be inferred from the decorations listed above, worship at St Stephen's is in the Anglican Catholic tradition. 'It speaks of the glory of God', says Fr Knights, 'but with a direct simplicity which belongs to the people'. Easy-to-follow booklets are provided at each service. There is a high standard of music with an emphasis on congregational participation. On Sundays, Wednesdays and Saturdays, tea and coffee are available after services in a small hall at the rear of the church. This hall is also used for meetings by a number of local groups.

The parish contains three large estates as well as many streets of large Victorian houses, some of which are family homes while others have been converted into bed-sitters or flats for single people. The congregation reflects the mixture of ages and backgrounds found in the neighbourhood.

Services: Sunday 10.30am Mass, 6.30pm Evening Service; Weekday Mass 11.30am Mon, 9.30am Tues, 8pm Wed, 11.30am Thurs, 7pm Fri, 4.30pm Sat; Confession 12noon Thurs, 7.30pm Fri, 5pm Sat □ Children: Dom Bosco Club for Confirmation candidates □ Wheelchair: level access through doors beneath clock tower; reserved places at front of nave □ Other details: small hall can be hired; bookstall □ Visiting: open for services only

St Stephen, Rochester Row

Rochester Row, SW1 □ Telephone: 834 0950 □ Bus: 2, 2b, 10, 36, 36a, 76 □ Tube/BR: Victoria, Pimlico □ Parking: on street □ Vicar: Rev Richard Chartres □ Address: 21 Vincent Square SW1 □ Telephone: 834 8981 □ Available: most times □ Other clergy: Rev Howard Pennington

When it was built in 1850, St Stephen's was an exhibition of wealth in a virtual no-go area known as 'Devil's acre'. The philanthropist Angela Burdett-Coutts financed the building to be a memorial to her father. Her generosity ran further; she built a church hall and schools, while providing a soup kitchen and setting up a college to train some of the youth of Westminster for a new life in Canada.

The church is a large neo-Gothic building with an off-centre steeple, the spire of which recently had its top removed, resulting in a most distinctive appearance. The stone of the exterior is millstone grit, naturally dark in colour, while inside there is lighter coloured Caen stone. The interior is spacious with wide aisles and a long chancel.

'Worship at the parish aspires to be reverent without being excessively elaborate.' This is the stated intention, which means in practice that the Communion services follow either ASB Rite A or the Book of Common Prayer, while the Family Service on Sundays is chiefly designed for children of primary school age and their parents, fulfilling the role of both service and Sunday school.

Rev Richard Chartres has been at St Stephen's since 1984 and has witnessed a growth in the numbers attending, such that the Parish Communion service now has an average congregation of 75. He has encouraged community involvement, leading to support for Christian Aid and the Queen Mary Hostel for the Homeless. He has also encouraged greater understanding and enthusiasm for worship. Members of the congregation now produce 'Family Packs' based on the Christian seasons, that teach people how to take Christianity into the home. Numerous activities including brownies, the Monday Club (for elderly people) and the Mothers Union are held at Napier Hall on Hyde Place, a short walk from the church.

Services: Sunday 7.15am Matins, 8am Holy Communion, 9.30am Parish Communion, 11.30am Family Service, 6pm Evensong; Weekdays HC Wed 9.30am, Thu 12.30pm, Fri 7.30am □ Children: especially welcome to Family service □ Wheelchair: ramps provided □ Other details: Napier Hall (available for hire) □ Visiting: open for services only

Westminster Abbey

Parliament Square, SW1 □ Telephone: 222 5152 (Chapter Office) □ Bus: 3, 11, 12, 24, 29, 53, 59, 70, 77, 77a, 88, 109, 159, 170, 177, 196 □ Tube: Westminster □ Parking: very difficult □ Dean: V Rev Michael Mayne □ Address: The Deanery, Westminster Abbey □ Available: contact secretary in office hours □ Canons: Revv Sebastian Charles, Anthony Harvey, Donald Gray; V Rev Colin Semper □ Precentor: Rev Alan Luff □ Other clergy: many other clergy

Westminster Abbey is inextricably linked to the history of the British Monarchy and the vast majority of its annual three million visitors come to see the tombs and chapels of past monarchs, and the quire where so many coronations, royal weddings and funerals have taken place, rather than to participate in worship. Yet the Abbey is most active as a place of worship and, aside from the comprehensive observance of Anglican services, there is also an hourly prayer, led from the pulpit in the nave. For this short prayer visitors are asked to sit or stand still and to participate, as most willingly do.

Throughout the week Matins, Holy Communion services and Evensong are held each day. These are conducted in either the nave or quire, though the smaller services are held in St George's Chapel, next to the west door, or in St Faith's Chapel, which is near Poet's Corner. At all times that the Abbey is open the two chapels are available to people for quiet prayer.

On Sundays there are five services, taken by the Precentor or the Chaplain, and held in the nave or quire. Matins and Evensong each Sunday is assigned to one of the Canons, who will preach at one of the two services and invite a guest to lead the other. These people may be friends, parish clergy or academics, women included. The Dean of the Abbey is often present to read the second lesson and to give the blessing.

At Communion services both Rites A and B as well as the 1662 Prayer Book are used, thus satisfying the widest possible range of preferences. Sunday services are attended by between 300 and 1,000 people, out of which only some 20 will be regular worshippers at the Abbey. The Abbey choir, so much a part of the unique atmosphere, can be heard at Matins and Evensong in the quire. At the 6.30pm Congregational service on Sundays whoever leads the service has an opportunity to introduce different features into the worship, such as other choirs, dance and drama.

At various times throughout the year, memorial and other special services are held here. The monthly news-sheet gives details of these and indicates the times at which the Abbey is open to the public. A number of the chapels are used for particular services: the Henry VII Chapel, for instance, is used for the marriages of the Order of the Bath and of those living in the precincts. If anyone associated with the Abbey should die, be it monarch or cleaning lady, they are entitled to have their coffin in the chapel overnight.

As regards the architecture and monuments of Britain's premier church building it is less feasible to attempt a summary than to refer readers to any of the countless texts that dwell on the Abbey at an appropriate length. Informative guidebooks are available to visitors at the Abbey itself.

Westminster Abbey, SW1

Services: Sunday 8am Holy Communion, 10.30am Matins, 11.40am Holy Communion, 3pm Evensong, 6.30pm Congregational Service; Weekdays 7.30am Matins (9.20am Saturday & Bank Holidays), 8am Holy Communion, 12.30pm Holy Communion (except Sat & Wed), 5pm Evensong (3pm Saturday) □ Facilities: amplification, deaf loop in south transept □ Wheelchair: ramp through cloisters □ Visiting: open Mon, Tue, Thu, Fri 9.20am–4.45pm; Wed 9.20am–4.45pm and 6pm–7.45pm; Sat 9.20am–2.45pm and 3.45pm–5.45pm; entry fee charged outside service times and Wed 6pm–7.45pm; shop open 9.30am–5pm Monday to Saturday

---

Church of England : Kensington and Chelsea

All Saints with St Columb

Colville Road, Powis Gardens, W11 □ Bus: 7, 15, 15a, 52, 52a □ Tube: Ladbroke Grove, Westbourne Park □ Parking: on street □ Vicar: Rev John Brownsell □ Address: The Vicarage, Powis Gardens, W11 □ Telephone: 727 5919 □ Available: most times □ Other clergy: Rev Jeremy Fairhead (221 2857)

This parish church in North Kensington—the area around Portobello Road—was built in 1861 to serve what was then a wealthy community. A hundred years later the fine houses were all in multiple occupation; slum landlords, poverty and racial tension were rife. The local council designated this area as one of the pockets of the borough in which it was to build housing estates: the result has been to make this an extremely densely-populated parish, and gentrification of the neighbourhood by housing developers has changed the social mix but not reduced the overpopulation. Now both black and white, well-established residents and newcomers, young and old, meet together each Sunday at All Saints. There are far more single people (of all ages) than families in the congregation, which is true of the area as a whole.

The church is Victorian Gothic, with post-war improvements. The altar, the font, and the stained glass are by Ninian Comper. However, in 1981 the altar was remodelled by Norman Davies. There is a side altar, the work of Martin Travers, which is used during the week. A side chapel, set in the south wall, has a large window through which passers-by can see the large crucifix which is illuminated at night. This is an Anglo-Catholic church, which tries to stay contemporary in both its form of worship and its approach to social problems.

Services: Sunday 11am Solemn Mass; Monday, Wednesday, Friday 6.30pm Mass; Tuesday, Thursday 7am Mass; Saturday 10am Mass; Morning Prayer—daily at 9.30am (except Monday), Evening Prayer—daily at 6pm □ Facilities: amplification □ Children: Sunday school; creche □ Wheelchair: full facilities—ramps, toilets for disabled etc □ Other details: church hall □ Visiting: open for services; foyer always open allowing view of interior

Chelsea Old Church (All Saints)

Old Church Street, SW3 □ Bus: 11, 19, 22, 31, 39, 45, 49, □ Tube: Sloane Square □ Parking: on street □ Vicar: Rev Prebendary C E L Thomas □ Address: 4 Old Church Street, SW3 □ Telephone: 352 5627 □ Available: most times during day

During the night of 16th April 1941, Chelsea Old Church, which dates back to the 13th century, was bombed. The tower collapsed and rubble and broken glass were scattered across Old Church Street. Many of the priceless monuments commemorating notable Chelsea families were badly damaged. Least affected was the 14th century chapel which had been re-modelled some two hundred years later by Sir Thomas More—the altar stood proud amid the ruins.

The More chapel was the first part of the church to be re-opened after a long wait of nine years. The re-built church was not completed until May 1958. Although in 20th century brick, it has the medieval-style tower and other features of the original. With seating for 400, the interior gives the feel of worshipping in a splendid museum, with the restored relics and monuments filling every space and corner of the church. Also within the church is a set of books given by Sir Hans Sloane (1661–1753), including a 1717 Vinegar Bible and two volumes of Foxe's Book of Martyrs (1684).

A choir of professional singers sing at weddings and special services and the bells are rung most Sundays and for weddings by request. Recitals are held from time to time in the church and the choir can be heard after Evensong on Sunday or sometimes on an evening during the week.

Next door to the church is the church hall, built at the same time as the vicarage and the re-building of the church. It has seating for up to 200. After services on some Sundays, the congregation adjourn here for tea and coffee. The hall, used by brownies during the week, is available for general hire and is used most frequently by theatre companies for rehearsals.

Chelsea Old Church overlooks the Thames and is set in a small colourful garden. The parishioners are encouraged to inspect the church garden and enjoy it while it is at its best. Outside the south wall of the church is a statue of Sir Thomas More by L Cubitt Bevis, unveiled in 1969.

Services: Sunday 8am Holy Communion, 11am Mattins, 12 noon Holy Communion, 6pm Evensong □ Facilities: amplification □ Children: children's service, Sunday 10am □ Wheelchair: level access □ Other details: hall □ Visiting: open 10am–1pm, 2pm–5pm, most days

Christ Church, Kensington

Victoria Road, W8 □ Bus: 9, 33, 49, 52, 73, 74 □ Tube: Gloucester Road □ Parking: street parking □ Clergy: Rev Julian Browning, Rev Sister Gerd CSA (Deacon) □ Telephone: 229 2662 □ Available: most times

Set on the quiet corner of Victoria Road and Eldon Road, and surrounded by a well kept garden, Christ Church is a fine example of an early Victorian village church. Once inside the church, which is small enough to have no heating problems in winter and has excellent acoustics, a warm and friendly atmosphere prevails.

Christ Church was built in 1851 as a Chapel of Ease to St Mary Abbots, for those living in the south-west corner of the parish. Today, services are held on Sunday mornings only, when a professional choir sing accompanied by the organ adding to the traditional ambience. After the service, coffee is served at the back of the church. For services at other times, worshippers attend at St Mary Abbots.

The life of Christ Church is organised by a Deacon Rev Sister Gerd CSA. She is a member of the Anglican Religious Community of St Andrew and works in partnership with a non-stipendary priest, Rev Julian Browning.

During the week, Christ Church is used for school services and a local Montessorri nursery who hire the vestry. Social activities are arranged both at Christ Church and St Mary Abbots.

Services: Sunday 8am Holy Communion, 11am Sung Eucharist 1st & 3rd Sunday (Morning Prayer 2nd, 4th & 5th) □ Children: Sunday school 11am, 1st & 3rd Sunday; children's service 10am 2nd, 4th & 5th □ Wheelchair: 1 small step □ Visiting: open for services only, or by arrangement; garden always accessible

Christchurch, Chelsea

Christchurch Street, SW3 □ Telephone: 351 7365/6 (St Luke's, Chelsea) □ Bus: 11, 19, 22, 49 □ Tube: Sloane Square, South Kensington □ Parking: on street □ Priest-in-Charge: Rev Simon Acland □ Address: c/o church □ Available: ring for appointment

Built in 1838–9, Christchurch was originally a Chapel of Ease to St Luke's, but because of the rapidly growing population it soon came to have its own parish. The church is very plain both inside and out, the highlight of the interior being the stained glass lancet windows in the sanctuary. A Mr Bryan, writing in 1869, attributes this austerity less to strict Protestant principles than to the poverty of the parishioners desiring its construction.

The church is small, and an intimate atmosphere is created by the mixed congregation of between 40 and 70 people. Services follow Rite B and the 1662 Prayer Book and are in the 'central tradition'. There is a strong boy's choir with additional adult voices. People are encouraged to become closely involved with the church, and members help prepare individuals for confirmation in special classes given for this purpose.

Christchurch is used extensively during the week by local schools, and by brownies and cubs. Exact details of the church's religious and secular programmes are unknown at the time of writing, pending the planned re-amalgamation with St Luke's (qv), its larger sister church.

Services: Sunday 8am Holy Communion, 11am Parish Communion or Morning Prayer with HC, alternately □ Facilities: amplification □ Children: children's church □ Wheelchair: a few small steps □ Other details: hall (available for hire) □ Visiting: open 10am–4pm weekdays

Holy Trinity, Brompton (with St Paul)

Brompton Road, SW7 □ Telephone: 581 8255 (office) □ Bus: 14, 30, 45, 49, 74, 264 □ Tube: Knightsbridge, South Kensington □ Parking: car park open for services □ Vicar: Rev Sandy Millar □ Address: Holy Trinity Vicarage, 73 Princess Gate Mews, SW7 □ Telephone: as church □ Available: during office hours □ Other staff: Adrian Burns, Administrator; Jeremy Jennings, Pastoral Director; 3 curates (all on 581 8255)

Holy Trinity, the parish church of Brompton and situated close to the Oratory, is an excellent example of a thriving evangelical church. The main act of worship, on Sunday evenings, is characterised by much lay participation, and includes an opportunity for the worshippers to talk amongst themselves and to get to know each other. The music features traditional hymns interspersed with modern songs led by a group of folk-style musicians, and the Bible-based talk (not referred to as a sermon) is entertaining and informal. A closed-circuit television system ensures that those with a restricted view of the chancel can follow the proceedings on colour monitors. These services are very popular and attendance can reach 1,000.

The church that houses this large congregation was dismissed as 'a poor, semi-Gothic structure' when it was consecrated in 1829, but over the years it has undergone numerous alterations and improvements. A recent development was the fully restored crypt, opened in 1986 by the Bishop of Kensington, which contains meeting rooms, offices, a bookstall and a coffee bar. The interior of the church itself is impressive and spacious with a number of interesting features, including the reredos in gold mosaic designed by J R Clayton and installed in 1885. Note also the marble chancel steps and balustrade with matching pulpit.

Central to the life of the church are the numerous pastorate and fellowship groups, meeting bi-weekly, which all regular worshippers are encouraged to join. Other organisations include Trinity Action which assists the elderly and disabled, and the Mission Task Force, which supports various missionaries. There is a weekly Women's Fellowship, a monthly Overseas Forum, and the church is also involved in healing: after the Sunday evening service there is a time of individual healing ministry, largely taken by lay people.

In order to help one keep track of the many forthcoming events and activities based here, the church publishes programmes about three times a year which give up-to-date information. These also include a 'who's who' of staff members and give contact details for the various groups and organisations.

Services: Sunday 8.30am Holy Communion, 11am, 6.30 Informal evening service; Wednesday 12.30pm Holy Communion (healing prayers once a month) □ Facilities: amplification, deaf loop, close-circuit television □ Children: creche (Sunday), Children's church Sunday 11.15am □ Wheelchair: good access, ramp, toilets for disabled □ Other details: hall for hire (contact crypt administration) □ Visiting: 9.30am to dusk daily

Holy Trinity, Sloane Street

Sloane Street, SW1 □ Bus: 19, 22, 137 □ Tube: Sloane Square □ Parking: on street, meters □ Vicar: Rev K L Yates □ Address: 97a Cadogan Lane, SW1 □ Telephone: 235 3383 □ Available: telephone for appointment

Holy Trinity has always been a fashionable church. Like many other Anglican churches— there are nine within half a mile—it was built at a time of great wealth

Holy Trinity, Brompton, SW7

and expansion when the Empire was at its height, and when the elegant townhouses that characterise Knightsbridge were also erected. Completed in 1890 to a design by John Dando Sedding, it is known as 'the Cathedral of the Arts and Crafts Movement', because many artists contributed to its rich decoration and furnishings. William Morris himself executed the east window, designed by Sir Edward Burne-Jones.

Originally, the local gentry would attend in the morning and their servants in the evening. Nowadays, the congregation reflects the cosmopolitan if impermanent nature of the community. Alongside local residents, there are many Europeans, Australians, New Zealanders, Canadians, Nigerians and Ghanaians, many of whom are diplomats or tourists. A special newsletter is produced three times a year to keep in touch with those from abroad.

Worship is in the 'central' Anglican tradition, and the services are noted for the quality of the music: the excellent organ, like those of Westminster Abbey, was designed by Walkers, and the church has superb acoustics.

Because of the fluctuating nature of attendances, there are no permanent groups or activities based at the church. Groups are set up as the need arises, and people are invited to become involved with the church, whether as an organist, flower-arranger or whatever, even if only for a temporary period.

Services: Sunday 8.30am Holy Communion, 10.30am Eucharist, 12.10pm Holy Communion; Wednesday 12.30pm Holy Communion; Thursday 1.15pm Holy Communion □ *Facilities: amplification* □ *Children: creche* □ *Wheelchair: level access* □ *Visiting: open service times only*

St Augustine of Canterbury

Queen's Gate, SW7 □ *Bus: 9, 52, 52a, 73, 74* □ *Tube: South Kensington, Gloucester Road* □ *Parking: difficult except Sunday and evenings* □ *Vicar: Rev K V Hewitt* □ *Address: 117 Queen's Gate, SW7* □ *Telephone: 584 1960* □ *Available: most times*

Service sheets at St Augustine's are available in English, French, Greek, Italian, Spanish, Portuguese, German, Arabic and Japanese—a measure of the number of tourists and visitors who worship here. During the summer, around two thirds of the congregation are non-residents, and church members make a special effort to welcome them, providing coffee and sometimes even a cooked meal. Surrounded by embassies, hotels and bedsits in cosmopolitan South Kensington, St Augustine's offers hospitality and fellowship to Christians from all over the world.

Worship is in the Catholic tradition, following ASB Rite B at Holy Communion and the Book of Common Prayer at Evensong. Lay participation is strongly encouraged. The church has a fine organ and good singers are always sought to enhance the beauty of Sung Eucharist.

Built in 1871–6, the church is undoubtedly one of William Butterfield's masterpieces. It presents a striking west front with bands of stone and red brick in typical Butterfield style. This 'streaky bacon' effect lost favour in the 1920s and the interior brickwork was covered in white paint, thus ensuring the recently installed reredos and Stations of the Cross by Martin Travers were the centre of attention. Tastes change however, and in 1975, Butterfield's patterns in brick and his glazed tile murals were again revealed, and they have since won the appreciation they deserve.

St Augustine's has a growing reputation as a centre for Christian Arts. A Performances of plays, such as Britten's *Noyes Fludde*, and liturgical music, such as Faure's Requiem as well as works by new composers, have taken place here to critical acclaim. The visual arts are also supported, as is evidenced by the modern allegorical fresco on the tympanum of the western arch. This was undertaken by a group of anonymous artists working, like their medieval forerunners, 'for the Glory of God'.

Services: Sunday 8am, 9.30 Holy Communion, 11am Sung Eucharist, 6.30pm Holy Communion, 7.30pm Evensong; Weekdays 6pm Evensong, (plus HC 8am Mon, Thur, Fri & Sat; 11am Wed; 6.30pm Tue & Wed) □ Wheelchair: shallow steps, wide door; allotted space inside □ Other details: adjoining hall, used extensively but can be hired □ Visiting: usually open in the daytime.

St Clement, Notting Dale

Treadgold Street, W11 □ Telephone: 229 5077 (Community Centre) □ Bus: 295 □ Tube: Latimer Road □ Parking: on street □ Parish Priest: Rev David Randall □ Address: The Vicarage, Sirdar Road, W11 □ Telephone: 584 1960 □ Available: by telephone □ Other clergy: Rev Brian Shipsides (603 3016)

Anyone attending the Sunday Sung Eucharist service at St Clement's may well be struck by the number of children at the service. There are six child servers in attendance and, just before Holy Communion, around 30 youngsters having just finished Sunday school join the 40 or so adults in the church. Most are well behaved though some toddlers grow a little restless and excited. Fr Randall has to speak a little louder but feels that the service would not be the same without them. The congregation reflects the ethnic mix of the area containing both white and Afro-Carribbean worshippers. Worship combines the dignity of the 'high' tradition with an inevitably relaxed and informal atmosphere created by the children. Notting Hill carnival is celebrated by a special service in carnival style.

Children from the parish school often make the seasonal banners that decorate the chancel, and links between church and school are very close. In 1979, St Clement's, then a rather run-down Victorian church, became the centre of a Community Development Project. Included in the scheme were plans for a youth clubhouse and a new school complex for the amalgamated C of E schools of St Clement's and St James Norlands. The church itself was fitted with chairs instead of pews while the vestry and choir room were converted into a community centre. This centre is used daily for a number of purposes, including Womens Fellowship meetings, an OAP group and Bingo sessions. There is a licensed bar which is open after services as well as for social functions at the centre.

Morning and Evening prayers are said by members of the congregation, and the church is kept open as much as possible for anyone seeking solace. A secluded side chapel is available for private prayer, and should the main entrance be locked, try the side door in Sirdar Road.

Services: Sunday 11.15am Sung Eucharist (Parish Mass); Friday 7pm Mass □ Facilities: amplification □ Children: Sunday school 11.15am □ Wheelchair: level access □ Other details: Community Centre; nave doubles as hall □ Visiting: usually open for private prayer as well as services

St Cuthbert

Philbeach Gardens, SW5 □ Bus: 31 □ Tube: Earls Court □ Parking: restricted parking available □ Vicar: Rev John Vine □ Address: Clergy House, 50 Philbeach Gardens, SW5 □ Telephone: 370 3263 □ Available: most times

St Cuthbert's is notable for its splendid interior and furnishings; it is a jewel of the late Victorian Arts and Crafts movements. Black Belgian and pale Torbay marble columns complement the vari-coloured marble facings on the walls. The art nouveau lectern stands out, fashioned in wrought iron and copper by Bainbridge-Reynolds, the most prominent among several artists in the early congregations. He is also responsible for the High Altar and the other features of the richly decorated sanctuary.

More important, however, than the contribution of any one artist is that of the Guilds. Parishioners were encouraged to learn and use the skills of stone- and wood-carving, enamel- and metal-work, and embroidery. The choir stalls, which have carved seat-backs (misericords), some of them humerous in conception, were made by the Guild of St Joseph; the Guild of St Margaret made vestments and the beautiful frontals; the greatest artistic contributions, however, came from the Guild of St Peter, who used carved stonework in many different and intricate patterns to cover all the interior walls of the church. The Guild system seems an appropriate and successful approach to the job of furnishing a place of worship.

Another luminary of the church art of St Cuthbert's was the Rev Ernest Geldart, who designed the awesome beech reredos, 44 feet high and carved with many Biblical scenes to illustrate the theme of the use of incense and lights in worship. St Cuthbert's was always a 'high' church, and in its history it has known conflict with unsympathetic laypeople and an ecclesiastical authority often cautious in regard to anything smacking of ostentation. Opulent it may be, but the atmosphere of the church is distinctly reverential, and the paintings, among which is the superb series of Stations of the Cross by Hans Winck (copied from the one in Antwerp Cathedral), do strike a subdued note.

The vicar, who has been here for over 17 years, has seen the congregation change considerably. It is now very mobile, rather than settled as it was, though it still includes many professional people. Numbers steadily increase, so redundancy plans—which had been mooted—will not now proceed, and an appeal may soon be under way to help with the extensive restoration work required. It is hoped that the two excellent Philbeach Halls will shortly be able to be put to valuable social and community use.

Services: Sunday 10am Holy Communion, 11am Sung Eucharist, 6pm Evensong; Daily 6pm Evensong; Mon to Fri 6.30pm Holy Communion □ Wheelchair: level access via the 'funeral door' □ Other details: two halls □ Visiting: anytime by request

St George, Campden Hill

Aubrey Walk, W8 □ Bus: 12, 88 □ Tube: Notting Hill Gate, Holland Park □ Parking: on street □ Priest-in-Charge: Rev Peter Myles □ Address: 25 Campden Hill Square, W8 □ Telephone: 727 9486 □ Available: telephone for appointment

St George's is situated in the area known as Campden Hill, just off Holland Park

Avenue south of Notting Hill Gate. These days it is a prosperous neighbourhood, but in 1864 when the church was built, Kensington Gravel Pits, as it was known, was a centre of slum housing and terrible poverty. The growing population in those days had been served by an iron church, built for use by the troops in the Crimea and then shipped back to England. St George's was its replacement, at the bequest of one John Bennett, and was designed in an eclectic Gothic style by E Bassett Keeling.

The main Sunday service is the Sung Eucharist at 10am. A Sunday school runs concurrently, and the children join the main service just before Communion. St George's is part of the large parish of St Mary Abbots, along with Christ Church, Victoria Road. Many church activities are organised together with these other churches.

St George's originally had a tall spire, and this can still be seen on the cover of early editions of *Peter Pan*, with Peter and Wendy flying around it. The author, J M Barrie, lived in Campden Hill Square. However, by 1950 the spire had become unsafe and it was dismantled. Soon afterwards, cracks were discovered in the wall of the apse so the whole area of chancel and sanctuary also had to be removed. Today the church is a blend of old and new building styles. Inside there are many original furnishings, but there is a new altar, of Welsh slate on brick.

Services: Sunday 8am Holy Communion, 10am Sung Eucharist, 6.30pm Evening Prayer, 7pm Holy Communion; Wednesday 12 noon Holy Communion □ Children: Sunday school 10am; creche □ Wheelchair: ramp □ Other details: library □ Visiting: open at service times only

Parish of St John and St Peter, Notting Hill

St John

Landsdowne Crescent, W11 □ Bus: 12, 88 □ Tube: Holland Park □ Parking: on street

St Peter

Kensington Park Road, W11 □ Bus: 7, 52, 59 □ Tube: Notting Hill Gate □ Parking: on street □ Vicar: Rev Harold Stringer □ Address: 25 Ladbroke Road, W11 □ Telephone: 727 3439 □ Available: daytime □ Other staff: Rev Bruce Collins (229 7275), Sister Denzil (229 2662)

These two churches, quite different in character and appearance, are run by the one vicar, Rev Harold Stringer, and a single parish team. They complement each other in order to play the widest possible role in the community.

St John's is a Gothic church surrounded by greenery at the top of the hill in Ladbroke Grove; its spire can be seen for some distance. The Sunday morning worship here is quite formal and along 'central' Anglican lines, attracting regular congregations of around 100. After services, coffee is served at the back of the church, and newcomers are made to feel welcome. There are a number of young families amongst the worshippers and creche facilities are provided for the Family Eucharist service.

At St Peter's, an Italianate church with a most attractive interior, services are less formal and are geared towards the young. At the Sunday Morning Worship music is provided by a contemporary instrumental group and many young people attend. The quieter Evening Prayer is held together with local Methodists. The Celebration of Praise service is again popular with young people. The church is regularly used for modern music concerts and other events.

There is also a wide range of study groups, some run jointly, including a Bible Reading Fellowship and a meditation class. A parish magazine is produced which, as well as listing the details of services and forthcoming events, carries forthright articles on a wide range of topics both secular and religious, local and international.

Services: St John's: Sunday 8am Holy Communion, 10.30am Parish Eucharist; Wednesday 7.30am Holy Communion. St Peter's: Sunday 10.30am Morning Worship, 6pm Evening Prayer (with Methodists); Monday–Friday 6.30pm Evening Prayer; Thursday 12.15pm Holy Communion □ Children: creche and Sunday school 10.30am (both churches) □ Wheelchair: easy access to both churches □ Other details: parish centre at St John's □ Visiting: only St Peter's open outside service times, for activities and Saturday morning

St John with St Andrew

Park Walk, SW10 □ Bus: 11, 14 □ Tube: Sloane Square □ Parking: difficult □ Vicar: Rev John O S Smith □ Address: 43 Park Walk, SW10 □ Telephone: 352 1675 □ Available: phone for appointment

This church is nestled among the houses on Park Walk which runs between the Kings Road and Fulham Road. Built in 1913, it replaced Park Chapel which had served for 250 years as an inter-denominational place of worship and, when plans were approved for the new church, the sponsor, Mr Hans Sloane Stanley, stipulated that it should be and always remain a 'low' Anglican church.

The rather plain Gothic-style red brick church is dominated by a tall buttressed tower. The lack of adornment is continued inside, where much brickwork is exposed and the woodwork strictly functional. The east window is the only one in stained glass.

Rev O S Smith is been incumbent here for over nine years and has a regular congregation of around 70 people, including many family groups. Communion services follow the Book of Common Prayer, while the ASB is used for Evening and Morning Prayer. Rev Smith has sought to create a caring parish atmosphere—one successful project is the good neighbours scheme whereby members of the congregation visit elderly or disabled people in the parish. The Friends of Ellesmere do similar work in a local old people's home. The church also provides, free of charge, a venue for the meetings of Narcotics Anonymous and Alcoholics Anonymous.

Services: Sunday 11am Holy Communion, 6.30pm Evening Prayer; Last Sunday of month 11am Morning Prayer, 6.30pm Holy Communion □ Children: creche, Sunday school □ Wheelchair: 1 step □ Other details: hall □ Visiting: open service times only; tours may be given by arrangement

St Jude

Courtfield Gardens, SW5 □ Bus: 74, 30 □ Tube: Gloucester Road □ Parking: small car park □ Vicar: Rev David Rymer □ Address: 18 Collingham Road, SW5 □ Telephone: 370 1360 □ Available: most times

An important part of the work of St Jude's is the coffee-bar situated in the Belfry, open four days a week. All are welcome to come and sit in a calm and comfortable environment, with the chance to chat if they feel like it. There is a full-time coffee-bar Outreach worker. The Police Charity have donated money for this facility as they regard it as very relevant to the social and welfare needs of many people. There is considerable contact with local hospitals and social services, to whom people may be referred for help.

A good deal of emphasis is also placed on making the church itself accessible and available to people, that is, to break through the 'stained glass barrier'. To this end Rev David Rymer meets regularly with the vicars and wardens of neighbouring parishes. 'Do it yourself' concerts are held to help promote a community spirit. A number of people have found comfort through the supportive capacity of St Jude's, and the opportunities that exist for informal counselling. There is also a Healing Ministry after some Sunday services.

St Jude's has a wide range of services, alternately using Rites A and B, and the 1662 Prayer Book. Guest preachers, from other denominations as well as Anglicans, are often invited to lead services. There are around 80 people on the Electoral Role of the church; this calls for a renewal of commitment every six years.

The church itself is similar to many other Victorian Gothic churches in the area and elsewhere, though it has a tall spire and some good stained glass and frescoes. The unusually slender pillars in the nave are made of cast-iron. In all St Jude's is a church addressing contemporary issues, and working with other local churches to create a coherent and relevant Christian presence in Earls Court.

Services: Sunday 8am Holy Communion, 11am Parish Communion, 6pm Evening service/Communion; Wednesday 7.30am Holy Communion; Thursday 12 noon Holy Communion □ Facilities: amplification, deaf loop □ Children: Sunday school □ Wheelchair: small step, ramp □ Other details: coffee bar □ Visiting: coffee bar open most times, otherwise ring church

St Luke, Chelsea

Sydney Street, SW3 □ Telephone: 351 7365/6 (office) □ Bus: 14, 45, 49 □ Parking: on street □ Rector: Rev Derek Watson □ Address: c/o church □ Available: telephone for appointment □ Other clergy: Rev Mark Butchers

By the end of the Napoleonic Wars, Chelsea had begun to spread north of the Kings Road, and there was need for a larger church than Chelsea Old Church. As a result, St Luke's was built, a large and expensive landmark of the Gothic revival, and consecrated in 1842. Designed by James Savage, the church boasts a pinnacled tower of some 142 feet and flying buttresses along the whole length of the nave.

The interior is high and spacious, and may well have been rather cold and forbidding before the introduction of pew heating. This has greatly added to the comfort of the congregation, which usually numbers between 70 and 100. The regular worshippers, who despite the prosperous image of the area are a real social mix, are welcoming and friendly. Services are in the 'central' tradition, following both ASB Rite A and the 1662 Prayer Book. There is a voluntary mixed voice choir. Close links have been established with the nearby Chelsea Methodist Church: rector and minister exchanged pulpits during the Week of Prayer for Christian Unity.

The labyrinthine vaults under St Luke's have been converted into offices, including a parish office, open daily. The Friends of St Luke's are a group of people who have special connections with, or affection for, the church, and they are actively involved in fundraising for restoration and maintenance.

Services: Sunday 8am Holy Communion, 10.30am Sung Eucharist or Morning Prayer and HC alternately, 6.30pm Evensong; Weekday HC Tue 6.30pm, Wed 11am □ Facilities: amplification □ Children: Sunday school and creche □ Wheelchair: ramps □ Other details: hall and vestry (available for hire) □ Visiting: open 12noon–2pm weekdays

St Luke, Redcliffe Gardens

Redcliffe Square, SW10 □ Bus: 11, 14, 22, 31 □ Tube: Earls Court □ Parking: spaces for members □ Vicar: Rev David Price □ Address: 1 Cathcart Road, SW10 □ Telephone: 352 7553 □ Available: most times

St Luke's is a fine example of a Victorian mock-Gothic church, set in its own grounds, surrounded by plane trees and standing in a commanding position: even in this area of tall houses, the church is a landmark.

The building was built by G and H Gordon, and was completed and consecrated in 1871. The church stands in a middle class area and was built with several doors, including one for carriages and an entrance for servants. The original capacity of the church was 1,000, though the side pews were later taken out and it now seats 400.

Inside, the church is large and impressive, and although the nave is quite dark, the sanctuary has large clear windows which illuminate the altar and choir stalls brilliantly. Other parts of the church still retain their stained glass. At one time a huge wrought iron cross hung over the sanctuary but it was removed during the war for fear it would drop. This cross can now be seen at the rear of the church.

The altar itself is impressive, dominated by a reredos containing statues of Christ flanked by Matthew, Mark, Luke and John; nearby are statues of Old Testament figures and plaques inscribed with quotations from the scripture. The organ is spectacular. Built by Norman and Beard in 1912, it has a vast array of pipes at the rear of the church, decorated with five large wooden angels blowing trumpets.

The church is evangelical in tradition—Rev Evan Hopkins, co-founder of the evangelical Keswick Convention, was once involved with the church—and uses the Alternative Service Book 1980, Rite A (although the 8am is still 1662). The congregation of around 100 take an active part in the service, helping with readings, intercessions and so forth, and also form the choir. Mr Price, the present incumbent, would like to encourage a greater degree of congregational participation. Mr Price is trying to get the church more involved in the community; the church aims to visit every home in the parish four times a year. He is also trying to set up and encourage home-based groups (such as prayer groups) in the area, tied to the church but not actually meeting there. All five Anglican churches in the Earls Court area are engaged in trying to set up a united outreach group.

Services: Sunday 8am Holy Communion, 10.30am Parish Communion 1st, 3rd & 5th Sundays (Matins and HC 2nd & 4th Sundays), 6.30pm Evening Service (HC 4th Sunday); Weekdays 8am Morning Prayer; Thursday 12 noon Holy Communion □ *Facilities: amplification, deaf loop, large print service books, Braille texts on request* □ *Wheelchair: ramp* □ *Other details: Parish Centre (hall available for hire; contact Mr Hamilton on 373 3628)* □ *Visiting: check with church*

St Mary Abbots

Kensington Church Street, W8 □ *Bus: 27, 28, 31, 52, 52a* □ *Tube: Kensington High Street* □ *Parking: nearby car parks, otherwise difficult except on Sunday* □ *Vicar: Rev Ian Robson* □ *Address: The Vicarage, Vicarage Gate, W8* □ *Telephone: 937 6032* □ *Available: most times* □ *Other staff: Parish Secretary (pm only) 937 2419; Rev Alan Boddy (937 2364)*

This is a famous church, the first church in Kensington and, indeed, the only one until the beginning of the 19th century. The present structure dates back only to 1872, but there has been a church on the site since at least 1100. Among the many memorials are several from the church of the period of William and Mary, who were the first Royals to move out to Kensington. King William presented the church with its pulpit, which is still in use, although the square Classical style church he knew has now been superseded by Gilbert Scott's large, Gothic design in stock brick faced in ragstone. The spire, at 278 feet, is the tallest in London, and the final stone of the spire was laid by the then vicar in person, who proceeded to hold a short service of dedication while still up in the scaffolding!

The original St Mary Abbots, as its name implies, was a monastry church, and somehow this has always been a centre of 'high' Anglicanism. There are five Sunday services, using either the ASB or the BCP. The main family service (ASB) is described by the present incumbent as a 'good example of an Anglican Parish Eucharist, demonstrating lay participation'. Well attended by a wide cross-section of the parish, with perhaps a fifth of the congregation visitors to the area, the service is supported by a choir and the newly-restored Hill organ. There are three services daily, and the church tries to be open to visitors as much as possible.

St Mary Abbot is home to a great many activities. This church hall is used daily by various community groups and by the BBC for rehearsals; a comedy theatre group who also use it are occasional performers at the church. There are frequent lunchtime concerts, including weekly concerts by pupils from the Royal College of Music, and organ recitals. Thursday evenings are for bell-ringing. The church is also the venue for a number of civic services, including the annual Mayor's service. After Sunday services, refreshments are provided at St Mary Abbot's school, to the west of the church.

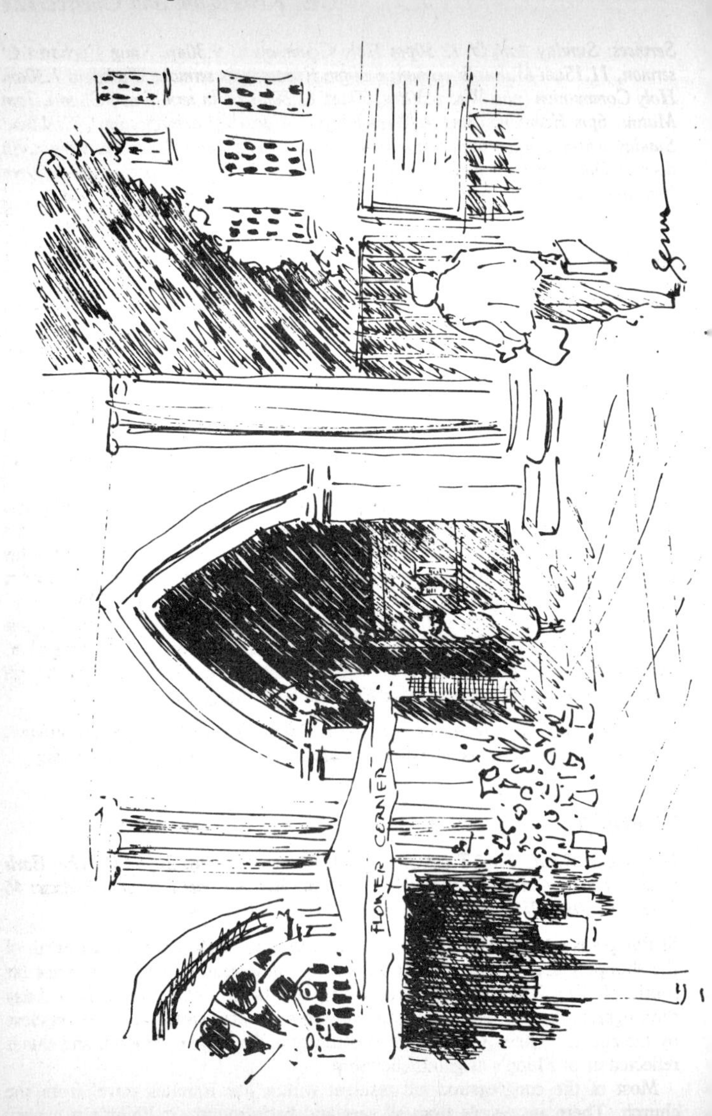

Gateway, St Mary Abbots, W8

Services: Sunday 8am & 12.30pm Holy Communion, 9.30am Sung Eucharist & sermon, 11.15am Matins & sermon; 6.30pm Evensong & sermon; Weekdays 7.30am Holy Communion (plus Wed 6.30pm; Thurs 11.30am & in term time 9.30am), 7am Matins, 6pm Evensong (sung on Wednesdays) □ Facilities: amplification □ Children: Sunday school 9.30am during term time; creche □ Wheelchair: level access via north door □ Other details: hall, in constant demand □ Visiting: open 7am–6.30pm (sometimes after 9pm); postcards available; occasional tours by Churchwarden

St Mary with St Peter

The Boltons, SW10 □ Telephone: 373 2810 □ Bus: 19, 45, 49 □ Tube: Earls Court, West Brompton □ Parking: on street □ Vicar: Rev Stephen Bartlett □ Address: 24 Fawcett Street, SW10 □ Telephone: 351 4204 □ Available: telephone for appointment

This attractive church, surrounded by prize-winning gardens, is kept open as much as possible during daylight hours for the benefit of impromptu visitors. It is surmounted by a six-sided spire in honey-coloured brick, with tiny trefoil windows let in each side. At the corners of the tower belfry is a choir of angels in black granite.

Inside, there is a subdued light from windows of both plain and stained glass, including a modern Nativity in the east window. The roof is supported on beams ending in carved corbels, each in the form of a saint bearing the instrument of his martyrdom. The general impression given by the white walls and orderly pews is of a 'low' church interior, but there is a statue of the Virgin and Child.

Services follow the ASB and the average attendance is around 100. This is quite a mobile neighbourhood and the changes are reflected in the congregation. Perhaps because of this there is little social activity centred on the church, though there is much involvement in charitable and community work.

Services: Sunday 8am Holy Communion, 10.30am Eucharist, 6.30pm Evensong □ Wheelchair: level access □ Other details: hall □ Visiting: open all day, every day

St Philip

Earls Court Road, W8 □ Telephone: 378 4847 (office) □ Bus: 31, 74 □ Tube: Earls Court □ Parking: car park at weekends □ Vicar: Rev Michael Forrest □ Address: 46 Pembroke Road, W8 □ Telephone: 602 5025 □ Available: most times

St Philip's is a large, 19th century Gothic church in brick, situated just north of the shopping area of Earls Court around the underground station, and not far south of Kensington High Street. Though Earls Court Road is a busy thoroughfare there are some quiet and very pleasant little streets and squares close by the church. There is a sense of community in the neighbourhood, and this is reflected at St Philip's as good fellowship.

Most of the congregation are resident within five minutes travel from the church. There are people from all ages and background. St Philip's is a busy place, and being open to the street it is much used for private prayer and contemplation. In summer quite a number of visitors find their way here. The 20–30 age-group within the church provide a focus of welcome to young people perhaps visiting London for the first time and, as so many do, staying in the short term in Earls Court. Outside the worshipping life there is some 'street level ministry' on the lines of help for the homeless and for people with mental health problems.

The church has embarked on a £400,000 conversion project which will put it in order for the next 50 years. The peripheral buildings, which are in poor condition, will be demolished, and a new hall will be created out of the south aisle. The church interior is to be realigned on a north-south axis. Entering the church one is immediately struck by the sense of lightness. There are no formal rows of pews, no heavy, obstructing pillars, and the lighting is good. In the chancel is a beautiful reredos made of Caen stone and alabaster; the altar rail is of alabaster with *vert antique*.

Services are held each Sunday and also three times a day during the week. There is a fine Walker organ and a good choir. Sometimes the services will also feature dramatic presentations, with children or adults acting out the Gospel texts. There are Bible study and prayer groups.

Services: Sunday 8.30am Said Communion, 10.30am Said or Sung Holy Communion, 4pm Occasional Services; Weekdays, times vary □ Facilities: amplification □ Children: creche, Sunday school □ Wheelchair: level access □ Visiting: open early morning to 7pm most days

St Saviour, Chelsea

Walton Street, SW1 □ Bus: 19, 22, 73, 137 □ Tube: Knightsbridge □ Parking: on street □ Vicar: Rev F H Anderson □ Address: 71 Cadogan Place, SW1 □ Telephone: 235 3468 □ Available: most times

St Saviour's, Chelsea, built in 1840 as a Gothic Revival church, was designed by Disraeli's uncle, the architect Basevi, who studied under the more famous Sir John Soane. The parish includes part of the wealthy residential neighbourhood of Knightsbridge, and the church itself is situated just opposite Harrods.

Services use the Book of Common Prayer, with a monthly Sung Eucharist using a choir of four voices, all professionals. The congregation is stable and consists mostly of local people aged over fifty. There are no study groups, but the Mothers' Union meets monthly and a special service is held on their behalf.

The church hosts weekly organ recitals and occasional concerts.

Services: Sunday 8.30am Holy Communion, 11am Matins and sermon (Sung Eucharist 1st Sunday), 12.15pm Holy Communion, 6pm Evensong; Weekday HC Wed & Sat 8.30am, Thu 10.30am □ Facilities: amplification □ Wheelchair: easy access □ Other details: hall □ Visiting: open for services only

St Simon Zelotes

Milner Street, SW3 □ Bus: 19, 22, 137 □ Tube: Knightsbridge, Sloane Square □ Parking: difficult except Sunday □ Priest-in-Charge: Rev Prebendary John Pearce □ Address: 34 Milner Street, SW3 □ Telephone: 589 5747 □ Available: most times at Vicarage

Just behind Sloane Street and among the squares of luxury flats lies St Simon Zelotes, its incongruously rural air created by its rough stone exterior. Built in 1859 to a Gothic design, the church has changed little since then, escaping the war quite without damage. As such, it provides a good example of a Victorian interior.

The congregation comprises local people, mostly elderly, though a few families worship regularly. Of the three Sunday services, Matins draw the largest attendance, usually around 60. As with Evensong, this service features both a sermon and a professional choir. Once a month there is a healing service, where anointing and laying on of hands are practised along with prayers for the sick.

Every Tuesday evening a Bible study class is held at the Vicarage, while regular monthly activities include parish breakfast, a 'Sunday Forum' with a guest speaker and a 'Prayer and Praise' session held at a member's home.

Services: Sunday 8am Holy Communion, 11am Matins, 6.30pm Evensong, (plus Holy Communion at 12.30pm every 1st Sunday, 11am every 3rd, and 7.30pm every 4th Sunday); Wednesday 11am Holy Communion □ Children: Sunday school 11am □ Wheelchair: 1 small step □ Other details: two halls □ Visiting: usually open during day; if locked, apply for keys at Vicarage

St Stephen

Gloucester Road, SW7 □ Bus: 49, 71, 264 □ Tube: Gloucester Road □ Parking: difficult street parking □ Vicar: Rev Christopher Colven □ Address: St Stephen's Vicarage, 9 Eldon Road, SW7 □ Telephone: 370 3481 (Vestry) □ Available: ½hr before and after 6pm service weekdays □ Other clergy: Revv Graham Morgan (381 3211), Robert Browne (581 3493)

A short distance north of Gloucester Road Underground station can be found the modest, unassuming exterior of St Stephen's. A Victorian Gothic church built in 1867 by Peacock, its true splendours lie inside: a long rectangular nave, with arches and twin transepts, leads to an impressive stained-glass west-window, beneath which is the baptistry and a Calvary. At the east end of the church is the sanctuary which contains the church's most notable feature, a magnificent carved reredos. It is very high, reaching to a rose window of deep blue glass. To the right of the Lady Chapel is a wooden Madonna (mentioned in one of Iris Murdoch's novels) and the memorial plaque to T S Eliot, churchwarden here for 25 years until his death in 1965.

The church lies firmly in the Anglo-Catholic tradition with a High Mass as the principal Sunday service complete with full ceremonial and a professional choir. It is not other-wordly, though, and preaching is taken seriously—sermons are critical and both socially and theologically aware. This style of worship partly reflects the needs of its unusual, eclectic congregation. Over recent years the once elderly congregation has been supplemented by an influx of young, often single people, professionals and students, who would not fit so easily into the life of a family-based parish church.

A significant number of Americans attend; some much so that the notice-board describes the church as 'Church of England/Episcopal' referring to the parallel tradition in the United States. An attempt is made to make all visitors feel at home, and after the service the clergy and congregation retire to the Parish Room to talk over a glass of wine. An American visitor has described St Stephen's as 'the friendliest of the London Anglo-Catholic shrines'.

St Stephen's does not try to develop its regular members in a ceaseless round of church-based activities, recognising that people may have busy and fulfilled lives. The congregation supports many charitable concerns, however, and individual members may be actively involved in such bodies as Amnesty International. The church is a member of the Kensington Council of Churches. In short, people come to pray and to receive instruction in the faith 'thereby equipping themselves for an apostolate in the world'.

Services: Sunday 8am and 9am Low Mass, 11am High Mass, 6pm Evensong and Benediction; Monday–Friday 8am and 6pm Low Mass (plus Tue 11am, Low Mass); Saturday 10am Mass □ Wheelchair: level access □ Other details: Parish room □ Visiting: open 10am–1pm Monday, Tuesday, Thursday and Saturday

---

Church of England : North and East London

Charterhouse Chapel

Charterhouse Square, EC1 □ Bus: 4, 279, 279a □ Tube: Barbican □ Parking: difficult □ Master: Mr Eric Harrison □ Address: The Master's Lodge, Charterhouse, EC1 □ Telephone: 253 0272

Charterhouse Chapel is a small private chapel, comparable to that of Lincoln's Inn. The Sunday services are attended by the residents of Charterhouse, people who have associations with it and perhaps a few visitors. Anyone may attend services but will not be entitled to view the rest of the premises (which provide accommodation for thirty elderly men), although guided tours are organised.

The history of Charterhouse is long and complicated. Founded in the 14th century as a Carthusian monastery, it later became a Tudor town house and finally a Jacobean 'hospital' or home for elderly gentlemen. It was only as a result of bomb damage in 1941 that the medieval plans of the monastery were made clear. Much of the monastic buildings were pulled down by Sir Edward North in 1545 but the chapter house and tower were left standing.

The present chapel was constructed from the old chapter house of the monastery. The interior has many 17th century features such as the carved screen and organ gallery, and handsome pews with carved pewheads.

Services: Sunday 9.45am Communion, 5.45pm Evensong, (the chapel is closed in August) □ Wheelchair: 2 small steps at the entrance □ Visiting: only available to the public during Sunday services; guided tours by arrangement, including Charterhouse itself

Christ Church

Albany Street, NW1 □ Bus: 2, 3, 53 □ Tube: Regents Park □ Parking: difficult except Sunday & evenings □ Priest-in-Charge: Rev Michael Markey □ Address: 4 Silsoe House, Park Village East, NW1 □ Telephone: 388 2166, 388 3095 (office) □ Available: best time is Monday 7–8pm at St Mary Magdalene

The brick-built Christ Church, with its slender clock tower and spire, stands on the north side of a housing estate across from its daughter church, St Mary Magdalene. Completed in 1878, it is the work of Sir James Pennethorne, an apprentice of John Nash who also worked with Pugin. The influence of these two architects can be detected in Christ Church's design.

Inside, the sanctuary area has rich Italianate decoration and, as its centrepiece, a large painting of the Transfiguration by Thomas Brigstock (after Raphael). Many of the furnishings, including the pulpit and lectern, are by Butterfield, and among the wealth of stained glass is a three-panelled window, designed by Dante Gabriel Rosetti, who lived locally, and made in William Morris' studio.

Christ Church was once a centre of the Oxford Movement, and many illuminati, including Manning, Hook and Pusey are recorded as having preached here. Today the 'high' traditions are carried on at the daughter church of St Mary Magdalene across the estate, while services here no longer feature incense or sung litany. Among the small regular population there is an emphasis on charitable work and social activities. The church has been under threat of closure, but a vigorous campaign seems to have prevented this.

Services: Sunday 9.30am Parish Eucharist; Tuesday 7.30pm Eucharist □ Children: 'Sunday school' meets Monday pm □ Wheelchair: ramp available □ Other details: Parish room □ Visiting: open 30 mins before and after services

Christchurch, Spitalfields

Commercial Street, E1 □ Bus: 5, 10, 15, 15a, 22a, 25, 40, 67, 225, 253 □ Tube: Aldgate East, Shoreditch, Liverpool Street □ Parking: on street □ Rector: Rev Eddy G Stride □ Address: 2 Fournier Street, E1 □ Telephone: 247 7202 □ Available: any reasonable time □ Other staff: Graham Marshall, crypt warden (247 7766); Janice White, parish worker (247 7304)

This imposing Hawksmoor church is in a most interesting area of London. Spitalfields has been the first settlement area for many immigrant groups, including Huguenots, Irish, Turks, Germans and Jews, and it now has probably the greatest concentration of Sylheti Bengali people in Britain. The Christchurch C of E School, for example, is attended only by Asian children, 98% of whom are Muslim and the rest Sikh or Hindu. Despite being a Christian institution, it is preferred to the local state school by many Asian parents because of the good reputation of both school and church, and the trust that has been built up in the community.

Three times a year every home in the parish is leafletted with information about the church, and there are monthly open-air services held outside the church. This evangelism and involvement with the community had led to a very mixed congregation of whom some are Asian. The church employs a parish worker with a special ministry to Asian women, and a Trust runs a house on Fournier Street for Bengali and other immigrant men in need of accommodation.

Another important part of the church's work is the use of the crypt as a residential centre for homeless alcoholic men. During the past 20 years, the Spitalfield Crypt Fund has enabled it to help over 650 men come to terms with their addiction. It is run as a Christian home with a second stage house in Stoke Newington.

Architecturally, the church is a true original. The west end has a raised portico with four huge Tuscan columns below a tower and spire that rise dramatically to 225 feet. The use of very steep buttresses creates the impression that the tower is fully as wide as the portico. Overall, the effect is very powerful, although Pevsner considered it ugly. The vast space of the interior is divided into aisle bays by enormous pillars.

Unfortunately, the church has not survived the test of time too well. Despite many repairs over the last 150 years, it was closed in 1956 as unsafe, and services were held in a temporary church nearby. Clearly, a great deal of money is needed both to restore and maintain this grand building and the Friends of Christchurch Spitalfields have done much to raise the necessary funds. Worship is now taking place in the church again, and in summer a ten day music festival is held here.

Services: Sunday 10.30am and 6.30pm (Holy Communion every Sunday at one or other of these times) □ Children: Sunday Club during morning service; creche □ Wheelchair: very difficult access; many steps (chair lift is planned) □ Other details: hall available □ Visiting: visitors are welcome during the day; if the church is locked, apply to Rectory for key

Gray's Inn Chapel

Gray's Inn Road, WC1 □ Bus: 17, 18, 45, 46, 171, 171a, 243 □ Tube: Chancery Lane □ Parking: difficult, except at services □ Chaplain: Canon Eric James □ Address: 308 Kennington Lane, SE11 □ Available: at services and by arrangement

The Gray's Inn Chapel sits tucked away in one corner of Gray's Inn Court. It is an extra-parochial chapel serving this small enclosure of the legal profession. There are twelve main services a year, equally divided between the three terms of the law houses. Details of the services are published in *The Times*.

The most unusual aspect of the chapel is that many of the worshippers are not Anglican. A great many are Welsh Nonconformists, for example, and others are Jewish. Thus while services are in the 'low' Anglican tradition, the chapel has developed a broad ecumencial base—members are encouraged to remain true to their own local church, but to worship together at the chapel as a special community. The congregation is almost always made up of the members of the Inn, judges and their families and friends, though all are welcome. The choir is considered of very high quality, and is composed of students at the Royal Academy and members of the Inn. Broadcasts are made from here for the BBC World Service.

The chapel's constant role is simply to provide a place for prayer and reflection. The interior is appropriately peaceful, finished to an uncluttered design by Sir Edward Maufe some 25 years ago.

Services: 12 services a year equally divided among the 3 Law terms □ Wheelchair: easy access, one small step □ Other details: the court refectory can be used as hall □ Visiting: open all day for private prayer.

Holy Cross, St Pancras

Cromer Street, WC1 □ Bus: 14, 17, 18, 30, 45, 46, 63, 73, 77a, 214, 221, 259, C11 □ Tube/BR: Kings Cross □ Parking: difficult except Sunday □ Parish Priest: Rev Trevor Richardson □ Address: 47 Argyle Square, WC1 □ Telephone: 278 5238 □ Available: most times

Financed by public subscription and donations from noble families, the Anglo-Catholic mission church of the Holy Cross was built in 1888 as a reaction to the dreadful slum conditions of the area and all the attendant problems. Almost a century on, Kings Cross still has its problems, most notably prostitution and the plight of the young homeless newly arrived in London, and this active church is in the forefront of those tackling these issues.

For example, the parish priest, Fr Trevor Richardson, is chair of a hostel in Camden which provides refuge and support specially for prostitutes and women who are at risk of becoming involved against their will in the sex industry. Fr Richardson is also Chair of the Alone in London Service, which runs a wide range of services to help young homeless people including counselling, education, shelter and resettlement programmes. Other residents are not forgotten, and the church is closely involved with the Kings Cross-Brunswick Neighbourhood Centre, which works to 'consolidate the existing voluntary groups and to strengthen the sense of community in this vulnerable inner city area'.

The church's own facilities are put to use, with the crypt housing a day centre for the elderly and providing a regular meeting place for local residents. Outside, there is a community garden with access for the disabled and a barbecue for community functions.

The church itself was designed by Peacock in the Gothic Revival style; its squat and now dark facade belies an interior that is bright and spacious under a high wooden vaulted roof. One's attention is immediately drawn to the chancel, firstly by the large rood and then by the magnificent High Altar behind. Although no longer used, this ornate affair in black and gold under its huge baldacchino remains an imposing centrepiece. Other decorations such as the inlaid marble Stations of the Cross give a clear indication of the church's liturgical tradition—indeed casual visitors might assume Holy Cross is a Roman Catholic church. The Roman Missal is used at services. The main Parish Mass attracts congregations of around 45, and there are a good number of young people attending. Regular events such as suppers with quizzes, functions and shows have helped create a strong sense of community amongst the worshippers and their neighbours.

Services: Sunday 8am Mass, 10.30am Parish Mass; Weekday Mass: 6.30pm Mon, Wed, Fri, 12.30pm Tues and Thurs □ Children: creche can be provided; Sunday school for 7–12 year olds □ Wheelchair: no access at present □ Other details: hall (for hire) □ Visiting: open every day; no leaflets or postcards, but tracts and community information

Holy Redeemer

Exmouth Market, EC1 □ Bus: 19, 38, 153, 171, 171a, 196, 221, 259 □ Tube: Angel, Farringdon □ Parking: difficult except Sunday □ Parish Priest: Rev Brian Boucher □ Address: 24 Exmouth Market, EC1 □ Telephone: 837 1861 □ Available: all days except Monday

Holy Redeemer, EC1

It is difficult to get a good view of this brick-built Italianate church, hemmed in as it is by neighbouring buildings and set on a narrow street, but one is certainly struck by the handsome tower looming above the busy Exmouth Market below. The church is clearly part of the local community and Fr Boucher is chaplain to the nearby Sadler Wells theatre as well as being on the street market committee.

Completed in 1888, Holy Redeemer was another of the Anglo-Catholic mission churches built in deprived and reputedly godless areas. The Italianate revival was gaining popularity by this time, and was thought to be well suited to the principles enshrined in the Oxford Movement. Services here continue to be traditional and Catholic in form, and the congregation is composed largely of local residents who have been attending for many years. Fr Boucher is keen to see the size of the congregation begin to increase along with the range of church activities and community work. At the moment the church runs popular jumble sales and holds an annual bazaar, and it helps support the Korean Mission.

The interior of the church looks not only Catholic but Italian, an impression borne out by the fact that it was modelled on that of the church of Santo Spirito in Florence. The first incumbent, Rev Eyre, was responsible for the design and as the church escaped war damage we are able to see it much as it was intended. The scene is dominated by the baldacchino over the High Altar; a highly ornate structure with gold angels and pillars apparently of red granite, one would never guess the whole thing is made entirely of wood. Other decorations are in the Italian manner, and there are several Renaissance style sculptures and paintings. The church has excellent acoustics and is often used by the BBC for recordings.

Services: Sunday 10.45am Sung Mass with sermon, 6.30pm Evensong & Benediction; Saints' Days 7.30pm Mass; Weekday Masses Tues 12.30pm Wed 9.30am, Fri 6.30pm, Sat 12.30pm □ Wheelchair: easy access □ Other details: hall (available for hire) □ Visiting: open from 8am until dusk; closed Mondays

Holy Trinity with St Mary

Shepherdess Walk, N1 □ Bus: 43, 76, 141, 214, 271 □ Tube/BR: Old Street □ Parking: on street □ Vicar: Rev Stuart Wilson □ Address: 3 Bletchley Street, N1 □ Telephone: 253 4796 □ Available: most times □ Other clergy: Rev Roger Reader (608 2345)

Hoxton, on the edge of the East End, is an area of light industry and blocks of flats. This early Victorian church (1848) was designed by Railton, best known as the architect of Nelson's Column. These days it is beginning to look a little shabby as the Kentish ragstone deteriorates in the polluted city air; the interior, though, is well-kept.

Among the church's fixtures are three items of particular interest: the Martin Travers reredos, the pulpit which is from the period of Sir Christopher Wren, and a Spanish confessional. The church houses a shrine to Our Lady of Walsingham, at which candles are always lit; a monthly mass is offered at the shrine.

The congregation at Holy Trinity is made up of mainly local people who reflect the area's multi-racial community and range in age from families with young children to the elderly. At the 10am service on Sundays there are about 90 people present, of whom 60 will be communicant members. Other services are attended mainly by a small number of, for the most part, older people, who also help out in maintaining the church. A Bible study group operates during Advent and Lent, and throughout the year the congregation have jumble sales and collections, giving 10% of the proceeds to charity. These and other activities take place in the former Parochial School next door.

Stuart Wilson has been the vicar of Holy Trinity since 1982. He has an assistant, who also works at Pentonville prison nearby. In response to the document 'Faith in the City' they have linked the parish with that of St Peter and St Paul in suburban Teddington, an act which should encourage friendship and better understanding.

Services: Sunday 8am and 6pm Low Mass, 10am Sung Mass; Holy Days 8pm Sung Mass; Weekday Masses Mon 1.15pm, Tues 7.30pm, Wed 8pm, Thu 10am, Fri 9.30am & 7pm, Sat 8am □ Children: Sunday school 10am □ Wheelchair: ramp □ Other details: hall (available for hire) □ Visiting: open 9am–6pm daily

Lincoln's Inn Chapel

Lincoln's Inn, Chancery Lane, WC2 □ Bus: 171, 171a □ Tube/BR: Holborn □ Parking: some spaces □ Preacher: Rev Felix Boyse □ Address: 19 Old Buildings, Lincoln's Inn, WC2 □ Telephone: 405 2980 □ Available: at services □ Other contact: Judge Edward Clarke, rtd

Lincoln's Inn of Court, situated on Chancery Lane, is a collection of buildings dating from the 15th to the present century. The chapel is easily distinguishable above the open cloisters, where on can easily imagine Dickensian solicitors interviewing their clients.

The chapel was built between 1619 and 1623 to replace a former chapel which had become ruinous. The interior has changed little, still having many of the oak box pews. The oak pulpit and desk were added in 1730 while the organ is now of modern specifications. Thanks to the precaution of removing the windows during the war, the chapel has four side windows contemporary with the original building. The Great East Window comprises panels containing the arms of the Treasurers of the Honourable Society of Lincoln's Inn, dating from 1680 to the present day. In them it is possible to see the arms of Royalty and of many famous and influential people.

The single weekly service at the chapel is Matins held only during the legal terms of January to March, May to July, and October to December. One can expect to hear some splendid music from the organist and choir, and a sermon by Rev Felix Boyse, or by a visiting preacher. The 1662 Prayer Book is used. A booklet of services for each term, and the relevant details are also published in *The Times* and *The Telegraph* on the Saturday preceding a service.

The chapel is only open for services, which members of the public are free to attend. During the Spring and Summer months, this presents an opportunity to walk through the well kept gardens that are normally out of bounds.

Services: Sunday 11.30am Matins with sermon □ Wheelchair: 2 flights of stairs □ Other details: halls, library, etc □ Visiting: open only for services

St Alban the Martyr

Brooke Street, EC1 □ Bus: 8, 17, 18, 22, 45, 46, 171, 171a, 243, 259, 501 □ Tube: Chancery Lane, Holborn □ Parking: difficult except Sunday □ Vicar: Rev John B Gaskell □ Address: Clergy House, Brooke Street, EC1 □ Telephone: 405 1831 (Vestry) □ Available: most times

In front of this church is a small courtyard. At its entrance one is met by a remarkable sculpture: *The Resurrection* by Hans Feibusch, which shows a taut but magnificent Jesus with arms outstretched. The artist, a Jewish-born German national whose pieces were banned and burned by the Nazis, puts passion and strength into his work—rare qualities in the English tradition of church art.

St Alban the Martyr is an ambitious and successful rebuilding of the Victorian original, little of which (bar the steeple) managed to survive the War. The new building has a boarded and decorated barrel ceiling instead of the former open timber roof; the arcade has been raised. Another work by Feibusch, a fresco of *The Trinity in Glory*, decorates the altar.

From its inception last century St Alban the Martyr has been a centre of Anglo-Catholicism, one of the foremost 'high' churches in London. Today it is still noted for the ceremony of its worship. There is an extremely good choir and the music in general is of a very high standard. Each year the BBC broadcasts an Evensong from the church and many other recordings have been made here. The organ is a Compton and is used frequently for recitals.

The congregation, young and friendly, come from all over London to find a service with this flavour. About 125 people attend the two Sunday Masses. The original St Alban's was one of the first great 'slum churches', with a mission to the poor of the area. Nowadays they are not so poor, but local parishioners do still attend, of course, and mix in well.

Fr Gaskell himself has become noted for his counselling abilities; he frequently acts as confessor and is always willing to talk informally to people about matters that concern them. Despite the far-flung nature of the congregation, the church does run several societies, one being a women's group which was formed as early as 1860.

Services: Sunday 9.30am Sung Mass, 11am Solemn Mass, 5.30pm Low Mass; Weekday Masses Mon to Fri 12.30pm, Wed & Fri 6.30pm, Sat 9.30am □ Facilities: amplification □ Wheelchair: 2 steps only at Brooke Street entrance □ Visiting: open 7.30am–3.30pm most days; closed weekend afternoons

St Andrew with Holy Trinity

Thornhill Square, N1

and All Saints

Carnegie Street, N1 □ Bus: 14, 17, 45, 221, 259 □ Tube/BR: Caledonian Road, Barnsbury □ Parking: on street □ Vicar: Rev Arthur Harvey □ Address: 5 Huntingdon Street, N1 □ Telephone: 607 6895, 607 4552 (office) □ Curate: Rev Moray Thomas □ Telephone: 837 0720 (am), 833 4701 (pm) □ Available: telephone for appointment

These are the sister churches of a parish formed in 1978, yet it would be hard to imagine two more contrasting buildings. St Andrew's is a large Victorian Gothic pile standing majestically at the centre of a tree-lined square, while All Saints, which was originally a 1960s church hall and looks like it, squats on a council estate nearby.

The churches are run by the vicar and curate and the services held in each suit the nature of the buildings. St Andrew's, built in 1854, is the more traditional, though still informal; it attracts about 80 worshippers on Sundays. It was designed to seat 1,200, but the interior has been divided by screens to suit present needs.

All Saints draws a small congregation from the surrounding estate, including several Senior Citizens who contribute greatly to the vitality of the church. As at St Andrew's, worship is informal and lay led. A piano provides a lighter touch than would an organ, and suits the homely atmosphere. The hall has been used for worship only since the 1970s so everything has been recently installed. The most notable feature is a modern stained glass window by Mark Angus, placed here in 1985. It is an allegory of *Peace* and bathes the interior in mauve and yellow light.

There is no demand for many church-based activities, but with help and contributions from parishioners, Rev Moray Thomas runs a lively parish magazine and, perhaps appropriate to this split-site parish, he sees on the role of the Church as two-fold: on a human level, it is 'a community of people who know, trust and provide a human resource' while spiritually, it is 'a place where people can receive from God, and accordingly re-adjust their values in a wider perspective'.

Services: St Andrew's: Sunday 9.30am Holy Communion (also 6.30pm every 2nd Sunday, 11am every 4th Sunday). All Saints: 3rd Sunday 11am Holy Communion □ Facilities: amplification □ Children: creche and Sunday school □ Wheelchair: easy access □ Visiting: St Andrew's is open only for services; All Saints is open every morning

St Anne, Hoxton

Hoxton Street, N1 □ Bus: 22, 48, 67, 149, 243 □ Tube: Old Street □ Parking: on street □ Vicar: Rev Alan Wynne □ Address: The Vicarage, 37 Hemsworth Street, N1 □ Telephone: 729 1243 □ Available: most times at the church

The parish church of St Anne, with the supervision of the vicar, Rev Alan Wynne, is undergoing a rejuvenation. In the first six months since his arrival in August 1986 his efforts to build an active parish church have led to an increase in attendance at Sunday Parish Mass from 12 to between 40 and 60.

Not wishing to tread on other churches' toes, the activities organised have been aimed at the young and the old, groups not fully catered for by the surrounding churches. A meeting on Tuesday evenings called 'Hoxton Ladies' is a combined keep fit and awareness class. The other two meetings, both on Wednesdays, are run by outside organisations: in the afternoons one of the parish sisters run a ladies club and in the evenings there is a Gamblers Anonymous group. Activities for the young are planned, to make the most of Fr Wynne's experience in teaching and the church's proximity to three schools.

The church has maintained the Anglo-Catholic traditions of its founding days, though nowadays members of the congregation give readings and assist with the administration of Communion. ASB Rite A is used at all services. Most of the newcomers to this growing congregation are young adults and young families, many of whom travel in from outside the area to attend the services. There are weekly confirmation classes, one for the children and one for adults, and during Lent there is a study group.

The church is of a Gothic design in red brick, built in 1865 by Francis Chambers. The interior is in keeping with the Anglo-Catholic tradition, having many shrines and statues around the church. Built as part of the church there is a large hall used for the activities, which has a stage and two kitchens.

Services: Sunday 11am Parish Mass and Sunday school; Wednesday 7.30pm Holy Communion; Saturday 12 noon Holy Communion □ Wheelchair: 3 steps to all entrances □ Other details: hall □ Visiting: open at 9am and 6pm daily for prayer as well as for the services and activities

St Clement

King Square, EC1 □ Bus: 4, 5, 55 □ Tube/BR: Old Street, Angel □ Parking: difficult except Sunday □ Vicar: Rev Michael Shier □ Address: The Vicarage, King Square, EC1 □ Telephone: 253 9140 □ Available: during the day

In the middle of a modern council estate stands St Clement's church, tucked behind a shopping mall but opposite a welcome patch of green that serves as a recreational area for the local residents. The church was one of several built to celebrate the victory at Waterloo, all of which have a classical portico with four massive columns.

The Vicarage is the only house (as opposed to flat) in the parish, the former Georgian residences having been demolished in the 1960s. The church itself suffered bomb damage in the War and lay dormant until 1953, so both the church and the community were involved in re-building their lives around the same time, in a parish that had changed beyond recognition. St Clement's has preserved the links with the community that were forged in those years, and seeks to provide a base for activities intended to generate self-help and to enhance people's lives.

The congregation includes members of extended families who live in or around the estate, elderly people and single parents. Along with the vicar, some are involved with church outreach and visit local people in their homes. This has met with a positive response and attendance at the church is increasing—at present about 30 come to the main 11am Sunday service. Worship is in the Catholic tradition: the Jerusalem Bible and the Roman Missal are used alongside the ASB and the BCP.

Services: Sunday 8am, 11am, 6pm Mass; Weekday Mass Mon 1pm, Tue 7pm, Wed 10am, Thu 7.30pm, Sat 10am □ Children: 'Sunday school' Thursday 5.30pm; creche for services □ Wheelchair: several steps, help required □ Other details: hall (available for hire) □ Visiting: always open during the day

St George, Bloomsbury

Bloomsbury Way, WC1 □ Telephone: 405 3044 (Vestry) □ Bus: 8, 14, 19, 22, 25, 38 □ Tube: Tottenham Court Road □ Parking: difficult; NCP under Bloomsbury Square □ Priest-in-Charge: Rev Michael Day □ Address: 7 Little Russell Street, WC1 □ Telephone: 831 9288 □ Available: generally

St George's is the parish church of Bloomsbury. Few people live here now, and those who attend services on Sunday are likely to be from outside the parish. Weekday congregations are more stable, with a large working population here, based on the British Museum and local offices. St George's also holds the chaplaincy for the visual arts, and a growing number of students from the Royal College of Art and elsewhere are beginning to attend here, although the congregation is predominantly middle-aged.

It is a welcoming church, with an organisation that makes visitors feel at home and runs many activities including charitable groups, regular recitals, and exhibitions in the crypt gallery. It is certainly a lively church, and this is in large part thanks to Fr Day, who has a variety of interests himself, being art historian, musician, and writer.

We shall not attempt to do justice to the splendid design of the church here, merely directing the reader to the excellent guide to the church, produced by Hugh Mellor. It is arguably the finest of Hawksmoor's churches, with London's most dramatic early Classical facade. The large portico is of six columns, set two deep; to the west a tall, stepped steeple rises, and this is topped by a statue of George I in Roman attire. The whole is said to be modelled on the Mausoleum at Helicarnassus, one of the seven wonders of the ancient world.

Services: Sunday 10am Eucharist and sermon, 6.30pm Evening Prayer; Weekdays 9.15am Matins (except Saturday), 1.10pm Eucharist (Wednesday to Friday only) □ Wheelchair: no access □ Other details: crypt, book room □ Visiting: open from 9.30am to 1pm daily

St George-in-the-East

Cannon Street Road, E1 □ Bus: 22a, 56 □ Tube: Shadwell □ Parking: some spaces in front of church □ No incumbent at present □ Curate: Rev Marcus Cook □ Address: as church □ Telephone: 709 9040

All is not what it may seem at St George-in-the-East. To the casual observer, Hawksmoor's imposing edifice in Portland stone may appear much as it always has, with the large apse protruding from the pedimented east wall, the recessed octagonal turrets along the nave, and the bizarre 160' tower which culminates in an open lantern looking like a little castle with Roman altars for battlements.

In fact, all this is merely a shell. There have been no services held in the main body of the church since May 1941 when the interior was totally gutted in an air-raid. The church lay derelict until 1960, when an architect, Arthur Baily, devised an ingenious plan for its renewal. He restored the walls and tower where necessary, and constructed a small, modern chapel in the east end. The galleries were converted to contain residential flats and the crypt became a hall. The nave has been left as an open courtyard, so if one stands in the new chapel and looks

St George-in-the-East, E1

back through the large windows, one can still see the original entrance to the church. In all, the conversion was a most imaginative way to alter Hawksmoor's edifice to suit modern needs while retaining the quirky splendours of the exterior.

Since January 1987 there has been no incumbent of St-George-in-the-East, but the church is now under the charge of the curate, Rev Marcus Cook. It continues to serve a small worshipping community and its future now looks brighter than it has done for some time. The hall is in great demand as rehearsal and workshop space, and it is perhaps through a fruitful interaction of artists and worshippers that St George's will be able to continue its Christian witness.

Services: Sunday 10.15am Holy Communion; Thursday 8pm Holy Communion □ Wheelchair: many steps; assistance required □ Other details: hall, etc □ Visiting: normally open at service times only; NB all that remains of Hawksmoor's work is exterior

St George The Martyr

Queen Square, WC1 □ Bus: 68, 77, 77a, 188 □ Tube: Russell Square, Holborn □ Parking: difficult except Sunday □ Rector: Rev Donald Werner □ Address: 13 Doughty Street, WC1 □ Telephone: 831 0588 □ Available: most times

Two students from Oak Hill Theological College were to be placed at St George the Martyr as part of their training and decided to make an 'undercover' visit to a service to check the place beforehand. By the time they left there was hardly a person in the church who did not know who they were and why they were there. This is indicative of the kind of friendly welcome one can expect at St George the Martyr.

The place is undergoing something of a revival. The size of the congregation is growing steadily and a broad cross-section of society attend, including people from various ethnic groups, students, nurses, and others unemployed or working, single or married. The rector maintains that every Christian has been given his or her own ministry by God and all are encouraged here to put this gift into practice. Many help with services; others have released a cassette of songs. Regulars affirm there is always some new aspect of the church's life that spurs them on. Worship here is charismatic and has an evangelical, outgoing feel. The 1662 Prayer Book is used at the 8am Sunday service, while the other Holy Communion services follow the ASB.

The church is set in a corner of the quiet Queen Square in Bloomsbury. Built in 1706, it stands a square, tall building with a spacious interior. It can hold some 550 people but the present regular congregation of around 100 are able to make the church feel full by using the central pews and conducting the services from the front of the chancel. A glass partition has been erected at the rear of the church to provide space both for a creche and for meetings.

Services: Sunday 8am Holy Communion, 10.30am Morning Service (HC 2nd Sunday), 6.30pm Evening Prayers (HC 3rd & 5th Sunday); Thursday 1.10pm (except summer months) □ Facilities: amplification □ Children: Sunday school and creche during Morning Service □ Wheelchair: level access □ Visiting: generally open

St James, Clerkenwell

Clerkenwell Green, EC1 □ Bus: 5, 55, 243 □ Tube/BR: Farringdon □ Parking: difficult, on street □ Vicar: Rev Jim Roberts □ Address: St James Vicarage, Wyclif Street, Northampton Square, EC1 □ Telephone: 253 1568 □ Available: at all times

The church of St James faces the trees and gardens of Clerkenwell Green, an attractive spot in an area increasingly given over to offices and workshops. The church's history can be traced back to 1100 when a nunnery dedicated to St Mary was built here. At the Dissolution, the nunnery church, by now re-dedicated to St James, came to be used as the parish church.

Unusually, the right to appoint vicars by parish elections was retained here until this century, and because of this a strong Low Church tradition with its emphasis on stirring sermons was established. This circumstance influenced the design of the present church, built in 1792 to replace the medieval nunnery church which had become a delapidated jumble of styles and additions. A local man, James Carr, was commissioned to design what is essentially a preaching house; with a curved gallery at the west end, similar to those in many Methodist churches. The prominent spire however, quite old-fashioned by this time, clearly shows Carr's debt to Wren and Gibbs.

The interior has several monuments salvaged from the old church and installed during the 19th century. These include a 16th century brass of John Bell, Bishop of Worcester, who was buried on the site, and various other memorial plaques. Many of the furnishings are still in their original condition.

At services, music is provided by a splendid organ, built in 1792 and restored to its rococo glory in 1978. The size of the congregation has dwindled as the area has become less residential, and now only 12 to 20 people attend on Sundays. Unless numbers increase, St James may be closed as a place of worship.

Ironically, the church is far from disused or impoverished. A steady income is provided by hiring out the church as a recording studio to record companies, and it is used for rehearsal by the Canonbury Chamber Choir. Also the crypt, transformed into a hall in 1912, as well as being used for dances, and by scouts and brownies, has been popular with gymnasts, musicians and dancers including Michael Clark, the well known exponent of modern ballet.

Services: Sunday 10.30am Holy Communion (occasionally prayers 6.30pm) □ Facilities: deaf loop, Braille service sheets by arrangement □ Children: creche; playgroup weekday mornings □ Wheelchair: difficult, 6 steps into church □ Other details: hall (available for hire) □ Visiting: open for services only

St James the Apostle

Prebend Street, N1 □ Bus: 271 □ Tube/BR: Old Street, Highbury & Islington □ Parking: difficult except Sunday □ Vicar: Rev Michael Markey □ Address: St James Vicarage, Arlington Square, N1 □ Telephone: 226 4108 □ Available: generally

The origins of this church lie in the founding, in the City, of a church of the same name by William Lambe of the Company of Clothworkers in 1545. Members of the Guild still hold the trusteeship of St James the Apostle, and the Guild helps to maintain the church in good condition. This new church was built in 1875, by the trustees, to replace the City church and to serve a new parish.

A peal of bells precedes the main Sunday service which takes place at 10am. Worship here is in the 'high' tradition, and the ASB Rite A is used, though Matins and Evensong are taken from the Book of Common Prayer. The attendance for the Sunday Eucharist is around 100. During the week though only a handful of worshippers will be present at any of the daily services.

It is hoped to replace the present Cumming Hall with a complex which will also include housing and may provide a 'drop-in' centre for the unemployed. Meanwhile the existing hall is used extensively, showing that the church, in this quiet Islington neighbourhood of private and council housing, is a lynchpin of community activity.

Services: Sunday 8am Holy Communion, 9am Morning Prayer, 10am Sung Eucharist, 6pm Evening Prayer; Weekdays 9am Morning Prayer (except Tue & Sat 8.30am), 6pm Evening Prayer (plus HC Mon & Fri 8.30am, Wed 11am, Thu 7pm, Sat 9am) □ Children: Sunday school and creche 10am □ Wheelchair: level access □ Other details: hall □ Visiting: open at service times only

St John the Baptist

New North Road, Hoxton N1 □ Bus: 76, 141, 271 □ Tube: Old Street □ Parking: on street □ Vicar: Rev Arthur Robinson □ Address: St John's Vicarage, Crondall Street, N1 □ Telephone: 739 9823 □ Available: most times

This church was built as one of four in commemoration of the Battle of Waterloo to be named after the four Gospel writers. There may have been some confusion at the consecration of St John's in 1826, for it came to be dedicated to the Baptist rather than the Evangelist.

Around the church is a courtyard which contains several broken headstones indicating its former use as a graveyard. The interior is of a classical design and rather plain, the most elaborate decoration being the ceiling panels depicting scenes from the Book of Revelation, which date from 1926. There is a wide gallery running along three walls which would have enabled the church to seat the congregations of 1,500 it was intended for, and used to attract.

One interesting feature is the tall pulpit set on rails in the floor. Tucked away under a balcony when not in use, it can be rolled out into the centre of the nave so that the preacher is in full view of everyone right to the back of the farthest gallery.

The pulpit has not been rolled into position for some years now, for the regular congregations of 35 people do not warrant the use of such an imposing structure. Due to the poor condition of some of the plaster ceiling, especially over the chancel, services are now held at a communion table under the north gallery providing the congregation with a smaller, more intimate space.

The church is reaching the end of its useful life and plans are being considered to build a smaller, multi-purpose building alongside that would better suit the area's needs. At the same time, a team ministry with the nearby St Leonard's, Shoreditch, is likely to be established to enable both congregations to work together more effectively.

Rev Robinson sees the role of the Church in this largely under-privileged area as that of preaching the Gospel, and reaching out to the neighbourhood. St John's also has a family care centre, an active youth club and Sunday school groups.

Services: Sunday 9.30am Holy Communion, 11.30am Holy Communion □ Children: Skywalkers youth group; Explorers & Pathfinders Sunday school groups (meet Sun 11am) □ Wheelchair: easy access □ Visiting: open only at service times

St Leonard, Shoreditch

119 Shoreditch High Street, E1 □ Bus: any to Liverpool Street □ Tube/BR: Liverpool Street □ Parking: on street □ Vicar: Rev Paul Turp □ Address: 36 Hoxton Square, N1 □ Telephone: 739 2063 □ Available: every day

The dynamism of Shoreditch Church as a living place of worship is apparent from the moment you enter. That gravitas which pervades most of the old London churches is there of course, given that the place has been shaped by the prayers of generations of East Londoners, but there is no doubt that over and above all that, this is a church for today's community. There may be a display of children's paintings, for example, an exhibition on mission work or on the local Mildmay Christian Charitable Hospital; whichever, this church certainly has the appearance of a working building, and not of a museum piece.

The church is meeting the challenge of inner city problems head on—and there is no shortage of these in the neighbourhood—and it is growing stronger in the process. Students come here, like it, and stay to develop their commitment in study groups and especially in prayer partnerships. A new member might get paired with various people for a while, for social events as well as for praying together.

Regular attendance at Sunday worship is around the 75 mark. Special services include the performance of an oratorio on Good Friday and candlelit carols on the Sunday before Christmas. Everyone is encouraged to participate fully in the services, with the singing, the prayers and helping to administer Communion. One may even be asked to preach.

'The 1,000 year experience of Shoreditch church is being poured into our community', says the vicar, Rev Paul Turp. Indeed, although the present church by George Dance with its famous tower dates from 1740, there has been a church on the site since Saxon times. Of the several interesting memorials, those that stand out are the rather macabre Tree of Life attacked by skeletons which dates from 1710 and the plaque commemorating Dr James Parkinson, who lived nearby. The bells of St Leonard's, of course, are featured in the nursery rhyme, replying 'When I grow rich'.

Services: Sunday 10.30am Holy Communion □ Facilities: amplification □ Children: Sunday school 10.30am; creche; day nursery □ Wheelchair: ramp □ Other details: hall (for hire) □ Visiting: open 12noon–2pm weekdays

St Mark, Myddleton Square

Myddleton Square, EC1 □ Bus: 19, 38, 171 □ Tube: Angel □ Parking: on street □ Priest-in-Charge: Rev Brian Boucher □ Address: 24 Exmouth Market, EC1 □ Telephone: 837 1861 □ Available: most times, except Mondays

St Mark's has graced Myddelton Square for over 150 years. In the recent past it has been somewhat neglected, but now steps have been taken to preserve the fabric, and the arrival of Fr Boucher, who also has care of Holy Redeemer (qv), has heralded a new lease of life for the church.

The number of services is limited and times have been altered to fit in with Fr Boucher's other commitments. They are 'high' Anglican in form, following Rite B and the 1662 Prayer Book, and the main service is described as Sung Eucharist with vestments. Around 40 people regularly attend, perhaps 40% of them from outside the parish, and there are signs of a gradual increase in the number of worshippers. There are few church activities, though Fr Boucher is keen to build up this side of things and to use the available facilities to the full.

The church is Gothic in style, with a solid square tower dominating the west front. It benefits greatly from its setting amongst the elegant Georgian houses of the square.

Services: Sunday 9.15am Sung Eucharist, 3.30pm Evensong (1st Sunday of month only); Saints Days 6.30pm Evensong □ Wheelchair: easy access □ Other details: hall □ Visiting: open only at service times

St Mark, Regents Park

St Mark's Square, Regents Park Road, NW1 □ Bus: 2, 74 □ Tube: Camden □ Parking: on street □ Vicar: Rev Tom Devonshire-Jones □ Address: 4 Regents Park Road, NW1 □ Telephone: 586 1694 (answer-phone) □ Available: leave message if not in

This is the church that became famous during the 1930s as 'the Zoo Church'. The vicar at the time used to organise Bank Holiday tea parties in the church grounds, and thousands of people must have enjoyed these as their next stop after visiting the Zoo. The parties continued through the war years, even when the bombs were falling all over London.

Sadly, the church was hit and burnt to a shell in September 1940, and though it was the first Anglican church in London to be completely rebuilt after the War, this did taken seventeen long years. The 'high' church tradition and the excellent music of the professional choir continue, but St Mark's has now definitely entered a new era. It is the young professionals and their families living locally who are becoming the mainstay of the congregation. The gardens are now used by a nursery school, which also utilises the crypt.

The church is Victorian Gothic with an impressively light and airy interior. The reredos, a triptych showing the life of Christ with saints including St Mark, is by Sir Ninian Comper, his last major work. Also by Comper are the Lady Chapel altarpiece, the church fittings and vestments, and much of the stained glass. Other glass includes the splendid rose window with the lion of St Mark at the centre and, by way of a feline contrast, portraits of the vicarage cats in the Benedicite window. This also features what must surely be London's only moon rocket in stained glass.

Services: Sunday 8am Holy Communion, 10am Family Communion, 11am Sung Eucharist; Wednesday 6.30pm; Thursday 8am; Friday 9.10am □ Children: nursery for weekday services □ Wheelchair: 2 steps □ Other details: crypt, garden □ Visiting: open at service times only

St Mary, Islington

Upper Street, N1 □ Bus: 4, 19, 30, 43, 279 □ Tube: Angel, Highbury & Islington □ Parking: easy on Sundays □ Vicar: Rev Graham Claydon □ Address: St Mary's Vicarage, Upper Street, N1 □ Telephone: 226 3400 □ Available: most times □ Other clergy: Rev Charles Yeats, Curate (251 3565)

Islington has long been a centre of evangelical Anglicanism. Since 1827 the annual Islington Clerical Meeting (later Conference) has brought together evangelical clergymen into what was the largest and most influential assembly of its kind. It was Rev Daniel Wilson, Vicar of St Mary's and founder of the Lord's Day Observance Society, who called the first meeting, and the church continues to uphold the evangelical tradition which is now further enhanced by a charismatic approach to worship.

This is best seen in the Family Worship service. Over 200 regularly attend including many children who are especially welcome and who are allowed to play, participate and generally express themselves as much as possible. The informal, lively service often incorporates drama and always relies on much lay participation. Sermons, which may be given by the vicar, Rev Graham Claydon, or a guest preacher, are thoughtful and challenging, true to the traditions of the church.

Since 1976 St Mary's has run a Neighbourhood Centre which has forged strong links with the community and provides facilities for a range of activities involving people of every age group. The crypt, currently used as a legal advice centre, is also to provide workship and rehearsal space. There are a number of home groups meting for Bible study, prayer and discussion. Since his arrival in 1980, Mr Claydon has encouraged these developments.

The church itself is an Islington landmark, especially its distinctive spire, modelled on that of St Bride's. This was one of the few parts of the 18th century church to survive bomb damage in the Second World War. The new interior has a low altar, clear glass windows and clean straight lines. There is no longer a chancel, the east end culminating in a large empty cross surrounded by murals depicting scenes from the life of Christ.

Services: Sunday 11am Family Worship, 6.30pm Evening Worship (Communion is in the morning or evening alternately) □ Facilities: deaf loop □ Children: Explorers Sunday group □ Wheelchair: ramp □ Other details: Neighbourhood Centre; crypt □ Visiting: open for services only

St Mary Magdalene

Munster Square, NW1 □ Telephone: 388 3095 (Crypt office) □ Bus: 2, 3, 18, 27, 30, 53, 137, 176 □ Tube: Regents Park □ Parking: difficult except evenings and weekends □ Priest-in-Charge: Rev Michael Markey □ Address: 4 Silsoe House, Park Village East, NW1 □ Telephone: 388 2166 □ Available: best time is 7–8pm Monday, in Crypt

St Mary Magdalene, the daughter church of Christ Church, is close to Great Portland Street, behind St Thomas' SPCK Bookshop. Built to R C Carpenters' design in 1852, it is in the Victorian Gothic style. It stands next to a large presbytery with a listed frontage, and is a smaller church than its parent.

Inside, however, it is surprisingly spacious, and boasts a large sanctuary area with a Pugin stained-glass window and a splendid decorated reredos. Flanking the sanctuary are two small chapels; to the left is the Lady Chapel, with carved screens, which is used for weekday services, and to the right is the Calvary Chapel. Whilst there is little of specific historical interest within the church there is much to please the eye, including the two-toned carved wooden roof, a highly ornate Sacrament House, a decorative rood beam surmounted by a large crucifix, and some stained glass.

The first incumbent was Edward Stuart, a member of the Oxford Movement and curate of Christ Church, who brought with him the 'high' traditions for which that church was once famous. These traditions now continue at St Mary Magdalene, where services feature sung liturgy, servers and incense. Fr Markey prefers the term Modern Catholic to Anglo-Catholic, feeling that it reflects the church's commitment to move with the times. Certainly, the church is becoming more active under Fr Markey's guidance and attendance is increasing, both among local residents on Sunday and people who work in the area during the week.

Services: Sunday 11am Parish Mass; Weekday Mass at Mon 6pm, Wed & Fri 1.05pm, Thu 7.30pm, Sat 9.30am □ Wheelchair: ramp available □ Visiting: open 30 minutes before and after services

St Mary the Virgin, Primrose Hill

Primrose Hill Road, NW3 □ Telephone: 722 3238 (Office) □ Bus: 31, C11 □ Tube: Swiss Cottage, Chalk Farm □ Parking: on street □ Vicar: Rev John Ovenden □ Address: 44 King Henry's Road, NW3 □ Telephone: 722 3062 □ Available: telephone for appointment □ Other clergy: Rev Stephen Masters

The silhouette of this red brick Gothic church, especially that of the apse, gives an impression of medieval France. Indeed, St Mary's, largely built by M P Manning in 1870–72, may appear a little forbidding at first, but the interior is a delightful contrast—it is painted white which gives an impression of space and brightness and acts as a perfect foil for the furnishings. These include a Bodley and Garner pulpit, and the reredos, a carved and gilded triptych, also by Bodley. The Great Rood, depicting the Risen Christ, is by Gilbert Bayes, and the west windows are the work of that prolific Victorian artist in stained glass, C E Kempe.

The interior was first whitened as long as 1903 by the third vicar, Percy Dearmer, famous for the 'English Hymnal' which did so much to revitalise liturgical music in this country. Music is still a feature of St Mary's: the church runs a musical society, monthly concerts are held here, and there is an excellent choir. Music is central to another tradition maintained at St Mary's, that of full Catholic worship with incense and dignified ceremonial. The Easter and Christmas services in particular attract local Roman Catholics, who prefer them to the Folk Masses now common in their churches.

The medieval custom of the 'lenten array' has been revived here. During Lent, all hangings and vestments are of rough, unbleached linen and all pictures are covered, in order to create a more sombre atmosphere. In particular, the rood is veiled so the worshippers may consider the suffering rather than the victorious Christ.

St Mary's attracts a large congregation and is used as a cultural and social centre as well as a place of worship—witness the concerts, the library and the Ploughman's Lunches (every first Thursday). The magazine is stimulating and witty. In 1986 the present incumbent, Rev John Ovenden, in an attempt to 'open the church to the whole community', initiated a Midsummer festival. Events were organised to suit all tastes including an art exhibition, a barbecue, an evening's music-making with Sir Georg Solti, and an ecumenical service with a sermon by broadcaster Gerald Priestland to which Catholics, Jews, Moslems and others were invited. The festival was a great success and it is hoped they may become a regular annual feature of this thriving church.

Services: Sunday 8am Holy Communion, 10.30am Parish Eucharist with sermon, 6pm Evensong (Sung 1st Sunday); Weekdays 6pm Evensong, plus HC Mon 6.30pm, Tue 8am, Wed 7am, Thu 10.30am, Fri 7.30am, Sat 9am □ Facilities: amplification □ Children: creche & Sunday school 10.30–11am □ Wheelchair: ramp □ Other details: library □ Visiting: caretaker present 10am–1pm, 3–6pm

St Mary the Virgin, Somers Town

Eversholt Street, NW1 □ Bus: 14, 18, 24, 27, 29, 30, 68, 73, 77, 77a, 134, 137, 188, 214, 253, 555 □ Tube/BR: Euston □ Parking: on street □ Priest-in-Charge: Rev Philip Dyson □ Address: St Mary's Church House, Eversholt St, NW1 □ Tel: 387 7301 □ Available: when in □ Other clergy: Revv Neil Gray (485 3147), Ivan Morris (267 8704)

St Mary the Virgin, on Eversholt Street, a few hundred yards from Euston station, was built in 1826 for the poor of Somers Town. It was the first attempt by the architect, Inwood, at a Gothic church and is a simple design, inexpensively built. Somers Town is still a traditional working class area and the church has a friendly atmosphere.

St Mary's is a large church and seating can be arranged for up to 700 people. The interior is in good order and the reredos in particular should be seen; on the theme of the Immaculate Conception, it is by Caroe and was salvaged from a Hampshire church when it closed in 1984.

The churchmanship at St Mary's is very 'high' and the Roman Rite is used at every service. The best attended act of worship is the Sunday morning Sung Mass, which is followed by a parish breakfast. The church hall, built in the 1960s, is used for a variety of purposes, including rehearsal by young actors who then put on shows for local schools and old peoples' homes.

Services: Sunday 10am Sung Mass, 6pm Mass; Weekday Mass at Mon 8am, Wed 9.30am, Fri 7pm □ Children: schoolchildren attend Wednesday Mass □ Wheelchair: 1 step □ Other details: hall □ Visiting: open for services only

St Matthew, Bethnal Green

St Matthew's Row, Bethnal Green Road, E2 □ Bus: 8, 8a □ Tube: Bethnal Green □ Parking: in the church yard □ Rector: Rev Christopher Bedford □ Address: The Rectory, Hereford street, E2 □ Telephone: 739 7586 □ Available: most times at the church □ Other clergy: Rev Patrick Allen (729 0878)

St Matthew's upholds a tradition of Anglo-Catholic worship which is enhanced by their use of modern texts in the services. There are daily Masses, though the best attended is the Sunday Parish Mass when children take part and members of the congregation give readings.

The nearby church primary school reflects the area's racial mix but despite the mixed beliefs of the pupils they all attend a weekly Mass and daily prayers. At these times great care is taken to respect all faiths and the emphasis is on celebrating a living religion. Other sections of the community have free use of the parish room. It is used for tenants association activities and for the church-organised handicapped club and mothers and toddlers group. The lounge, adjacent to the parish room, is used for the council run creche and 'surgery'.

Rev Christopher Bedford has been at St Matthew's since 1981. With his ambition to deepen the quality of Christian life in the parish his active role in community organisations and those activities taking place in church premises has led to an increase in numbers of those attending services; now around 70 people can be expected at Parish Mass.

The church is set in its own grounds and is situated at the Brick Lane end of Bethnal Green Road. It was built in 1746 in a classical style by George Dance the Elder. Twice the interior has been destroyed by fire, first in 1859 and secondly in 1940. The second restoration, creating a bright and spacious interior, was not completed until 1961. Most of the fixtures one would expect in an Anglo-Catholic church are to be found, though they make use of modern materials and designs: the Stations of the Cross are ceramic, the High Altar a block of wood, and the glass doors leading to the east gallery have been decorated by sandblasting.

Services: Sunday 10.30am Parish Mass, 5.15pm Mass; Daily 9am Morning Prayer, 5pm Evening Prayer; Weekday Mass Mon & Thu 9.30am, Tue 7pm, Wed 5.30pm, Fri 12.30pm, Sat 5.30pm □ Facilities: amplification □ Children: Sunday school 10.30am; Children's Club Thursday 5pm □ Wheelchair: ramps □ Other details: lounge, Parish Room with bar, hall □ Visiting: open daily from Morning to Evening Prayer

St Michael

Camden Road, NW1 □ Bus: 24, 29, 134, 253 □ Tube/BR: Camden Town, Camden Road □ Parking: very difficult □ Vicar: Rev Alan Richard Page □ Address: 1 Bartholomew Road, NW1 □ Telephone: 485 1256 □ Available: most times

While the churchyard trees have provided relief from the scaffolding and demolition work that have dominated this stretch of the Camden Road recently, St Michael's itself has long been almost obscured by the neighbouring exhaust-blackened buildings. When the development by Sainsbury's on the adjacent site is completed, however, the church will be once more in view, its grimy Gothic standing in stark contrast to the shiny 'High Tech' style of the superstore.

The brick church, designed by Bodley and Garner, and completed in 1881, is largely unchanged and as such is occasionally included in tours arranged by the Victorian Society. The bare stone interior is sombre and dignified; the statues and the seven sanctuary lights are typical High Church decorations of the period. From 1876 the congregation had been worshipping in a rented shop, using an altar and font acquired from other churches. This shop still stands and is busier than ever—it is a licensed betting office.

St Michael's, in poor condition and unable to finance repairs, is not one of the glories of Anglican architecture, nor is it a busy focus of parish life. Fr Page places emphasis on the quiet 'prayerful' nature of the Mass, but there are no other activities. He is closely involved with the nearby voluntary-aided primary school, whose pupils are drawn from the various ethnic groups in the parish.

Apart from this, Fr Page is available for those who need him irrespective of their involvement with the church. After 15 years at St Michael's, Fr Page is not overly optimistic about the future but adds 'though the congregation is small, it is extremely loyal'.

Services: Sunday 10.15 Mass; Weekday Mass at Tue 7.30pm, Wed 8pm, Fri 7.30pm, Sat 10am □ Wheelchair: 1 step, easy access □ Visiting: open for services only

St Pancras

Upper Woburn Place WC1 □ Telephone: 387 8250 (Vestry) □ Bus: 14, 18, 30, 68, 73, 77a, 170, 188, 239 □ Tube/BR: Euston □ Parking: on street, meters □ Vicar: Rev Douglas J L Bean □ Address: 12 Fitzroy Square, W1 □ Telephone: 387 6460 □ Available: at services □ Other staff: Rev David Lawson (387 9300) Chris Nottage, verger (387 8250)

St Pancras has justifiably been called the outstanding example of a Regency parish church. Also, by virtue of its position opposite Euston station, it has been described in the parish magazine as 'the grandest waiting room in Christendom'—many people enter for a moment's prayer, reflection or rest before catching their trains.

Built between 1819 and 1822 in the style of a Greek Temple, it was designed by William and Henry Inwood, who visited Greece to ensure their designs were authentic. The exterior is in a white stone and the white fluted Ionic columns occur throughout the building. The tower is based on a Greek original and the hexastyle portico makes it a prominent sight on Euston Road. Also visible from the road are the Caryatides, female figures, that support the side vestries. These were originally made too tall and had to have a section removed from their middles in order to fit.

The interior has more obvious English features, with boxed pews and an ornate pulpit carved from a Fairlop Oak grown in Hainault forest, yet the Greek influence is continued with the Ionic columns found almost everywhere. The largest are those found in the recessed sanctuary. These are so large that if built from stone or marble they would be too heavy for the floor to support, and so are hollow with a covering made from marble chippings, paste and glue.

In 1880 when the Victorian vogue for dark colours prevailed, the interior was duly painted and the windows replaced with stained glass. Later work in 1889 included the reordering of the chancel and the removal of the front pews. In 1980 the colour of the walls was returned to that intended by the architects. The floor, which was also darkened with paint, is slowly being worn through to the light coloured stone. At the end of the last century, St Pancras was very much a 'low' church and a very fashionable preaching hall with services attracting up to 1,500 people. Nowadays, the church has been restored to its 'high' traditions, but the largest attendance is that of 50 for the Sunday Sung Mass (ASB). The Book of

Common Prayer is used for the early Sunday Holy Communion and for Evensong. The church is periodically used for commemorative services, and is the venue for both the BMA and the British Rail carol service.

Services: Sunday 8am Holy Communion, 9.30am Matins, 10am Sung Mass, 6pm Evensong; Weekdays 8am Morning Prayer (Wed & Thu), 1.10pm Holy Communion (Wed & Holy Days), 5.45pm Evensong (Wed & Thu) □ Wheelchair: several steps □ Other details: hall □ Visiting: open 8am–6.30pm daily

St Pancras Old Church

Pancras Road, NW1 □ Bus: any to Kings Cross □ Tube/BR: Kings Cross □ Parking: on street □ Priest-in Charge: Rev Philip Dyson □ Address: St Mary's Church House, Eversholt Street, NW1 □ Telephone: 387 7301 □ Available: at services

Though a number of London churches lay alim to having a village atmosphere, none is so convincingly rural as St Pancras Old Church, set on a grassy hillock in public gardens that were once graveyards. The small Romanesque church, despita a long history encompassing near ruin and extensive Victorian restoration, has retained an extraordinarily, if not whimsically, countrified look. Clad in stone, it has an ancient-looking carved west door arch and a truncated 'dovecote' south tower. The contrast with the nearby network of garages and railway arches behind Kings Cross and St Pancras stations is both immediate and striking.

Tradition has it that there was a church on this site in the 4th century, even before St Augustine's mission to Britain and only a few years after the martyrdom of the young St Pancratius himself. There is no proof of this, but the case for the antiquity of the site was strengthened by the rediscovery, during Victorian refurbishing work, of the old altar stone which had been hidden from Cromwell's troops. The distinctive shape of the crosses on the stone would seem to date it in the 6th century. The stone was relaid in the High Altar, where it remains. Other interesting features of the interior are the exposed Norman north wall which has tiles from the Roman era, the Blomfield reredos, and a Sacrament House in the south tower by Martin Travers, who directed the 1948 repairs to the church following war damage.

The simple interior seats around 65 people but can hold more when, for exampke, it is used as a concert venue. Between 20 and 30 people attend Sunday services here. The Catholic style of worship was re-instated in the 1880s and continues under the incumbency of Fr Philip Dyson. Parochial activities tend to be based at the church of St Mary the Virgin, Sojmers Town (qv) where Fr Dyson also has charge.

Because of its picturesque quality, the Old church has become very popular for weddings, and up to 40 are held here each year. Unfortunately, the church has been the victim of vandalism and desecration, and so, despite its history and great charm, the church is locked outside service times.

Services: Sunday 10am Mass, 6.45pm Benediction (Lent & Festivals only); Weekday Mass at Tue & Thu 7pm, Sat 10am □ Wheelchair: steps to garden, then level access □ Visiting(open for services and events only

St Pancras Old Church, NW1

St Silas with All Saints and St James

Penton Street, N1 □ Bus: 30, 73, 214 □ Tube: Angel □ Parking: on street □ Vicar: Rev A T John Salter □ Address: 87 Richmond Avenue, N1 □ Telephone: 607 2865 □ Available: most times except Monday □ Other clergy: Rev Dennis Pauley

Built by S S Teulon in 1864 to a typical Victorian Gothic design, St Silas has survived better than many churches built of Kentish ragstone. Today, the exterior looks new after sandblasting 10 years ago. Inside there have been some major structural changes to accommodate a new chapel for weekday use, which has been constructed from the old vestry. The main worship area is a wide open space with chairs rather than pews under a fine wooden roof. There are few items of interest, but one should not miss the delightful collection of wooden statues carved in Oberammagau which are displayed around the interior. The new chapel at the rear of the main church has a wooden reredos by Noyes-Lewis, best known as the illustrator of the first Sunday school stamps.

The Sunday Mass attracts 50 or so people and over the years it has attracted a substantial number of regular Black worshippers. The church has strong connections with both the West Indies and Africa and a former curate is now Archbishop of Central Africa. Today, over one third of the congregation is Black—an unusually high proportion for an Anglican church. The services follow Rite B and are standard High Church with lay readers and servers. During the week seven or eight people attend services in the new chapel. One of the most important secular activities of the church are its weekly jumble sales which many local residents and visitors attend.

Fr John Salter also has charge of St Dunstan-in-the-West, the ecumenical church in the City. It is perhaps not surprising then that St Silas' church is also used for worship by a Byelorussian Orthodox congregation; their Solemn Liturgy is said monthly here.

Services: Sunday 8am Mass, 11am Parish Mass; Tue, Thu, Fri 10am Mass; Wednesday 7pm Mass □ Facilities: occasional services for Deaf and Blind □ Children: Sunday school, 11am □ Wheelchair: access via fire escape □ Visiting: open for services and all day Saturday

The Student Chaplaincy (Christ the King)

Gordon Square WC1 □ Bus: 14, 18, 24, 29, 30, 68, 73, 77, 77a, 134, 137, 176, 188, 253, 555 □ Tube: Russell Square, Euston Square □ Parking: difficult □ Chaplain: Rev Nicholas Darby □ Address: 2 The Cloisters, Gordon Square, WC1 □ Telephone: 387 0670 □ Available: most times

This huge Victorian Gothic church in the heart of Bloomsbury is a place of worship for university and polytechnic students. Run by students, under the guidance of Rev Darby, the church functions as a chaplaincy to the various inter-collegiate halls nearby. The atmosphere at services is lively and convivial, with students assisting and even preaching at the evening service. At present there is a congregation of about 120 people on a Sunday morning and about 40 in the evening. The services are fairly 'central' with an emphasis on sacramental worship. There is a student counsellor available at the church and the pastoral assistant is normally a recent graduate.

The building belongs to the Catholic Apostolic Church but has been leased to the Chaplaincy since 1963. The church has cathedral-like dimensions and is practically impossible to fill during regular service—and so most of the activity takes place in the smaller space of the chancel, which the present chaplain has adapted to fit this purpose. Only on special occasions like the Annual Thanksgiving Service for people who have dedicated their bodies to Medical Research which some 700 people attend, does the church ever appear full.

Architecturally, the church was considered by Sir John Betjeman to be a gem of the Victorian Gothic and there are several features worth noting. Its architect, J Raphael Brandon, drew much from great abbeys and cathedrals and his design shows a good sense of proportion. The altar itself is of fine Derbyshire marble and alabaster with fossil shellfish clearly visible—a strange reminder of the Darwinian debate in which the Church was engaged at the time of building.

Services: Termtime: Sunday 10.30am Eucharist and sermon, 7pm Evening service; Weekdays morning and evening prayer as announced. Vacation: Sunday 10.30am Eucharist □ Facilities: amplification □ Wheelchair: level access at west end □ Other details: hall (available to Christian and student groups) □ Visiting: open all day during term, chapel only during vacation; guidebook

---

Church of England : Southwark

Christ Church

Blackfriars Road, SE1 □ Bus: 45, 59, 63, 76, 109, 141 □ Tube/BR: Blackfriars □ Parking: difficult during the week □ Rector: Rev Canon Peter Challen □ Address: Christ Church Rectory, 49 Colombo Street, SE1 □ Telephone: 928 4707 □ Available: most times □ Other staff: 10 Chaplains

Although this is a lively place there is only a small attendance on Sundays and at the weekday (Thursday lunchtime) service. All the activity connects up with Christ Church's commitment to ministry and witness in the workplace.

This modern church replaces one lost in the War. The building was funded by the John Marshall Trust, after whom the hall is named. In the hall and its adjoining rooms a number of local organisations have set up shop. There is also the British Association for Art Therapy who come here for drama practice. And then there is the church's own mission: SLIM, or South London Industrial Mission, which represents the work of ten chaplains of all denominations, all employed in schools, offices, factories and other institutions. In 1967 the parish and SLIM combined and the appointment of a rector/senior chaplain gave the church a unique ecumenical constitution.

On this theme, stained glass windows in the church portray the traditional work and life of the parish in their upper portions, with, by contrast, changes in industry and the city-scape below. In 1984–5 more windows were installed, representing the rapid change of the last quarter century: they feature some famous names, including Sainsbury's, a local employer, and some less famous ones. Trades Unions have a window, which announces that there are twelve branches that meet here.

A group of unemployed people created the altar frontal, made of wool, which depicts details from the stained glass windows. A large backdrop of an old city centre was donated to the church by the National Theatre; this hangs on the east wall of the sanctuary, poignantly surmounted by a cross of brass. Not many people live around here any more, but of those who come there is a mix of ages and ethnic groups, and there are study groups. The services are often taken by the various chaplains of SLIM.

Services: Sunday 9.30am; Tuesday 7.45am; Thursday 12.50pm □ *Wheelchair: ramps; toilet for disabled* □ *Other details: Vestry, 6 offices, hall, library, lecture room, etc* □ *Visiting: open only for services and activities*

St George the Martyr

Borough High Street, SE1 □ *Bus: 10, 21* □ *Tube/BR: Borough* □ *Parking: difficult except Sunday* □ *Rector: Rev David Howes* □ *Address: The Rectory, Manciple Street, SE1* □ *Telephone: 407 2796* □ *Available: at all times*

This Georgian church is at least the third on the site. Opposite an earlier St George's stood the famous Tabard Inn, where Chaucer had his pilgrims gather before setting off for Canterbury. The present church features in Dickens' *Little Dorrit* and has thus become the venue for the annual service of the Charles Dickens Society. Unfairly described as a poor imitation of a Wren church—it does have a very City-like steeple—St George's was designed by one John Price and completed in 1736. The stained glass in the east window brings together many of the associations with its figures of pilgrims, Little Dorrit and St George the Martyr himself.

Services at the church are characterised by congregational singing, a touch of humour and a good measure of informality. Neither 'high' nor 'low', the church has developed what Rev David Howes describes as an 'amalgamated and hybrid' style of worship to suit the needs of the parishioners and to reflect their various backgrounds. Thus, services are based on the ASB but may include material from other texts and may also be left open-ended to stimulate discussion amongst the worshippers. Lay participation is strongly encouraged and is much in evidence. Many families attend, and once a month the Eucharist service is adapted for children and includes their favourite hymns.

The enthusiasm of the services is carried over into social concerns based at the church. Along with five other local churches, St George's runs the Manna Centre which provides food for the homeless sheltering under London Bridge. Members of the church are involved individually with such organisations as Amnesty International, Samaritans and the Anti-apartheid movement. The crypt is used as a social centre after the services and on Friday evenings, and the church has three halls which provide a venue for numerous groups, including cubs and scouts, a playgroup and a 'Retirement Club'.

Services: Sunday 10am Eucharist, 6.30pm Evening Prayer; Friday 7.30pm Prayer meeting □ Facilities: special facilities at September service for the Blind □ Children: Sunday school 11–12noon; special Eucharist monthly □ Wheelchair: no facilities; assistance given □ Other facilities: crypt with bar, 3 halls □ Visiting: open Monday, Wednesday and Friday lunchtimes

St Mary Magdalene

Bermondsey Street, SE1 □ Bus: 1, 70, 70a, 198 □ Tube/BR: London Bridge □ Parking: carpark opposite □ Rector: Rev T Wooderson □ Address: The Rectory, 193 Bermondsey Street, SE1 □ Telephone: 407 5273 □ Available: at service times

The first record of the church of St Mary Magdalene in Bermondsey is as a chapel attached to the local priory (1296). No evidence of this original building remains, as the church has undergone much construction and alteration as various sections became unsafe or more space was needed. The earliest parts of the building can be dated back to the 15th century, but basically the church as it now stands is that of the rebuilding of 1680. In 1829 the portico was removed and the west elevation and tower were dressed in the present Gothic style. The interior of the church owes its appearance to the 1880s when new pews, lectern and pulpit were brought in.

The church also contains memorials to several families of the parish, some of which date back to the 17th century. The most interesting of these are the Gaitskell Hatchments (diamond-shaped paintings of the family coat of arms). Made for funerals, they were used to decorate the side of the funeral carriage during the procession and subsequently left at the church *in memoriam*. They are probably the precursors of the modern wreath.

The main Sunday service here is an unusual mixture of the traditional Anglican Communion and modern evangelism. The Communion service is punctuated by gospel singing, which is accompanied by guitar and tambourine and clapping; speakers preach in an evangelical style. Thus the service is relaxed while still retaining the Anglican Communion service at its core. The mixture has proved very popular—when Rev Wooderson arrived the ageing congregation numbered around 20; now up to 70 people attend a modern, lively service. The congregation reflects the multi-cultural nature of the area with African, Chinese and other Asian members. On Tuesdays a completely traditional Communion service is held.

This is an active church. There are House Fellowship Groups, informal Bible study and prayer groups which meet regularly in members' homes; there is a youth group which meets on Sunday afternoons at the church; and recently an Alcoholic Anonymous group has been started up. The south aisle of the church has been walled off to provide an extra room where tea and coffee are served after services and other meetings are held.

Services: Sunday 8am (2nd Sunday only), 10.30am Holy Communion, 6pm Evening Prayer, 7.30pm Fellowship service; Tuesday 1pm Holy Communion □ Facilities: amplification □ Children: Sunday school 10.30am; youth meeting Sunday pm □ Wheelchair: access by side door □ Other facilities: hall □ Visiting: open most times

St Matthew

New Kent Road, SE1 □ Bus: 1, 53, 63 □ Tube: Elephant and Castle □ Parking: on street □ Priest-in-Charge: Rev Angus Galbraith □ Address: The Rectory, Merrick Square, SE1 □ Telephone: 407 1707 □ Available: most days □ Other clergy: Curate, Rev Andrew Davey

St Matthew's Anglican church combines a strong Eucharistic tradition with a heavy involvement in the life and work of the local community. It is also linked with Crossway United Reformed Church through joint services and a mission to local people. The two churches produce a newspaper called *Crossroads* which has a circulation of over 1000 copies and 'seeks to reflect the life of the local community and to discover God's will within it'.

It is St Matthew's Rectory in Merrick Square, a short walk from the church, that provides the facilities for some of the large number of activities laid on. The list is a long one: a coffee group for the retired, a mother and toddler group, monthly residents meetings, the Befriender Club, and a bereavement care service are just some of them and go towards making this church an important centre for the community. The Rectory is also used for the placement of students from Salisbury and Wells Theological College providing six weeks of urban training including work with secular agencies for four days a week. There is also a hall adjoining the church where a youth club meets every week, jumble sales are held at weekends and there are two studios used by four local artists. Lunch is provided following the Friday lunchtime services designed to attract people who work locally.

Built in 1867 in a Gothic style, it is quite large, the pews and balcony being able to seat over 200 people. The condition of the church is a little shabby. No restoration work has taken place for years now and so the paintwork and general condition gives the impression of it being run down. There are, however, new plans to redevelop, using the present church and hall as a shell and converting the interior into a new church hall and other facilities for the community together with 29 flats. There will be a coffee-bar and a 'Drop-In' Club for elderly and for homeless people.

Services: Sunday 10am Sung Eucharist; Tuesday 10.30am House Communion; Weekday HC Mon & Wed 8.30am, Fri 1.05pm, Sat 9.30am; Weekdays 5.30pm Evening Prayer □ Facilities: amplification □ Children: Sunday school 10am; creche □ Wheelchair: easy access, 2 low steps □ Other details: hall □ Visiting: open only for services and activities

Southwark Cathedral

London Bridge, SE1 □ Bus: 8a, 10, 17, 21, 35, 40, 43, 44, 47, 48, 70a, 133 □ Tube/ BR: London Bridge □ Parking: on street □ Provost: The Very Rev DL Edwards □ Address: Cathedral Office, 9a St Thomas Street, SE1 □ Telephone: 407 3708 □ Vice-Provost: Canon P Penwarden □ Precentor: Canon G Parrott

Southwark Cathedral is rather overshadowed by St Paul's and Westminster Abbey, and indeed it is not very 'cathedral-like' but simply a large church. It was only in 1905 the Church of St Saviour and St Mary Overie was made Cathedral of the newly created Diocese of Southwark. This act undoubtedly saved the church for it was in a poor state of repair, and the nave had to be rebuilt before the consecration.

However the church had a long and interesting history of its own, before having cathedral status thrust upon it. From around 860 AD there has been a place of worship on this site and the interior of the present cathedral carries much evidence of its past. On the south wall, for example, are the remains of the 13th century arcading; elsewhere is a mosaic made of Roman tiles found in the crypt, and in the sanctuary, whose walls are some 700 years old, is a statue of the first Prior of Southwark. Some of the history of Southwark is celebrated in such features as the Shakespeare and Chaucer windows, depictions of Southwark ferrymen, and the Harvard Chapel in memory of John Harvard, son of a local butcher who founded the famous university in the USA.

Other features of interest include one of the oldest wooden effigies in England, that of a knight buried c. 1275, and the dramatic black and gilt tomb of Lancelot Andrewes, Bishop of Winchester.

The cathedral is famed for its music, having a fine organ and choir, and for the quality of its preaching. It is this that brings the majority of the large congregation to what is considered the mother church of south London. The support for the church can be seen in the number of voluntary workers who do everything from cleaning to manning the bookstall and arranging flowers for every Sunday service.

A new role is being adopted by the cathedral, that of a 'City church'. This is in response to the growing number of office blocks springing up along the banks of the Thames. Lunchtime services are now held regularly with Holy Communion celebrated. Lunchtime recitals often follow with live piano or organ music or recorded choral music being played. There is often a dialogue on specific problems of belief or life in this modern world.

Social or community work tends to be looked after by the parish churches, rather than the cathedral. However, new buildings are being erected between the cathedral and the Thames to provide rooms for private counselling, teaching, exhibitions, better facilities for the choir, and drama. Thus those who live and work in this neighbourhood and in the widely spread diocese will be able to find refreshment in the broadest sense of the word.

Services: Sunday 9am Holy Communion, 11am Cathedral Eucharist, 3pm Cathedral Evensong; Monday to Friday 12.30pm Matins, 12.45pm Holy Communion, 5.30pm Evensong (sung on Tuesdays and Thursdays); Tuesday and Thursday 8am Holy Communion; Saturday 11.30am Matins, 12noon Holy Communion, 4pm Evensong □ *Facilities: amplification, deaf loop, large print and Braille books* □ *Children: creche, Sunday school* □ *Wheelchair: good access* □ *Other details: new buildings under construction; see text* □ *Visiting: open all day*

Parish of Waterloo
St John
Waterloo Road, SE1
St Andrew
Short Street, SE1 □ Bus: any bus to Waterloo □ Tube/BR: Waterloo, Waterloo East □ Parking: difficult □ Both churches, contact: Deaconess Penny Casemore □ Address: Parish Office (St Andrew's), Short Street, SE1 □ Telephone: 633 9819 □ Available: office hours Mon–Fri by telephone (answer-phone)

Formed four years ago by the merger of two smaller parishes, the parish of Waterloo has two churches, St John and St Andrew, serving a single congregation. Each church takes its turn, on alternate weeks, to hold the Sunday morning service. Weekday services are held at St John's. On Sunday there is an average attendance of around 40; these are nearly all local people, mainly working class. The congregation is not elderly, the average age being mid-thirties, with some children and single parents.

It is a caring parish; the congregation is divided into four 'sharing groups', based on a geographical division of the parish. New members of the congregation are encouraged to join one of these groups, to get involved with their work and pass onto the staff the names of people who need to be visited or helped. A rota is arranged for church duties such as giving readings, cleaning the churches and organising social events.

One of four churches built in the area by Francis Bedford in celebration of the British victory at Waterloo, St John's was completed in 1824. It is Baroque in style, with an enormous portico and an elegant spire. Its five doors lead into a large interior, restored in the 1950s after wartime bombing. Among its interesting features are an unusual white cylindrical pulpit and a large wall painting of the Crucifixion by Hans Feibusch. The organ is valued at £250,000, and there is a fine peal of bells, used for practice by bellringers' groups.

The church seats 500, on wooden chairs bracketed into rows; these are removed during the week, since the church is often used for rehearsals and auditions by theatre groups, including the RSC. The church is ideal for this purpose since it is a large open space with completely flat wooden block floor. A major restoration of the crypt has recently taken place. Much of the space has been transformed into a suite of rooms, with extensive facilities. It is used during the week as the North Lambeth Day Centre; activities on offer include arts and crafts, pottery and woodwork. At weekends the crypt is used for church functions; there are parish lunches and social evenings every five to eight weeks. The parish's youth club meets here on Mondays. Also in the crypt is a small chapel, used for the numerous weekday lunchtime services.

By far the smaller of the two churches, seating 150, St Andrew's was built in the mid-1950s and is simple in design. The interior is 'open-plan', with the sanctuary area containing a small communion table, and modern wooden choir stalls. The church has bench pews and an attractive panelled ceiling.

The Parish Office is contained within the church, as is the office of the Upstream Children's Theatre, a parish project. The church is very much involved with the stage, having its own studio theatre upstairs, where productions are often staged, both by Upstream and by outside theatre groups. The lower hall is loaned out on a permanent basis to the Lee Strasberg Acting Company of America. The Southwark Singers also use the church for rehearsals, and two or three times a year there is a series of lunchtime recitals.

Services: Sunday 10.30am Holy Communion (alternating between the two churches), 6.30pm Evening Prayer (check with church for venue); Mon, Thu, Fri 12.30pm Holy Communion (said) at St John's □ Facilities: some large print service books available □ Wheelchair: St John's: some steep steps leading to main entrance. St Andrew's: level access □ Children: small Sunday school during morning service □ Other details: St John's: crypt, used in week as day centre. St Andrew's: studio theatre, lower hall □ Visiting: St John's: open at service times only. St Andrew's: available any time the Parish Office is open; ring bell for assistance

---

The Church of Jesus Christ of Latter Day Saints (Mormons)

Joseph Smith (1805–44), visionary founder of The Church of Jesus Christ of Latter Day Saints, had his first revelation at the age of fifteen, declaring he had been chosen to restore the Gospel and the true Church. Guided by visions, Smith found and translated a set of gold tablets whose contents were published in 1830 as the Book of Mormon. This text, although regarded as the revealed Word of God, supplements, rather than replaces, the Bible. The first Church meeting took place in April 1830 with six members attending. Today the Church is a worldwide organisation of well over 4.5 million people, with much wealth and influence in its American heartland.

The Church is so structured and organised that a member will find the same patterns of worship and evangelism operating wherever he or she may be in the world. Each chapel is at the centre of a Ward, presided over by a Bishop, and a number of Wards make up a Stake. Amongst lay members there are Elders, Patriarchs and Apostles, all of whom have the authority of ministry, including missionary work and supervising worship. Services begin with a Sacrament meeting involving the whole congregation which is afterwards divided according to age and gender into study classes. Further, each group has specific responsibilities; the young men concentrate on evangelising for example, whilst women run the Relief Group, whereby the Church's vast resources are mobilised for emergency relief of disaster areas.

Many chapels including Hyde Park Chapel have become repositories of genealogical information. It is a central facet of the Mormon faith that family relationships are both sacred and eternal. Being therefore able to trace and identify their ancestors, many members have them baptised by proxy in order to save their souls and to be re-united with them for the bodily resurrection following the Last Judgement. This emphasis on the sanctity of family life lies behind the system of 'Family Home Evenings' each Monday as a supplement to chapel worship.

Further information can be obtained from Hyde Park Chapel.

Hyde Park Chapel

64–68 Exhibition Road, SW7 □ Telephone: 584 7553/4 □ Bus: 14, 30, 49, 73, 74 □ Tube: South Kensington (Museum exit) □ Parking: on street, difficult □ Hyde Park Ward: Bishop Larry Hess □ Address: 17 Randolph Crescent, W9 □ Telephone: 286 3226 □ Britannia Ward: L Kent Dansley □ Address: 41 Lennox Gardens, SW1 □ Telephone: 584 0938 □ Available: someone always at visitors' centre

The Hyde Park Chapel of Jesus Christ of Latter Day Saints, looking more like a modern office building than a church, stands in stark contrast to the elegant Victoria and Albert Museum nearby. Built in 1959 to a design by Sir Thomas Bennett, the chapel is largely nondescript though easily recognised by virtue of its slender, tapering gold spire. The main hall and worship area is designed to have no horizontal lines, presumably to create an uplifting atmosphere. There is a very large postwar organ, regularly used for recitals.

The reception hall is given over to a visitors' centre where the history of the Mormon faith and its relationship to the life of Christ is illustrated through paintings and photographs. There is also a video room where visitors are encouraged to see films on a wide range of subjects, from the history of the Church's founder, Joseph Smith, to moral discussions on the sanctity of marriage and the beauty of family life. There are always willing volunteers to show you around and share their beliefs with you.

The majority of non-Mormon visitors to the chapel come here for the Genealogy Centre, one of the largest in the UK. With access to over 80 million names on microfiche and copies of almost all the parish records in England, it is possible to trace one's family back to the 1500s. All are welcome to use the facilities and there is a regular meeting every Wednesday at 7pm for genealogy buffs.

Both the Hyde Park and the Britannia wards hold their meetings in the chapel. Both have a predominantly American membership and the main difference is that the Britannia ward is reserved exclusively for the younger members and single members of the Church (18–30 year olds). It has about 700 members with, on average, 170 attending the Sacrament meeting in any given week. Although smaller, with a membership of 574, the Hyde Park ward has a regular turn-out of 270. Both wards follow the usual Sunday format.

The chapel has its own well equipped sports/function hall and many social events take place, including dances, exhibitions and sports. In addition, the Britannia ward replaces the Monday family evening with social gatherings because of the nature of its membership. All are welcome but non-members should be prepared for attention from missionaries keen to share their faith.

The next most central Mormon place of worship is the North London Ward Chapel at 88 Archway Road, N19. A former synagogue, it attracts a cosmopolitan, though mostly British, congregation. The Sunday Sacrament meeting begins at 10am. Telephone 458 4225 for more details.

Services: Hyde Park Ward: Sunday 10am Priesthood & Relief meetings, 10.40am Sunday school (inc adults), 11.45am Sacrament meeting. Britannia Ward: 3pm Sacrament meeting, 3.40pm Sunday school (inc adults), 4.40pm Priesthood & Relief meetings □ Facilities: amplification □ Children: cry room; Sunday school □ Wheelchair: several steps; help always available □ Other details: Genealogy Centre, open office hours □ Visiting: fully staffed visitors' centre, open 10am–9pm daily

The Church of Scotland

There are several Scottish Protestant denominations of which the largest and the best known is the Church of Scotland. It differs primarily from the Church of England in that it is presbyterian (governed by lay elders) and not episcopal (governed by bishops).

The Scottish Reformation took place later than that of Henry VIII's in England and Wales. This was largely due to the Catholic faith of the Scottish monarchy. The driving force behind the changes was John Knox, a fiery Scottish preacher. He had spent much time on the continent, where he met John Calvin, who influenced him greatly. By 1560 Knox and his followers had succeeded in having the Mass abolished and papal authority rejected. Knox clashed with Mary, Queen of Scots, who wanted to make the church episcopal, and it was not until much later, 1690, that a fully presbyterian system was formally adopted.

The Church of Scotland has remained largely the same since that time, although its history has not been smooth. It has been subject to various secessions, the largest of which was the Disruption of 1843, when nearly a third of its clergy left to form the Free Church of Scotland (qv). By 1929, most of the breakaway denominations had united and been re-absorbed into the main Church once again.

The denomination has two churches in London, both of which also act as centres of Scottish culture, fellowship and social activity. Although attended mainly by Scottish expatriates from London and the South-East, and also by visitors to the capital, they are by no means exclusive, and anyone is welcome to attend services. For further information contact either of the churches listed here.

Crown Court Church

Russell Street, WC2 □ Telephone: 836 5643 □ Bus: 1, 4, 5, 6, 9, 11, 13, 15, 68, 77 □ Tube: Covent Garden, Aldwych, Holborn □ Parking: meters □ Minister: Rev Kenneth G Hughes □ Address: The Manse, 53 Sidmouth Street, WC1 □ Telephone: 278 5022 □ Available: telephone for appointment

'Like preaching to a procession' was the way that Rev Joseph Moffatt, minister at Crown Court from 1917–1962, described his work. It is still an appropriate description for a congregation that to some extent fluctuates according to family and work commitments. With St Columba's, Pont Street, this church is a point of reference for Scots, be they young people in London for the first time or established residents. Visitors from all over the world are also welcomed.

Crown Court is in the middle of theatreland, across the road from the Theatre Royal, Drury Lane. The original church, dating from 1719, was committed to mission work in Covent Garden, under the pioneering hand of Dr John Cumming, minister from 1832 to 1879. His successor, the Rev Donal MacLeod, became minister to two churches when St Columba's was opened in 1884, drawing many of Crown Court's congregation. A year later, Rev Alfred Phillips was inducted as minister of Crown Court and the two churches became separate. Later, the old church became inadequate and the present Crown Court was built in 1909.

St Columba, SW1

It has a most attractive interior: dark, polished wood dominates, highlighted by discreet lighting. The Royal Arms of George I, King when the original church was built, can be seen over the Communion Table. There are several striking stained glass windows—including one of John Knox who, through his association with Calvin, provides Scotland's most direct link with early Presbyterianism.

As in many Presbyterian Churches, there is emphasis on the preaching of the Scripture. Services are traditional; Elders assist the Minister in administering Holy Communion, and a choir leads the worship at both Sunday services. During the Morning Service, the church operates one of the oldest Sunday schools in the country, dating from 1814.

The church today continues its wide-ranging ministry to the immediate area in addition to its obvious Scottish emphasis. It keepts in close touch with elderly Covent Garden residents and is also represented on the Covent Garden Forum. A mid-week service is held on Thursday lunchtimes. 'Crown Court', says the brochure, 'stands ready to welcome all visitors, from wherever they may come, who wish to enjoy our fellowship and worship in the Scottish tradition. We hope they will feel very much at home in this sanctuary of the Scottish nation'.

Services: Sunday 11.15am (Shortened Communion, 1st Sunday), 6.30pm; Thursday 1.10pm; (Quarterly Communion & Gaelic service, 1st Sunday of March, June, October and December) □ Facilities: deaf loop, some large print hymnbooks □ Children: Sunday school during morning service; creche □ Wheelchair: difficult, several steps □ Other details: hall for community and church activities □ Visiting: open to visitors 11.30am–2.30pm, Tuesday to Thursday during June, July and August; otherwise by arrangement; souvenir stall open after services

St Columba

Pont Street, SW1 □ Telephone: 584 2321 □ Bus: 9, 11, 19, 22, 46, 49, 137 □ Tube: Knightsbridge, Sloane Square □ Parking: on street □ Minister: none at time of writing

An elegant modern building in Kensington, St Columba's is both a place of worship and a social centre for Scottish people in London. It has over 1,500 members, and around 500 people attend the Sunday services, which are in the Presbyterian tradition.

The original St Columba's was built in 1884, as a companion to the Crown Court Church of Scotland in Covent Garden. Destroyed by fire in 1941, the church was rebuilt in the early 1950s with money from a fund set up by the congregation. The church is an attractive piece of architecture, from the pleasant exterior and tall clocktower to the uncluttered interior, with its wide nave and narrow transepts. The decor is grey, with many blue fittings, including the choirstalls, pulpit tester and the chandeliers. There is also a beautiful rose window. Mounted into the walls are the armorial crests of all the counties of Scotland, and above the doorway at the south entrance are the personal coat of arms of the Queen Mother; as a Scot, she takes a personal interest in the church, and laid the foundation stone in 1950, returning to attend the Silver Jubilee in 1980.

Downstairs is a large hall with a proscenium stage and stackable chairs. It forms the cornerstone of St Columba's thriving Scottish community centre, whilst on

Sunday afternoons lunch is served here for the congregation. Community is the keyword at St Columba's. Whilst the congregation itself is scattered all over London, the church acts as a focal point for religious and social activities. There are Bible study and fellowship groups, with an active Congregational Fellowship which supports missionary and other church activities. There are connections with the London Scottish Regiment (who hold their annual Church Parade here on Remembrance Sunday) and the Royal British Legion. The social activities are varied, ranging from cub scouts to Scottish country dancing.

Both congregation and clergy help with community ventures. The church is involved with the Centrepoint Night Shelter in Soho, and the soup kitchen at St Martin-in-the-Fields. It also finances a home for the elderly in Putney. Young Scottish people alone and in London for the first time can get friendly advice at St Columba's. On Sunday the church has a service unit desk, manned by volunteers, which supplies help with cleaning, gardening, shopping and the like for the elderly and people in need.

Services: Sunday 11am, 6.30pm; Thursday 1.10pm (Quarterly Communion, last Sunday of January, April, June and October) □ *Facilities: amplification, deaf loop* □ *Children: Sunday school during morning service; creche* □ *Wheelchair: several steps* □ *Other details: suite of halls in full use; library* □ *Visiting: open to visitors 'at all times'; bookstall*

Congregationalist Churches

Not all Congregationalist churches joined the URC when it was formed in 1972; some became unaffiliated, while the remainder became members of either the Congregational Federation, or the Evangelical Fellowship of Congregational Churches, examples of which follow this introduction. The fact that not all churches made the same decision is indicative of the extent of independence and self-determination that each church, or indeed congregation, maintains.

Modern Congregationalism began with the Reformation when some Christians took Luther's doctrine of the priesthood of all believers to its logical conclusion: that where two or three meet together in the name of Christ they constitute a church that is independent, though part of the Universal Church. It is held that this system represents the earliest form of church order. There is an ordained clergy, though no credal test of membership. Congregationalism has long been evangelical in tone, with a strong reputation of preaching. Between them, the two Congregational denominations have around 17,000 members in the UK.

For further information, contact any of the churches listed below.

Kentish Town Congregational Church (Evangelical Fellowship of Congregational Churches)

Kelly Street, NW1 □ Bus: 27, 46, 53, 134, 137, 214 □ Tube/BR: Camden Town, Kentish Town, Kentish Town West □ Parking: on street □ Minister: Rev I Blayney □ Address: 13 Oakwood Avenue, Hutton, Brentwood, Essex □ Telephone: (0277) 223501

Built in 1807, this is the oldest independent church in the area, though the congregation has dwindled in recent years. At present they meet only once a month, and the church is used more regularly by the Calvary Church of God in Christ (qv)—a thriving Pentecostalist group.

The church is now in a poor state of repair, and the whole site is due to be redeveloped for the benefit of the local community. It is intended to provide a new sanctuary for worship along with two halls for community use with bookstall and coffee shop facilities. Also on the site will be four shared units of accommodation for mentally-handicapped people under the 'Care in the Community' scheme, and other housing accommodation for local needs. The project is being organised by a steering committee which includes representatives of Camden Society for Mentally Handicapped, a local voluntary agency. For further details contact the minister.

Latimer Congregational Church (Congregational Federation)

Ernest Street, E1 □ Telephone: 790 8796 □ Bus: 10, 25, 225 □ Tube: Stepney Green □ Parking: car park at church □ Minister: Rev RV Sago □ Address: The Manse, Ernest Street, E1 □ Telephone: as church □ Available: most times (by telephone) □ Other staff: Asst Minister G Grierson

Emerging from Stepney Green Underground station, one finds oneself facing the Ocean Estate, a large, post-war residential development built by the GLC. Close by, on Ernest Street, is the Latimer Congregational Church, the only church on the estate.

The church has a long history, tracing its origins back to 1672 (and before) when it was based in the City. Moving to Mile End in 1835, the church flourished until World War II, when many members perished, and the church building was bombed.

A new church was built on the present site and was opened in 1953. The building was designed to function not only as a place of worship but also as a focus for the community and its activities. The church hall is used by the local community; three other rooms, including games rooms, are also available. The church's weekly calendar is full, events including a women's meeting on Mondays at 2pm (with guest speakers) and a midweek meeting on Thursday evenings with fellowship, prayer and praise; this is led by a lay person, Miss Vera Page.

Wednesday is a particularly busy day. There is a coffee morning, and a mums and toddlers' group during the day, while in the evenings there is a Bible study and prayer meeting, followed by games—snooker, pool, darts and Scrabble are all played. Outside groups use the facilities at other times, including the Gingerbread single parents' group, which meets on Thursday evenings. The Blood Transfusion Service uses the hall regularly.

On Sunday, there is evening worship ministering to a local working class congregation, predominantly elderly but with a smattering of people in their thirties. On the first Sunday of the month, a Family Service is held in the morning to which children of any age are welcome.

Services: Sunday 6pm Evening worship, 11am Family worship (1st Sunday in month); Thursday 5pm □ Facilities: amplification, large print hymnbooks □ Children: welcome to Family worship □ Wheelchair: ramp at rear entrance, chairlift to upstairs □ Visiting: open at services, can be opened at other times (telephone The Manse)

Orange Street Congregational Church (Evangelical Fellowship of Congregational Churches)

Orange Street, WC2 □ Bus: any to Trafalgar Square □ Tube: Leicester Square, Charing Cross, Piccadilly Circus □ Parking: difficult except Sunday □ Deacon: Mr HE Stough □ Address: 47 Holland Park, W11 □ Telephone: 727 6807 □ Available: most evenings

Tucked away behind the National Gallery lies Orange Street Congregational Church, so close to Trafalger Square and yet so easily missed. A good time to seek it out would be any Wednesday from 4.30pm when the church opens it doors for reading and relaxation. Refreshments are served at 5.15 and this 'open house' session, held in the crypt, concludes with Bible study from 6 to 7pm.

The church has an interesting history dating back to a chapel built in 1693 by Huguenot refugees. In 1776 the chapel passed into the hands of the Church of England, and amongst its incumbents was Rev Augustus Montague Toplady, the writer of 'Rock of Ages'. The Congregationalists acquired the chapel in 1787, though the present building dates only from 1929.

Sundays at Orange Street are very busy. As well as the Congregationalists, a Chinese group (at 2pm) and an Evangelical group (6pm) also use the church. The Congregationalists meet at 11am; the attendance is small but regulars come from distant suburbs, and there are occasional visitors from overseas. There is no minister at Orange Street, so services are led either by one of the deacons or by a guest preacher. Every third Sunday there is a lecture at 3pm.

Services: Sunday 11am (Holy Communion 1st Sunday); Wednesday 6–7pm Bible study □ Wheelchair: 2 steps up to chapel, flight of stairs down to crypt □ Other details: crypt □ Visiting: open Wednesday after 4.30pm & Sunday only

Trinity Congregational Church (Congregational Federation)

St Matthew's Road, SW2 □ Telephone: 274 5541 □ Bus: 3, 28, 35, 37, 50, 59, 109, 133, 159, 189, 195 □ Tube: Brixton □ Parking: small car park, easy street parking on Sunday □ Minister: Rev Dr Alan Argent □ Address: The Manse, 125 Sudbourne Road, Brixton, SW2 □ Telephone: 274 0853 □ Available: almost any time, always someone to answer phone

Close to St Matthew's Anglican church is the smaller, but almost as impressive, Trinity Congregational Church. A listed building graced by a large portico, it often attracts visitors as it is one of the few churches in the area that actually looks like a church. It was opened in 1828 as a non-denominational church, but subsequently became Congregationalist. The interior is dominated by the large organ and carved pulpit, and has seating for 250 people if one includes the pews of the curved gallery. Although time has taken its toll, a major restoration is now under way which will see the return of this handsome and well-loved building to its former glory.

Services, although formal in structure with sermon and hymns, are informal in character. During the Sunday morning service, for example, the children attending before Sunday school are encouraged to speak out and ask if there is anything they do not understand. Dr Argent is keen on involving people in the life of the church; thus some members form the choir, others give readings, children taken the collection, and there are six or seven lay preachers attached to the church. The loyal and active congregation includes people from many different backgrounds; in addition to the local working people there are a number of academics and artists, many of whom travel from outside the area, perhaps returning to the church they grew up with. The average age is between 20 and 30, with some teenagers and children.

Outside activities are numerous, including Bible study meetings, and a range of discussion groups and social clubs. Dr Argent sees the church functioning as a 'home'—members of the congregation, adults and children alike, are welcome to pop in any time to use the facilities, such as a large hall for games and cosy sitting room. Members usually keep in touch if they leave the area; many return to visit and can be assured of a warm welcome. The church magazine is mailed to friends all over the world.

Services: Sunday 10.30am (Holy Communion 1st Sunday), 6.30pm (Holy Communion 3rd Sunday) □ *Facilities: amplification, large print servicebooks & hymnbooks* □ *Children: Sunday school after morning service* □ *Wheelchair: several steps, help available; good access to hall & wide door toilet* □ *Other details: hall with sitting room, etc* □ *Visiting: usually open only for services*

Union Chapel (Congregational Federation)

19 Compton Terrace, N1 □ *Telephone: 226 1686* □ *Bus: 4, 19, 30, 43, 263a, 279, 279a* □ *Tube: Highbury & Islington* □ *Parking: on street* □ *Minister: Rev Janet Wootten* □ *Address: 19a Compton Terrace, N1* □ *Telephone: 354 3631* □ *Available: most times at chapel*

When viewed from Upper Street, which is separated from Compton Terrace by gardens, the chapel seems somewhat out of place, resting in a row of terraced houses; yet when entered there is revealed one of the grandest and most unusual Victorian church interiors.

The first chapel on the site was built in 1806 by a group of nonconformists at Highbury Grove. Growth of Islington's population in the first half of the 19th century led to the decision to build a new and larger chapel in 1875. The chapel

Union Chapel, N1

was designed so that a large congregation of up to 2,000 people would all be able to see and hear the minister equally well. This requirement resulted in an irregular octagonal design by James Cubitt, completed in 1877. There is a balcony on all sides facing the marble pulpit, and as it does not sit over the nave area there is no need for supporting pillars that would have otherwise spoilt the view. Modelled on the Romanesque church of St Fosca at Torcello, near Venice, the chapel established Cubitt's reputation as an architect. It has remained much as he created it.

The chapel's capacity is too large for today's congregations, but its suitability for large gatherings, and its excellent acoustics (unexpected by Cubitt when he built it), has led to its use for other activities. The chapel has a policy of opening its doors to the local community for social needs, and to the national and international comunity for cultural, academic and commercial activities, in addition to providing a venue for denominational events. For example, charity concerts are held here, as well as live BBC recordings, and the chapel has featured in a video by the pop group The Housemartins.

The single weekly service on a Sunday morning led by Rev Janet Wootten, who arrived here in 1986, is in traditional nonconformist style. It is attended by 20 to 30 people who are mainly young, and attendance figures are increasing.

Aside from the chapel itself, the building houses a lecture hall, a large and a small hall (the large one having a balcony) and a vestry. In 1982 English Heritage recognised the chapel's architectural importance and offered a grant for the renovation of the halls, while 'The Friends of Union Chapel' was set up as a registered charity to raise the balance. Despite their condition, one of the halls is used for a Rudolph Steiner playgroup that takes place every weekday. Further activities are the brownies and a Bible study group.

Services: Sunday 11am, (Communion 1st Sunday; Family Service 4th Sunday) □ *Facilities: amplification* □ *Children: Junior Church, Sunday 11am* □ *Wheelchair: level entrance at the rear, toilets for disabled* □ *Other details: halls (for hire), vestry* □ *Visiting: open at service times only*

Evangelical Churches

Christianity in this country has long contained strong evangelical elements—almost for as long as there has been Protestantism. Indeed, the evangelical movement is quintessentially Protestant, basing its teaching on the Gospels, and affirming the supremacy of the Bible, the depravity of man, the importance of personal conversion and salvation by faith in the atoning death of Christ.

Evangelicalism is not a denomination as such, but it may be present as a theological wing within a Church, such as the Anglican Church for example, and it characterises many largely autonomous churches which may be affiliated with others of similar beliefs and practices. The emphasis on autonomy and personal responsibility militates against more formal links, and makes splits and secessions not uncommon; the present evangelical associations contain churches whose origins lie variously in the Methodist, Baptist, Congregationalist or other nonconformist traditions.

At services the central feature will be the sermon which may be delivered by a minister or lay preacher, while there will be little in the way of sacraments. Communion may be taken at a separate meeting from the main act of worship or it may be only fortnightly, for example. The buildings are plainly decorated, perhaps with only a simple cross indicating its purpose, though there will usually be facilities for the baptism, ie total immersion of adults.

Churches included here belong variously to the: Fellowship of Independent Evangelical Churches (HQ 681 7422); Union of Evangelical Churches (HQ 0375 672 826); and the Old Baptist Union (HQ 0742 352739), a member of the Evangelical Alliance.

Also included is the Christian Brethren church at Rossmore Hall.

Camberwell Evangelical Church (Union of Evangelical Churches)

65 Bethwin Road, SE5 □ Bus: 3, 36, 36a, 109, 131, 133 □ Tube: Kennington □ Parking: small car park □ Pastor: Rev FC Hintze □ Telephone: 703 3290 □ Available: by appointment □ Other staff: Archdeacon, 3 Deacons

This simple modern church accommodates an average attendance of 90 people for the Sunday morning service. The majority of the congregation are under-forties, some West Indian, mostly English, but few with strong local ties. It is a mobile congregation, for people soon move away to better housing in other parts of London. The church accents family worship and there is a room adjoining the main one where services are held, where young families can hear the service over a loudspeaker system.

The history of the church hall just off Bethwyn Road is one of mission to to the deprived youth of the area. It was built in 1810 and named after Sir John Kirk, a benefactor of the Shaftesbury Society, the charity associated with the great reformer of that name. The hall was also used as a school by the Ragged School movement. There is a collection of plaques which commemorate some of the notables associated with this mission.

Following in these footsteps the Evangelical Church has a full programme of activities to interest kids in the neighbourhood today. A 'sausage sizzle' on

Sunday evenings invites all to come for free food and coffee. For the older folk there is a film club, and a women's meeting is held on Tuesday afternoons. Women will be escorted to and from church on request if they are worried about their safety.

Services: Sunday 11am, 3pm Evening Gospel, 7.45pm Bible reading/Prayer ☐ Facilities: amplification ☐ Children: Sunday school 3pm; creche; youth groups ☐ Wheelchair: no access ☐ Visiting: open at service times only

Dalling Road Evangelical Church (Old Baptist Union)

Dalling Road, W6 ☐ Bus: 27 ☐ Tube: Ravenscourt Park ☐ Parking: not difficult Sunday & evenings ☐ Minister: Rev Leslie Clark ☐ Address: 25 Greenend Road, W4 ☐ Telephone: 995 0180 ☐ Available: mostly during the day; telephone for appointment

The Dalling Road Church was obtained in 1956 by an Old Baptist Union congregation founded in Fulham late last century. The building was bought from the Methodists, and the architecture is appropriately reminiscent of a Methodist chapel. The interior is large and spacious, with wooden pews seating up to 250 people. The preacher's table is on a raised dais at the front of the church. In recent years, the church has been redecorated and many improvements have been made.

The church serves the Old Baptist Union of Greater London, although the majority of the congregation lives within a mile. Each service has an average attendance of 40, and the congregation is very active, both within the services (helping with readings and music) and outside. There are afterchurch fellowship meetings at private houses, and weekly meetings at the church, such as 'Prayer, Care and Share' on Tuesday evenings, an event which involves prayer and Bible study in a family atmosphere, and the informal Wednesday Fellowship. Sunday school is styled Junior Church and also involves Bible classes. The ladies meeting on Monday afternoons is well attended, as is the mums and toddlers group on Wednesday morning.

The Old Baptist Union is a small group of evangelical Baptists founded in 1880. The Articles of Faith are organised after the principles of the General Baptists of 1611 and 1660. The Union is not sectarian, advocating fellowship with other Christians; it is a member of the Evangelical Alliance and the Free Church Federal Council.

Services: Sunday 11am, 6.30pm; Tuesday 8pm 'Prayer, Care and Share' Prayer Meeting and Bible Study; Wednesday 8pm, Wednesday Fellowship ☐ Facilities: amplification, overhead projector (for words of hymns) ☐ Children: Junior Church and creche at service times; also Bible class ☐ Wheelchair: some steps, but not steep ☐ Other details: school hall, meeting room etc ☐ Visiting: open for services and activities; bookstall and library available

Gedling Mission Hall (Fellowship of Independent Evangelical Churches)

Sweeney Crescent, SE1 □ Bus: 47, 47a, 70, 188 □ Tube: London Bridge, Tower Hill □ Parking: space for 12 cars in grounds □ Secretary: Mr David Gilbert □ Address: 39 Shipwright Road, SE16 □ Telephone: 232 2897 □ Available: telephone in the evenings

This hall was opened in 1960, but the Mission to which it is home dates back to 1881. At that time, services were held in a converted stable in Gedling Street (hence the name). The present building has a suite of rooms and two halls separated by a folding partition which can be combined to make one large hall for special occasions. The chairs can be stacked away when not needed, and a curtain is drawn across the pulpit area when the hall is not in use for worship.

Most of the congregation are local, living within 500 yards of the Mission Hall, and many of them are elderly. Services are Free Church in style, with hymns, prayer and an emphasis on preaching. They are flexible in format, allowing visiting preachers scope to choose the direction which the services may take. There is no incumbent at the time of writing and therefore most of the preachers are lay people. In addition to the two Sunday services at the Hall there is a Morning service held jointly at Rotherhithe Evangelical Free Church near the Rotherhithe Tunnel.

In the week, the Hall is used for various activities. On Monday afternoon, the Women's Fellowship (mainly older women) meets, and there is a prayer/Bible study meeting on Tuesday evenings.

The Mission Hall is used on occasion by other Christian groups, such as Christian Endeavour, for meetings and events. The Mission itself is often involved with other churches at Easter and similar festivals, and also has involvements with charitable and community work. There are connections with the Shaftesbury Society, which helps to provide schools for handicapped children.

Services: Sunday 6.30pm Evening Service (followed by Holy Communion, 2nd Sunday); Tuesday 7.45pm Prayer Meeting & Bible Study □ Facilities: amplification; some large print Gospels □ Children: Sunday school 2.30pm, children's club, 6pm Wednesday, 6–12 year olds □ Wheelchair: some shallow steps at entrance □ Other details: hall, classroom, etc □ Visiting: open around service times

Rossmore Hall Evangelical Church (Christian Brethren)

1 Rossmore Road, Marylebone Road, NW1 □ Bus: 159 □ Tube: Marylebone □ Parking: on street □ Elder: A Graham □ Telephone: 723 4211 □ Available: at services □ Other contacts: Choy Jeankan (624 8314)

The first Brethren meeting in Britain took place in Plymouth in 1831, thus giving rise to the popular term Plymouth Brethren. Members prefer the name 'Christian Brethren', a designation broad enough to embrace their fellow Christians, all of whom are welcome to services. There is no central organisation, no headquarters, no statement of beliefs for members and no formal federation links between churches; however there are many similarities between them and a strong sense of a spiritual bond. The most obvious characteristic of this evangelical Bible-based group of churches is that there is no ordained clergy—male members and guest speakers take turns to lead services.

Founded in 1962, the group meeting at Rossmore Hall is a small fellowship, the largest congregations numbering around 30. A significant proportion of these are students from elsewhere in Britain and abroad, who attend only while in London for their studies. Although this prevents a settled community developing, it does create an atmosphere of youth and vitality not found at many provincial Christian Brethren meetings.

The hall, now 200 years old, is in a terrace of houses. On the white-washed wall that faces the street are noticeboards and posters that indicate its use. Inside there is a single large room on the ground floor. Although simple, it has something of the busy clutter of a schoolroom with its wooden chairs and posters on the walls.

Sunday commences with Morning Worship, which includes the Breaking of Bread. The Family Service is geared more towards hymn-singing and the preaching and ministry of members or other Brethren. Every other Sunday afternoon there is a young people's Bible study, whilst the only weekday activity is the Wednesday evening Assembly.

Services: Sunday 10am Morning Worship, 11.30am Family Service; Wednesday 7.30pm Assembly Bible Study and Prayer □ Wheelchair: level access □ Visiting: open at service and activity times only

Westminster Chapel (Fellowship of Independent Evangelical Churches)

Buckingham Gate, SW1 □ Telephone: 834 1731 □ Bus: 11, 24, 29 □ Tube: Victoria, St James Park □ Parking: on street □ Minister: Rev Dr RT Kendall □ Available: after services at chapel □ □ Other Contacts: Rev Anthony O'Sullivan (assistant to the minister)

Westminster Chapel may not be as famous as the nearby Abbey and Methodist Central Hall, but it is an imposing building in its own right with a strong tradition of worship dating back to 1842. That was the year a group of Congregationalists first used a small hall on the site for services. It was soon found to be insufficient for their needs and the present large chapel was built in 1865. It boasts a fine Romanesque facade complete with a solid, square tower. Inside, a huge organ case dominates the east end, above a raised pulpit which indicates the emphasis placed on preaching here. The pews and galleries are arranged in an oval shape again focusing attention on the pulpit. The dominant colours are the purple-blue of the ceiling and the dark polished oak of the woodwork, giving the chapel a rich, dignified air.

The chapel left the Congregational Union, which it regarded as becoming too liberal, in the 1950s and formed the Fellowship of Independent Evangelical Churches. The Congregational notion of church autonomy is retained, although the democratic structure has to be viewed alongside the tendency of the chapel's notable ministers to dominate the proceedings. One such minister was Dr Martin Lloyd-Jones, who died in 1981, whose preaching drew a large flock from well beyond London. His successor, Dr RT Kendall, continues the tradition of expository preaching, writing and evangelism, and guest evangelists are often invited to preach here.

The whole congregation, often numbering around 600 on a Sunday, is invited to participate in the chapel's work. 'Pilot Lights' is a training scheme for the street evangelism that takes place every Saturday at various local venues. 'Evangelism Explosion' is a thoroughgoing seventeen-week course including much practical experience to equip people for door-to-door evangelism. Trainees sit a final examination. The chapel also runs a variety of youth clubs and a ladies' meeting. News of events is contained in a Sunday Reminder leaflet, while the more weighty *Westminster Record* contains sermons recently delivered at the chapel as well as articles and news in more depth.

Services: Sunday 10.15am, 5.30pm Prayer Meeting, 11am, 6.30pm Worship; Monday 6.30pm Prayer Meeting; Wednesday 6.45pm Fellowship; Thursday 1.10pm Lunch-time Service □ *Facilities: amplification, deaf loop, large print Bibles and hymn books, Braille hymn books* □ *Children: Sunday school; Teenagers' Class, Sunday 3pm; creche during Sunday morning service* □ *Wheelchair: 5 steps, no ramp* □ *Other details: two large halls, large meeting-room (Lloyd-Jones Hall), reference library* □ *Visiting: open at service times only; book and tape shop open 5.30–6.30pm and 7.45–10.45pm Fridays*

Jehovah's Witnesses

The Jehovah's Witnesses trace their beginnings to a small Bible study group founded by Charles Taze Russell in the early 1870s in Allegheny City, Penns, USA. In 1879 he published the first issue of *Zion's Watchtower & Herald of Christ's Presence* and, soon after, other groups sprang up in neighbouring states following the ideas put forward by Russell's magazine. These groups were united under Russell's leadership in 1881 and through the publication of services in newspapers at home and abroad, and members' personal evangelism, the movement quickly spread.

It was not until 1931 that the name 'Jehovah's Witnesses' was adopted and this date also marks the time when the organisation placed greater emphasis on the structure of Bible study and on extensive door-to-door evangelism. From the headquarters in Brooklyn, New York, they link and co-ordinate the work of over 2 million people in 200 lands. They publish weekly editions of *The Watchtower* and *Awake* as well as the yearbook and many other books.

Each congregation gathering in the Kingdom Halls all over the world follows the same format of meetings in the weekly schedule and uses the same topic for discussion at the Watchtower meetings. This meeting is mainly Bible study and it is complemented by a public lecture and 'Private Home Bible Study'. There are also two meetings for training Witnesses to be better proclaimers: the 'Theocratic Ministry School' where the actual training takes place, and a discussion meeting.

Every Witness is expected to devote thirteen hours a month to this evangelical work. All visits are recorded, to avoid the householder being seen too often, and notes are taken of the subjects broached and the attitude of the interviewee; thus, promising conversations can be resumed sooner than those which did not bode well. Certain Witnesses take this activity to be their main work, often doing part-time jobs so that they can go visiting for most of the week.

Camden Kingdom Hall

7 Pratt Mews, off Pratt Street, NW1 □ Bus: 24, 27, 29, 68, 134, 137, 214, 253 □ Tube/BR: Camden Town, Camden Road □ Parking: on street □ Presiding Overseer: Mr David Rastall □ Address: 105 Queens Crescent, NW5 □ Telephone: 346 8499 □ Secretary: Mr Michael Brown □ Available: evenings and weekends

Attendance here has increased so much over recent years that the Witnesses have been divided into three separate congregations—Kilburn, Camden and Holloway—who use the Hall on a shift basis. Even so, the 170 seater Hall is usually packed at service times, and much larger premises are being sought.

Tucked away at the end of a mews occupied by light industrial units, the Hall was formerly a builders merchant's showroom. Both its design and the interior decor can be described as functional. It is used for two main types of service: during the week, Witnesses meet for Ministry School comprising supervised Bible readings and study, while on Sunday there are Watchtower meetings. In addition, one of the small home groups, who normally meet at members' houses for talks, meet at the Hall.

Over twenty nationalities, all ages and many walks of life are represented in the congregations, and newcomers are most welcome, especially to a Sunday service. Three times a year, joint assemblies are held in a large Hall (a converted cinema) just off the North Circular, which has facilities for baptism. Those who have decided to become Witnesses, after having attended meetings and talked it over with the elders, are baptised on the occasions.

There are no charitable or social programmes organised by these congregations as such, although in practice a good deal of help is provided on an individual basis in the course of the door-to-door ministry.

Services: Sunday 10am, 3pm, 6pm Watchtower meeting and lecture; Wed, Thurs & Fri 7.30pm Theocratic Ministry School; (Tues 7.30pm Home Group) □ Facilities: amplification; sign language on request □ Wheelchair: level access □ Visiting: all are welcome to services

Chelsea Kingdom Hall

Sydney Hall, Pond Place, SW3 □ Telephone: 584 3097 □ Bus: 14, 45, 49 □ Tube: South Kensingtion □ Parking: difficult □ Presiding Overseer: Mr David Muxlow □ Telephone: 722 4845 □ Available: at the services □ Other contacts: Andrew and Sue Taylor □ Address: 75 Stourhead House, Tachbrook Street, SW1 □ Telephone: 834 4105

When Sydney Hall, formerly a Temperance Hall, was acquired by the Watchtower Society in 1959, the first congregation was made up of people living in south west London who had previously been meeting at Craven Terrace in Paddington. When the Fulham Congregation had sufficiently grown in numbers it split into two and now, after another division, three congregations meet at the Hall; Chelsea, Fulham and Walham Green.

This co-habitation leads to Sunday being very active as Chelsea worship from 10 to 12am, Fulham from 2 to 4pm while Walham Green start at 5pm and bring the day to a close at 7pm. In each case the meeting has two parts, starting with a 45 minute 'Bible educational talk' followed by an hour discussing the weekly Bible study article in *The Watchtower*.

For the second meeting of the week, the Theocratic Ministry School, each congregation has its own evening. At times when the congregations need to split into smaller groups, the ante-room and library are used, making full use of the space available in what is a small building for the number of people who use it. For this reason they are on the look-out for another place of worship, but with the high price of property in the area, this may prove difficult.

Their present building on Pond Place, a quiet road that joins Fulham Road at the Kensington end, was built in the late Victorian period. The simply decorated main hall or auditorium has free-standing chairs for 150 and there is a stage with a lectern and a writing board on the back wall used in the educational talks. Thanks to the electrical ingenuity of one of the members, there is a comprehensive public address system that combines on-stage amplification and a link with the cassette player to provide the musical accompaniment.

Amongst the 80 adults and 25 children that attend the meetings of the Chelsea congregation some 30 nationalities are represented. Although there are no social activities for the congregation, each member goes out for many hours each month to meet people in their homes.

Services: Sunday 10am, 2pm, 5pm Watchtower meeting and lecture; during week 7.30pm Theocratic Ministry School □ *Facilities: amplification; also large print books, sign language, Braille, available on request* □ *Wheelchair: 2 small steps* □ *Other details: hall, ante-room, library* □ *Visiting: open only for services*

Paddington Kingdom Hall

11 Monmouth Road, Westbourne Grove, W2 □ *Bus: 7, 15, 27* □ *Tube: Bayswater* □ *Parking: difficult* □ *Presiding Overseer: Mr Fred Cattel* □ *Address: 62 Charefield Court, 2 Shirland Road, W9* □ *Telephone: 286 2741* □ *Available: at services and in the evenings* □ *Other contact: Mr John Naughton* □ *Telephone: 727 2448*

As happens with most Kingdom Halls in London, the original congregation that came to Monmouth Hall in 1977 has grown so that now, as well as the Paddington congregation, there are three others, one of which is the Spanish congregation. This has the same programme of meetings as the others except that they are in the Spanish language.

The Hall itself was built in the 1840s as a Baptist chapel, serving as such until it was vacated in 1967, and then used as an art studio. When the Witnesses bought it in 1977, the money was raised by members together with a loan from the Watchtower Society which is now paid back. Thanks to this, the Hall has undergone a renovation, transforming the basement rooms into a library, a kitchen, a second hall that seats 30 and there are now well equipped toilets.

Upstairs, the auditorium follows the simple lines of Kingdom Halls, containing only what is necessary for worship. As there is seating for only 138 people, a number which is sometimes smaller than attendance, the overflow can sit downstairs and have the meeting relayed to them via the PA, also used for the taped musical accompaniment. Of the three meetings held each week, only two, the Theocratic Ministry School and the Watchtower meeting (called the Public Bible Lecture), are held at the Hall. The third is the Private Home Bible Study which is on Sundays.

Based in an area of cosmopolitan population, the fact that around twenty nationalities are represented within the congregations is of no surprise. Add this to the variety of ages and social backgrounds, and it is possible to say that the members are mixed in every way.

Services: Monday 7–8.45pm Theocratic Ministry School; Thursday 7–8.45pm Public Bible Lecture □ *Facilities: amplification* □ *Wheelchair: several steps; help available* □ *Other details: library, small hall* □ *Visiting: open only for services*

Lutheran Churches

The impact of Martin Luther's Reformation was felt most strongly in his native Germany and in the Baltic States, but now there are Lutheran Churches based in countries all over the world whose histories are linked and who have common characteristics based on Luther's catechism. Luther taught a return to the essentials of Christianity with the central tenet of 'Justification by Faith alone'. The only authority is Scripture, and the Church is a community of believers, not a hierarchy. An important principle is worship in the vernacular tongue.

Lutheranism has been represented in Britain since the mid-1600s and the right to worship in their own tongue was fully granted to German Lutherans by the Crown in 1689. Perhaps because of this language gap, Lutheranism did not spread amongst the English (although the 18th century monarchy was Lutheran, by and large). Only in this century has there been any surge in membership numbers, due to the arrival of refugees after the War. In 1948 the Lutheran Council was founded to co-ordinate welfare, and to provide venues for worship for the various national groups. Currently, its membership includes Estonian, Finnish, German, Hungarian, Lithuanian, Polish and Swedish Churches, as well as the United Lutheran Synod representing English-speaking congregations.

The future of some East European congregations is becoming precarious as the refugee generation grows older, and fewer people still speak the national tongue. By contrast, other European churches whose numbers in this country have increased due to trade links and EEC contacts have prospered. In this category are the Norwegian and Icelandic congregations who are not formal members of the Council. Indications of the worldwide spread of Lutheranism are provided by the formation of a Chinese congregation, and Lutheran worship being conducted in Swahili at Collingham Gardens.

For further information, contact the Lutheran Council of Great Britain, 8 Collingham Gardens, SW5 (373 1141/5566)

Christuskirche

19 Montpelier Place, SW7 □ Telephone: 589 5305 □ Bus: 9, 14, 19, 22, 30, 52, 52a, 73, 74, 137 □ Tube: Knightsbridge □ Parking: very difficult, except Sundays □ Pastor: Rev Dr Albrecht Weber □ Address: 78 Station Road, SW13 □ Telephone: 876 6366 □ Available: telephone for appointment □ Other staff: ARN Ratcliff (Hon Treasurer) 6 Portland Terrace, The Green, Richmond, Surrey

There have been German Lutheran congregations in London for hundreds of years. Originally, the German population was based in the East End, but in later years a community became centred here in the Knightsbridge area. A Lutheran chapel existed in St James' Palace, but this was closed down by Edward VII. There was a need for a place of worship for this growing community, and Christuskirche (Christchurch) was built.

A small building in a Gothic style, Christuskirche stands in Montpelier Place, one of the network of streets behind Harrods. In appearance, it is similar to a late Victorian Anglican church, with its high gabled roof, stone-vaulted sanctuary and stained glass. A large wooden pulpit stands to the left of the sanctuary. Beneath the church is a hall where activities are held and coffee is served after services.

There is one regular German language service each week. The congregation, whilst consisting mainly of German people and people of Swiss, Austrian and East European backgrounds, also contains some British people with an interest in, or connections with German language and culture. Since the German community in the area has largely dispersed to suburban areas, most travel from outside the district to attend. Two other Lutheran congregations—of the Polish and Latvian churches—meet at Christuskirche, holding monthly services.

Services: Sunday 11am (Holy Communion twice monthly, all services normally in German) □ Children: Sunday school twice monthly (5–13 year olds) □ Wheelchair: several steps, help required □ Other details: hall below church □ Visiting: open at service times only

Finnish Seamen's Mission

33 Albion Street, SE16 □ Telephone: 237 4661 □ Bus: 47, 70, 188 □ Tube: Rotherhithe □ Parking: not difficult □ Pastor: Rev Jarmo Kökkö □ Address: at church □ Telephone: 237 1261 □ Available: most days; phone for appointment □ Other clergy: Rev Leo Norja (0375-372 835)

Despite its title, the Finnish Seamen's Mission is not solely for seamen, nor is it simply a place for worship, but it is certainly for Finns. The Mission is both church and social centre for the 2,500 or so Finns who live in London, as well as tourists, au pairs, students and, of course, sailors from the 260 Finnish ships that dock in London every year.

A wide range of groups and acitivities are based here, organised by the six full-time staff with voluntary help from members of the congregation. There are regular events such as film shows and concerts, a canteen and shop selling Finnish goods and books, and even a traditional Finnish sauna. One of its most valuable functions is as an 'open house'—Finns can call anytime to drink coffee, socialise and chat in Finnish. All this explains the impressive number of visitors—an estimated 25,000.

The Mission, founded over a century ago, has had to widen its horizons considerably. Although seamen still make up some 20% of the congregation, the present church, a multi-purpose building completed in 1958, was designed to meet the needs of a growing community. Many Finns have married British people and settled here; unlike many Lutheran congregations, this one has a good many young families among the 70 or so regular worshippers. There is even a monthly family service conducted in both English and Finnish.

The church, and especially the separate tower, is in a very angular style. The interior is remarkable for the ivy that is growing down the hall behind the altar adding welcome colour and warmth to the grey stone and rather utilitarian fittings.

Services: 1st Sunday 11am Family service & Holy Communion (in Finnish and English); Other Sundays 6pm Service & Holy Communion; (Last Sunday of month 4pm Au Pair and Students Meeting); Tues, Wed, Thurs 9.45pm Evening Prayer; (All services in Finnish unless stated) □ Facilities: amplification □ Children: Sunday school with Family service; Saturday school for Finnish language and culture □ Wheelchair: level access to church, no access to canteen □ Other details: large hall, canteen, shop, sauna □ Visiting: open weekdays 2pm–10pm, weekends 2pm–8pm; tours by arrangement

Lutheran Church House

8 Collingham Gardens, SW5 □ Telephone: 373 1141 (Lutheran Council) □ Bus: 30, 49, 74, 264 □ Tube: Gloucester Road □ Parking: difficult □ Pastor: Rev Ron Englund, (Special Ministries) □ Telephone: 373 5566 □ Available: everyday □ Other clergy: Pastor Patkai (Hungarian congregation) 373 0747, Pastor Baldvinsson (Icelandic) 730 5131

Lutheran Church House, a rambling Victorian family house and a listed building, is owned by the Lutheran Council. It contains four flats, and various offices concerned with the management of Church affairs. The organisation, after the manner of the building, tends towards a certain labyrinthine quality, as there are so many language groups and nationalities involved.

Past dark panelled walls and up a flight of stairs is the room used for worship, with its altar table and small reed organ. The Hungarians meet at 4pm on three Sundays in the month, and the Icelandic congregation has an 'open house', with hymn singing, every Sunday night. On the first Sunday of the month there is a service in Swahili, which is unusual in that it attracts Christians of various denominations who appreciate the opportunity to worship in their own tongue (Swahili is the *lingua franca* of East Africa).

On Friday evenings an informal discussion and social group called the Collingham Group meets here. It is composed mostly of young people from all kinds of backgrounds, and while the emphasis is Christian, Muslims and Hindus attend occasionally. There is usually a film show and/or music, and someone on hand to answer any questions that may arise. There is no formal membership and newcomers can be sure of a warm welcome.

Services: 1st Sunday 11am Swahili service; 3 Sundays each month 4pm Hungarian service; Sunday evening Icelandic 'open house' □ Wheelchair: no access □ Other details: hall can be hired □ Visiting: all welcome to call during day

Marienkirche (St Mary's)

10 Sandwich Street, WC1 □ Telephone: 388 9586 □ Bus: 14, 17, 18, 30, 45, 63, 77, 77a □ Tube/BR: Euston, Kings Cross, Russell Square □ Parking: difficult except Sunday □ Pastor: Rev Boneberger □ Address: 22 Downside Crescent, NW3 □ Telephone: 794 4207 □ Available: most days □ Other staff: Mr Edding, Warden of Student Centre

Founded in 1692, St Mary's is the oldest German-speaking congregation in Britain, though members now meet to worship in the most recent Lutheran church in London, built in 1978 as part of the International Lutheran Student Centre. The congregation was originally formed amongst craftsmen brought over to help rebuild the City after the Great Fire, and the name is taken from St Mary's Chapel in the Savoy Palace, where they first held regular services.

The building of the new church and Centre with accommodation for 80 students was a joint venture undertaken by the Lutheran Council of Great Britain and Marienkirche who owned the site and who had been worshipping in a small chapel there since 1949. Overseas funding was obtained, and a successful design submitted by the architects, Maguire and Murray. The present Marienkirche, the fourth in the congregation's history, is in the basement of the Centre. Pastor Boneberger relates how some members were a little nonplussed by the change which brought them into contact with young people from all over the world, but it is now agreed that the relationship is beneficial for both parties.

The building as a whole has won acclaim for the way it respects the character of the surrounding buildings and makes the most of the limited space. The church itself, despite being below street-level, is well lit by three lunette windows which are echoed by the large semi-circular window surrounding the door. The interior is sparsely furnished and dignified despite the curious multi-coloured organ. Above the communion table is a stark yet serene statue of the Crucified Christ by Elisabeth Frink, specially commissioned by the congregation.

Services are in German and around twenty mostly elderly people attend. It is thought that more German-speaking visitors would come if only they knew of the church's existence. They would discover a traditional service with full liturgy, as befits the former church of German-speaking members of the Royal Family, back in the days of George I and II.

Services: Alternate Sundays 11am or 4pm (Services normally held in German) □ Wheelchair: several steps down; lift available by arrangement with Warden □ Other details: shared facilities with Centre □ Visiting: open only for services; otherwise by arrangement with Warden

Norwegian Seamen's Church (St Olav's)

1 Albion Street, SE16 □ Telephone: 237 5587 □ Bus:47, 70, 188 □ Tube: Rotherhithe □ Parking: on street, not difficult □ Pastor: Rev Helge Petterson □ Address: c/o church □ Available: by phone, most times

Like other seamen's missions, the Norwegian church was set up for the spiritual welfare of sailors who might otherwise fall prey to the many temptations of the

East End, but it now stands as both church and social centre for the expatriate community as a whole. Norwegians come from all over London to attend. Though the docks are now some distance away, the church has not lost sight of its original aims and runs a minibus service for the seamen.

Designed by a Norwegian architect, Seaton Dahl, the church is in an 'English Renaissance' style, with a tower modelled on the spire of Oslo Cathedral. Topped with a Viking ship weather-vane, the tower is one of the landmarks of Rotherhithe. The appropriately martime motif is continued inside the church, for hanging from the ceiling among the wooden chadeliers is a model of the *St Olav*, a Norwegian ship. The church interior is panelled in English oak. The church was designed with all its various purposes in mind: the hall can used as an extension of the church, there are separate rooms for social activities, and there is a shop.

The foundation stone of the present church, which replaced the original church of 1872, was laid by Crown Prince Olav, who is the present King of Norway. Nothing was known then of the role the church would play during the Second World War, when the government in exile was based in London. The church became an effective cathedral, and an important focus of Norwegian resistance.

The services, which feature much hymn singing and occasionally a gospel choir, attract around 60 worshippers including a good proportion of young people and even some seamen.

Services: Sunday 11am Service & Holy Communion; Gospel evening once a month (All services normally in Norwegian) □ Facilities: amplification □ Children: Sunday school at service times; Norwegian language classes □ Wheelchair: 3 steps □ Other details: hall, shop, etc □ Visiting: open weekdays 3pm–10pm and all day at weekends; tours by arrangement

St Anne and St Agnes

Gresham Street, EC2 □ Bus: any to St Paul's □ Tube: St Paul's □ Parking: on street □ Pastor: V Rev Robert Patkai □ Office: Lutheran Church House, 8 Collingham Gardens, SW5 □ Telephone: 373 0747 □ Available: by phone, office hours □ Other clergy: Rev Ron Englund (St Anne's Music Soc) 373 5566

This small, red brick, Wren-designed church is unique amongst City churches in that it is used for Lutheran worship (in three different languages), and also remarkable for the range and variety of music that can be heard here.

The Latvian and Estonian Lutherans have used the church since 1966, and they invited the English-speaking St John's congregation to worship here also. This latter group was formed as some Lutherans, mostly of German descent, preferred to speak, and hence worship, in English. St John's is now 250 strong and the average Sunday attendance is 75. The services are usually led by Dean Robert Patkai. The Estonians and Latvians, dwindling congregations whose members have an average age of 70, worship on Sunday afternoons.

The music at St Anne and St Agnes began with Bach Vespers. These are full services which feature a Bach cantata in exactly the setting the composer intended—a Lutheran act of worship. Organised by Pastor Ronald Englund, the

St Anne and St Agnes, EC2

range of the musical services has widened to include Telemann cantatas, choral Vespers led by St Anne's choir, a Gospel service and even Jazz Vespers.

In addition to this sacred music, the church is also used as a venue for various recitals and concerts, including world premieres of new works and performances of little known pieces by such composers as Handel, himself a Lutheran. Musical groups from all over the world, including Yugoslavia, Chile, Finland and the USA, have performed here. The concerts are an important means of raising funds for the church and financing the necessary restoration work. The three small congregations pledged £14,000 between them for this work, and this speaks eloquently for their faith and commitment, for they do not own St Anne and St Agnes; it is merely held on lease from the Dean of St Paul's.

The attractive church is well worth saving. It is one of only three that Wren designed to a 'cross-in-a-square' pattern, and despite extensive damage and rebuilding, the original form has been retained. Unusually for a City church, it is not overwhelmed by adjacent buildings, but is set back from the road in its own graveyard and gardens. The stone bell tower is the oldest part of the church and benefits greatly from the setting. The interior is well lit, and, in accordance with Lutheran tradition, plainly but handsomely furnished with dark oak panels and matching pews. Over the doorway is a small figure of Father Time—an apt signature perhaps for this church with its emphasis on the excellent musical heritage of Lutheranism.

Services: Sunday 11am (English speaking congregation), Sunday pm (Latvian and Estonian congregations). Many special musical services—ring Pastor Englund for details □ Children: Sunday school 9.45–10.45am (5 years +) □ Wheelchair: 1 small step, help available □ Other details: hall available for hire □ Visiting: open only for services and concerts; bookstall

St Georgs-Kirche (St George's)

55 Alie Street, E1 □ Telephone: 709 9663 (Hostel) □ Bus: 10, 25 □ Tube: Aldgate, Aldgate East, Whitechapel □ Parking: difficult □ Pastor: Rev Boneberger □ Address: 22 Downside Crescent, NW3 □ Telephone: 794 4207 □ Available: most days □ Other staff: Warden

St George's is a monument to the once flourishing German community in Whitechapel. One can imagine how it must have looked, and how comforting the sight of it must have been, to the German labourers who trudged past every day. Though run down and in need of repair, St George's is still a handsome Georgian building.

Built in 1763, St George's is the oldest surviving German church in Britain; over the pulpit is a Royal Arms in memory of King George II, who had died only three years previously. Both the pulpit and the pews are in old dark wood, but the interior is far from gloomy, being well lit by two stained glass and several plain glass windows.

The entrance is via a courtyard that was formerly the graveyard, and the church is flanked by buildings that were once part of a popular school, run by the pastors, where local children were taught in both English and German. The school was closed, and the church's standing irrevocably altered by the sinking of the

St Georgs-Kirche, E1

Lusitania in 1915 and the consequent outbursts of mob violence against all things German. One of the school buildings is now used as a hostel for visiting groups of students and schoolchildren from Germany, but the church has never regained its former importance.

None of the congregation now lives locally, and attendance at services, held only on the second and fourth Sundays in the month, averages 17. However, the church may gain a new lease of life if the Chinese Lutheran community decides to worship here on the alternating Sundays, as has been suggested. The church has few visitors, but probably deserves more, being a significant part of the fascinating history of the East End. After all, St George's is only a few minutes walk from the Tower of London and other sights.

Services: Alternate Sundays 11am Preaching service (Holy Communion once a month, all services normally in German) □ Wheelchair: several steps, help required □ Visiting: by arrangement with Warden, or ring 2nd floor bell

Swedish Church

6 Harcourt Street, W1 □ Telephone: 723 8209 □ Bus: 1, 6, 7, 8, 15, 15a, 16, 16a, 30, 36, 36b, 176 □ Tube/BR: Edgware Road, Marylebone □ Parking: difficult except Sunday □ Rector: Rev Lennard Sjoström □ Telephone: 723 5681 □ Available: 11am–1pm daily except Monday □ Other clergy: Rev Mats Hagelin

Unlike many other early Swedish churches founded outside the mother country, the London congregation has retained its distinctively Swedish character throughout its long history. The congregation was founded in 1710 and included craftsmen, merchants, seamen and travellers. The first church was built in 1728 in Wapping, an area with a growing Swedish community, but by the end of the last century, it was clear that the church's position was no longer appropriate. Two new churches were planned, one in Rotherhithe for the seamen (see below) and the present Harcourt Street church, serving the West End where many Swedes were then settling.

Built in 1911, this attractive, high-roofed building has a small steeple visible some distance away. The interior, with its stained glass, barrel-vaulted ceiling, elaborate chandeliers and wooden bench pews, is indistinguishable from many Anglican churches. This is perhaps surprising, given the strong Swedish identity of the church, but then, while the exterior was designed by Axel Herman Hegg, the interior was the work of a Mr Wrigglesworth. The reredos, which features a copy of Leonardo's *Last Supper*, and the altar were both brought from the earlier church in Wapping.

Over a hundred Swedes, including many children, attend the Sunday service here. Most are permanent residents, but there are always some students, tourists and embassy officials among the congregation. Although few Swedes now live locally, the church has an important social and cultural role, and over a thousand people maintain contact with it. On Wednesdays and Thursdays services are followed by social events, while after the monthly children's service there is usually a party. Occasional concerts are also held at the church. There are few organised clubs, but the building is open every day for Swedes to meet friends and use the facilities.

There is also the Swedish Seamen's Church at 120 Lower Road, SE16. Unlike the nearby Finnish and Norwegian Seamen's Missions which have developed into churches used by their respective communities as a whole, this is still used mostly by Swedish seamen. The Pastor is Rev Anders Fehn (237 1644/1956).

Services: Sunday 11am Eucharist; Wednesday 8pm; Thursday 12 noon; alternate Saturdays 10.30am Morning Prayer (All services normally in Swedish) □ *Facilities: amplification, deaf loop* □ *Children: Sunday school 11am; monthly service 3pm Saturday* □ *Wheelchair: no access* □ *Other details: large hall, sports facilities, library, etc.* □ *Visiting: open daily 10am-9pm except Saturday 10am-6pm*

The Methodist Church

The Methodist Church has its origins in the eighteenth century. It grew out of an Evangelical Revival led by, among others, John Wesley (1703–1791). With his brother Charles (1707–1788), Wesley formed the 'Holy Club' whilst at Oxford University, in order to reinforce and systematise the religious faith and practices of its members. After his ordination into the Church of England, Wesley took to open-air preaching, proclaiming that 'the world is my parish'. He drew large crowds, and ultimately began to recruit lay preachers, and started to open his own chapels, beginning with the Foundry Chapel in London.

At first, these buildings were unregistered, since Wesley did not like the idea of his followers being seen as dissenters, but he gave in and, in 1787, he agreed to the licensing of Methodist chapels as dissenting meeting houses. The split between Methodism and the Church of England became more pronounced after Wesley's death when, in 1795, the Plan of Pacification permitted Methodist preachers to administer the Sacraments and to hold marriage and funeral services in Methodist chapels.

The early history of the denomination brought various secessions, beginning with the New Connexion in 1797 followed by others at intervals; in the early twentieth century, however, most of these groups reunited and the World Methodist Council was formed, which nowadays consists of 62 groups spread over 90 countries.

The Methodist Church regards itself as part of the Church Universal, and believes in the priesthood of all believers; thus, ministers are not 'ordained' as such. Among the tenets of Methodist belief is the recognition of two Sacraments of Divine Appointment—the celebration of the Lord's Supper, and Baptism. It stresses the importance of a personal relationship between Man and God, and emphasises the workings of the Holy Spirit. It is also imbued with a sense of social responsibility, and exhibits this through practical charity—hence the large number of Methodist Missions concerned with helping the poor, the vulnerable and the underprivileged. As a Church, Methodism is ecumenical, and anyone who accepts Jesus Christ as saviour, regardless of denomination, is welcome to receive Communion in a Methodist Church.

The origin of the term 'Methodism' is in dispute, although Wesley did define a Methodist as being 'one who lives according to the method laid down in the Bible'.

Today, Methodism flourishes all over the world, particularly in the United States where there are some 14 million members. UK membership is in the region of a quarter of a million. London plays an important part in the history of the denomination, for it is here that Wesley lived and set up Wesley's Chapel (qv) which still stands as the Mother Church of world Methodism, attracting many pilgrims annually. Visitors should note that neither alcohol nor smoking are allowed on Methodist premises.

The Methodist Church, whilst having its own service book, has no compulsory liturgy and individual ministers can adapt the rite according to their needs. Hymn singing is a central part of services, as is the preaching of the Word. In the following entries the names of the ministers have not been given, simply because the Methodist circuit system, whereby ministers regularly move on to new churches and missions, would soon invalidate such information.

For further information, contact the Methodist Information Department, 1 Central Buildings, Matthew Parker Street, SW1 (Tel: 222 8010)

Camden Town Methodist Church

Plender Street, NW1 □ Bus: 3, 24, 27, 29, 31, 53, 74, 134, 137, 214, 253 □ Tube: Camden Town, Mornington Crescent □ Parking: difficult; some meters □ Contact: Superintendent Minister □ Telephone: 607 2155 □ Available: by telephone anytime □ Other staff: Mrs Doreen Smith (secretary)

Camden Town Methodist Church is an attractive Victorian edifice—with a listed frontage—built in 1889 by the Primitive Methodists to replace an earlier chapel in the area. The original name, 'New Camden Chapel', can still be seen inscribed on the portico. The building is on Plender Street, just off Camden High Street. Its services to the community have been both evangelical and secular—for instance, the chapel provided the catering for the deep shelters in the Underground stations during the World War II.

The chapel is on the first floor of the building and is rather attractive, with its beamed roof, gallery and stained glass windows. The ground floor is let as a private residential community, providing long-term accommodation for eleven or twelve young people living, working or studying in London.

In recent years the area has become very cosmopolitan, and this has been reflected in the growing congregation, which has a very wide mixture of ethnic groups, including West Indian, African and Chinese. There is also a total spread of ages—from two to eighty-four—and many families. The congregation is active, with many social activities and religious/fellowship groups. New members can be assured of a warm reception.

Services: Sunday 11am; occasional evening services as announced □ Children: Sunday school 11am (2–13 age group) □ Wheelchair: 2 flights of stairs □ Visiting: open for services and meetings only; bookstall

Chelsea Methodist Church and Pastoral Centre

155a Kings Road, SW3 □ Telephone: 352 9305 □ Bus: 11, 19, 22 □ Tube: Sloane Square □ Parking: NCP Kings Road □ Contact: Superintendent Minister □ Available: by appointment

The large foyer of Chelsea Methodist Church offers a quiet retreat from the busy King's Road. Known as the Welcome In, this foyer has easy chairs, coffee tables and a hotel-style reception desk, and is open to all.

The church building is modern, having opened in 1984 to designs by Bernard Lamb. (It is the second church on the site, the original 1903 building being demolished after war damage. Of this, only the hall remains.) The church interior has blue walls and a wooden ceiling, and is modelled on the catacombs of Rome—'the Church Underground'. On the walls by the entrance are the names of the twelve disciples written in a graffiti style, with 'Christ is Risen' added in even larger lettering. On the opposite wall is the reredos, designed with the theme of doves and flowers—to signify the Resurrection—a theme continued in the design of the kneelers. The specially designed chairs are arranged on three sides around the small area so that everyone can see one another. Eighty to ninety people fill the church on Sunday. In addition to the main church is a small chapel, used for quiet prayer and meditation.

The church has two small meeting rooms, used by many groups, including Narcotics Anonymous, a nannies (and charges) group, and a girls club: the girls learn art, cookery and games of all kinds, and are given a basic grounding in Biblical knowledge which includes taking examination papers under Methodist auspices.

The other work of the church splits into four. A Servite community administers 21 sheltered flats, for the elderly, attached to the building. The Chelsea Pastoral Foundation counsels on an individual basis and also runs counselling courses. There is also AVEC, a service agency for church and community work, a non-denominational charity which, through running courses and seminars, tries to focus attention on how the church can best serve the community. Finally, of course, there is the Welcome In; the volunteers who run this service supply tea, coffee, soup and sandwiches to anyone who needs them, and also provide a 'listening ear'. There is no evangelistic motivation evident.

'This church', proclaims lettering outside, 'welcomes people no matter where they come from, who they are or what they believe'.

Services: Sunday 11am (Holy Communion every 1st Sunday), 6pm (Holy Communion every 3rd Sunday) □ Children: Sunday school □ Wheelchair: ramp □ Other details: Welcome In reception foyer, meeting rooms, etc □ Visiting: open 9am–9pm weekdays; closed Saturday; open Sunday for services only

Kings Cross Methodist Mission

Crestfield Street, WC1 □ Bus: 14, 17, 18, 29, 30, 45, 46, 63, 73, 77a, 221, 254, 355, C11 □ Tube/BR: Kings Cross, St Pancras □ Parking: difficult; meters □ Contact: Minister □ Telephone: 833 1432 □ Available: by appointment

Kings Cross Methodist Mission, along with Archway, Camden Town, Kentish Town, Caledonian Road, and Islington, comprises the London Mission North and Central Circuit of the Methodist Church.

Methodists began meeting in the Kings Cross area between 1801 and 1807, and opened the church on the present site in 1825. At that time, it was on the edge of the countryside. The church building itself has, like London, changed considerably. Alterations were made in 1866 (to accommodate an organ), in the twenties and thirties (when the building was extended) and also in the fifties, when the church gallery was closed and additional floors created above it.

The church itself seats sixty people. Simple in design, it has many friendly touches, such as flowerpots on the windowsills and pinboards at the back covered in colourful posters and notices. The large hall behind the church has a full proscenium stage. Cubs and scouts meet here on Wednesday. Other rooms include a small and cosy parlour, with its own Communion table and pulpit; here, the Slavic Fellowship holds a regular monthly meeting. The parlour is used on Wednesdays for the church's Fellowship meeting, with hymns, prayer and Bible study.

The congregation has had a varied recent history. In 1950–51, it was joined by the members of the St John's, Clerkenwell congregation, and later, in April 1973, by the German Methodist congregation from Drayton Park. The congregation is small, but all visitors and members of the community are welcome.

Services: Sunday 11am, 5pm; Wednesday 8pm Fellowship meeting □ Wheelchair: easy access, 1 step □ Other details: hall (available for hire) □ Visiting: open 30 mins prior to services

Lambeth Methodist Mission

1–5 Lambeth Road, SE1 □ Telephone: 735 2166 □ Bus: 3, 10, 44, 59, 109, 159 □ Tube: Lambeth North □ Parking: small car park □ Contact: Superintendent Minister □ Available: most times

There has been a Methodist Mission in Lambeth since the early 1800s, although the present premises were built in 1963. Since the area has, for many years, been one of London's poorer districts, the Mission's community work has been involved primarily with poor and homeless people. Today, the work is centred around the single homeless, who can get food, clothes and friendly advice at the Mission's two Drop In Centres, one at the Lambeth Mission itself and one at Vauxhall Methodist Church (qv).

Although these Centres are the only major community activities run by the church itself, the Lambeth premises are used by many outside groups for the benefit of the community. These include an after school playgroup, a local Community Action Centre and three Alcoholic Anonymous groups. Theatre groups, and an orchestra, use the church hall for rehearsals. The church itself also runs cub, scout and brownie packs.

The Mission church is ideal for its various activities having a large hall, several smaller halls and offices incorporated into the building. These facilities are shared with St Mary's, an Anglican church. Both the Mission and St Mary's were bombed during the war, and the two congregations pooled their money to build the present Mission, which was completed in 1963. On Sundays, there are separate services, the Anglican service at 9.30am and the Methodist Family Service at 11am as well as a joint evening service.

The format of the services can be varied, with a music group often taking a leading role. Lay preachers are encouraged to lead worship. The congregation is a mixture of Afro-Caribbean and white people, with no single age group predominating. The Sunday school caters for all ages, having both junior and senior classes.

Services: Sundays 9.30am (Anglican Communion, St Mary's congregation) 11am Family Service, 6.30pm Joint service, Anglican & Methodist (plus monthly joint service at 10.15am) □ Facilities: amplification □ Children: Sunday school 11am □ Wheelchair: ramp □ Other details: Drop In Centre, hall, meeting room □ Visiting: open for services and activities only

Notting Hill Methodist Church and Ecumenical Centre St Andrew

240 Lancaster Road, W11 □ Telephone: 229 7728 (office) □ Bus: 7, 15, 15a, 52, 52a, 295 □ Tube: Ladbroke Grove □ Parking: on street □ Contact: Minister □ Available: most times

Ecumenical Centre

7 Denbigh Road, W11 □ Bus: 7, 12, 15, 15a, 27, 28, 31, 52, 52a, 88 □ Tube: Notting Hill Gate □ Parking: on street

The Methodist church holds services on two sites in Notting Hill. The main centre of worship for the Methodist community is St Andrew's, a Victorian church on the edge of a recent housing development near Ladbroke Grove; also important, however, is the Notting Hill Ecumenical Centre, a church/community building where some services and many activities are held.

Built in 1880 on Lancaster Road as a typical galleried Methodist church, St Andrew's remains largely unchanged, except for the worship area, now structured completely in the round, so that the congregation are gathered around the table and lectern, symbols of the Sacrament and the Word. Also, two sides of the gallery have been partitioned off and converted into offices. The church interior has been painted in a salmon pink colour and there is an unusual rough-hewn wooden cross at the rear, the pieces for which came from a local house being renovated by the Notting Hill Housing Trust; the church's links with housing and housing renewal are important.

The main Sunday service is at 11am, the format combining traditional Methodist worship with modern material, and relates to the daily life of the members as much as possible. People meet after services for coffee. About 150 people attend regularly. The congregation is a mixture of different ages, races and social groups, everyone from unemployed people to a Member of Parliament! Almost half are of Afro-Caribbean descent, and people of many races are made to feel welcome and are enabled to contribute to the life of the church. Lay participation is extensive; there are about 25 'worship leaders' and half-a-dozen local preachers.

The church's downstairs hall is divided into three. One part is used exclusively by the church youth group, another part by a day nursery, and the third, largest section is used for church functions and also (on weekdays) as the nursery's play area.

On Denbigh Road, about a mile away from the Lancaster Road church, is the Notting Hill Ecumenical Centre, a place of worship owned and run by the Methodist church. Services are held here on Sundays at 10am. Two other churches, the Bible Way Church and the Spiritual Baptists, also worship at the Centre.

The main purpose of the Centre is to provide a service for the local population. During the week it is the home of the Denbigh Centre, a psychiatric day centre sponsored by the Borough (open 9am to 5pm Monday to Friday) and a Save the Children Fund playgroup based in a small hall at the rear of the church (open between 9.30am and 12noon). A covered space under the church is used as a play area. Also in the building, apart from the main hall, are various offices, including those of the National Committee on Racism in Children's Books, a charitable organisation which publishes its own monthly magazine.

There are various evening activities, including a youth group for gay and lesbian young people, CND, and GROW (a group for people who wish to seek personal growth within an accepting group). The hall is also available for hire for jumble sales, etc, on Saturdays. There are occasional band practices and public meetings of all kinds, including pre-election forums.

Services: St Andrew's: Sunday 11am Morning Worship (Holy Communion 1st Sun & Festivals), 6.30pm United Worship (at St Peter's C of E, qv). Ecumenical Centre: Sunday 10am Holy Communion (plus services of other groups) □ Facilities: St Andrew's has amplification & deaf loop; Braille hymnbook □ Children: 'Christian Education' plus creche, 11am Sunday (St Andrew's) □ Wheelchair: both have many steps, help required □ Other details: halls, etc □ Visiting: St Andrew's generally open 10am–12noon weekdays; Centre open weekdays

St George's Methodist Church

Cable Street, E1 □ Bus: 22a, 56 □ Tube/BR: Shadwell, Stepney East □ Parking: on street □ Contact: Minister □ Address: 240b Cable Street, E1 □ Telephone: 790 0535 □ Available: by appointment

In its more formal days the church was known as St George's Methodist Centenary Chapel, since the year of its initiation (1838) was a hundred years after the conversion of John Wesley. The Chudleigh Memorial Hall was added in the 1930s and now houses the Day Centre, at present the hub of the church's work. The present church is smaller than the original and was completely renovated in the 1960s.

The single Sunday service is very informal and participatory; sermons are more like a discussion, and the prayers are built around much sharing of people's needs. Mutual support is the key; and it is unusual to find this emphasis built into church services, as distinct from the activities, to such an extent.

The Day Centre at the church forms part of the work of the Methodist East End Mission. Five students from the Social Studies course (also run by the Mission) work 20 hours a week at the Centre. For some years the project has provided support, shelter, food and medical care to men and women, many of whom are unemployed and homeless, and suffer ill-health as a result. They are generally not members of the congregation, often coming from further afield. St

George's also caters for other needs, accommodating several community groups. These include Alcoholics Anonymous and youth club on Fridays between 5pm and 8pm. On Thursdays, there is a well-attended coffee morning. People who find the East End—or life itself—tough going, will find at St George's a source of hope and encouragement that has helped many carry on.

Services: Sunday 11am □ Wheelchair: ramp available □ Other details: hall (available for hire); Day Centre □ Visiting: open only at service times

South London Methodist Mission

Bermondsey Central Hall, Bermondsey Street, SE1 □ Telephone: 407 2014 □ Bus: 47, 78, 188 □ Tube/BR: London Bridge □ Parking: on street □ Contact: Superintendent Minister □ Available: office hours & Sunday □ Other staff: Sr Jane Clark (Deaconess), Rita Queen (secretary)

Bermondsey Central Hall, the home of the South London Methodist Mission, has served the area for nearly a hundred years. The inspiration behind the Mission, and the Hall, came in the last century, when Henry Meakin (later Reverend) was given pastoral charge of the Locksfield Mission, near Elephant and Castle. At that time it was poorly attended and had earned the title of 'the white elephant of London Methodism'. Meakin's work was successful: the chapel became vastly overcrowded, and other premises had to be borrowed. He then conceived the idea of a Central Hall for South London. At the time of its opening in 1900, it boasted tip-up seating for 2,200 and 'a rostrum and orchestral arrangements of the most modern character'. In common with many other Methodist Missions, the work combined 'aggressive evangelism' with social relief and cultural activities, ranging from a soup kitchen and a mother and baby clinic to concerts and film shows.

After the Second World War the vision remained much the same, but the social picture altered dramatically, as the docks closed and Bermondsey lost many of its industries. This resulted in a vastly smaller congregation as the local population diminished; it became clear that change was on the way. It came in the 1960s. The hall was demolished, although the old Victorian frontage was retained, giving some idea of its original grandeur. Residential accommodation has been built adjoining the Hall, providing bedsitters for elderly ladies and students, and flats for Mission staff. Also attached is the Bermondsey and Landsdowne Medical Mission, a general practitioners surgery.

The present 100-seat chapel is adapted from the surviving entrance hall of the original building. The Sunday morning service has a congregation of around 50, with 20 attending the evening service; both congregations are made up of local people. Activities include a popular weekly coffee morning, a daily lunch club, a meeting for women and an advice centre. So, despite the fact that the premises are vastly scaled down from Meakin's original Hall, the work of the South London Mission continues with vigour, helping to alleviate such problems as poverty, hardship and unemployment.

Services: Sunday 10.30am Prayer meeting, 11am & 6.30pm (Holy Communion as advertised); Wednesday 9am Prayer & Praise, 7.30pm Fellowship meeting □ Facilities: amplification □ Children: Sunday school 11am □ Wheelchair: access to ground floor □ Other details: offices for Mission and MENCAP □ Visiting: open for services and at other times; if locked, apply office

Stepney Methodist Church and East End Mission

Commercial Road, E1 □ Telephone: 790 3366 □ Bus: 5, 15, 40 □ Tube/BR: Aldgate East □ Parking: on street □ Contact: Superintendent Minister □ Available: by appointment □ Other staff: Gail Elkington (Assistant Lay Preacher)

Stepney Methodist Church has all the physical attributes of a Town Hall rather than a place of worship—the actual church is but one of a large complex of rooms that make up the headquarters of the East End Mission. The church is both a local place of worship and the centre of the Mission's work in the community. That work is symbolised by a sculpture in the sanctuary depicting Christ's hands washing the feet of a discipline, which is in turn superimposed upon a cross.

The East End Mission was founded in the 1880s and its first home was St George's Cable Street (qv), now a sister church in the same circuit. It was a Mission of social action, a clear departure from the previous Wesleyan Circuit system. The premises became too small and in 1907 a new, purpose-built centre was opened in the Commercial Road. This enormous complex became headquarters of a whole network of Mission Centres which fed, clothed, challenged and taught the poor in huge numbers.

The coming of the Welfare State removed much of the worst poverty, but some of the same problems remain in every generation. Now the Mission runs the Bethany Hostel for Homeless Mothers and Babies, a charity shop open every weekday, and a Social Studies Centre, where, each year, twelve students study Religous Education and Sociology to 'A' level and also spend twenty hours a week on placement in the Mission's various enterprises. Apart from the Commercial Road initiatives, the Mission runs projects at other venues too. Memory House is a home for the elderly in Leigh-on-Sea, and for the community's young people, the Mission provides the Lambourne Campsite and Holiday Centre and an International Student Hostel.

The small congregation of the church itself comprises people of all ages, races and backgrounds. The assistant pastor is involved in race relations work and this is an important part of the church's work. Worship is along traditional Methodist lines, and Holy Communion is celebrated here every Sunday.

Services: Sunday 10.30am Holy Communion, 6.30pm Evening Service □ Children: Sunday school □ Wheelchair: ramp □ Other details: hall, lounge, etc □ Visiting: open for services and activities only

Vauxhall Methodist Church

Worgan Street, SE11 □ Telephone: 582 1313 □ Bus: 44, 77, 170 □ Tube/BR: Vauxhall □ Parking: on street □ Lay assistant: Simon Radcliffe □ Telephone: 735 3573 □ Available: most times

The small Methodist church in Vauxhall is run by a lay worker, Simon Radcliffe. There are close links with the Lambeth Mission, with the two liaising with their community activities and often taking services at each other's churches.

Recently, the church was refurbished; the hall is now carpeted and has free-standing chairs, enabling it to be also used as a conference centre. This hall seats

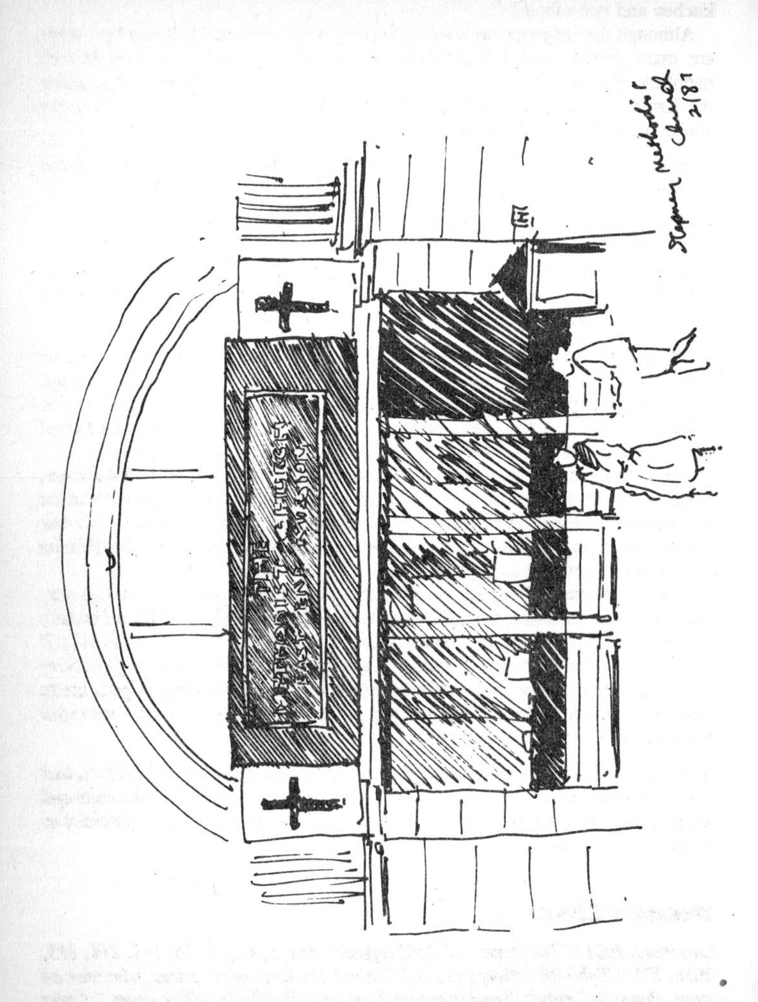

Stepney Methodist Church and East End Mission, E1

50 people; also incorporated into the church is a smaller hall (seating 30), a kitchen and two offices.

Although the congregation is small, varying between 6 and 20 in number, there are many groups and activities involving outside people as well as church members. The main activity is the Drop In Centre for homeless people (see under the Lambeth Mission). There is an Over-60's Club which meets on a Tuesday afternoon, and on Wednesday evenings there is a 'Kids Club'.

Services: Sunday 11am □ Wheelchair: level access □ Visiting: open for services and activities only

Victoria Methodist Church

Westmoreland Terrace, SW1 □ Telephone: 834 5896 □ Bus: any to Victoria □ Tube/BR: Victoria, Pimlico □ Parking: on street □ Contact: Minister □ Available: by appointment □ Other staff: David Ray (Church community worker)

'Very little glamour, nothing spectacular, no headline-grabbing story, but in God's Mercy, doggedly standing for Christ in the midst of the city'. This apt description, taken from a 1986 report, indicates the role played by Victoria Methodist Church in the local community. On Sunday, the church is a place of worship whilst on other days the facilities are used as a community centre.

The church interior is virtually square and functional in design. On Sundays, portable screens are put up around the worship area to create a more intimate atmosphere. These, and the chairs, are stacked away when not in use. The one Sunday service has a small but committed congregation who are very welcoming to newcomers and visitors.

The church itself, the lower hall and the lounge are all available for hire at very reasonable rates and local groups make full use of them. The Church Community Centre activities are varied, ranging from rehearsal groups, ballet classes and brownies to Alcoholics Anonymous, Narcotics Anonymous and the Gateway Club (for young mentally handicapped people). There is a playgroup which meets here four mornings a week, three youth clubs and a pensioners' food co-op (which has been featured on TV and radio).

Services: Sunday 11am □ Facilities: Braille hymnbooks □ Children: Sunday school 11am □ Wheelchair: difficult access; several steps and stairs □ Other details: halls and lounge (available for hire) □ Visiting: open 8.30am–9pm weekdays; open Saturday as required; open Sunday for services only

Wesley's Chapel

City Road, EC1 □ Telephone: 253 2262 (office) □ Bus: 5, 43, 55, 76, 141, 214, 243, 263a, 271 □ Tube/BR: Moorgate, Old Street □ Parking: some spaces; otherwise on street, meters □ Contact: Superintendent Minister □ Available: office hours □ Other staff: Assistant Minister, curator, etc

Wesley's Chapel is the Mother Church of world Methodism, and is therefore a place of pilgrimage for Methodists from all over the world. Up to 10,000 a year visit the chapel, but it must not be forgotten that it is also a local church with a cosmopolitan congregation who are both welcoming and active.

John Wesley himself was the driving force behind the building of the chapel. Forty years after opening the first Methodist church in a disused arms works, he bought the site for the present building. The Chapel was opened on All Souls Day 1779. Wesley himself lived in the house next door, now preserved as a museum, and is buried in the chapel grounds. Outside, in the courtyard, a statue of John Wesley stands Bible in hand.

The building is in the Georgian style, with Victorian additions, including the stained glass. Inside, the chapel is in excellent condition, having been fully renovated in the 1970s. There are many fine features. The Adam-style ceiling is the largest flat unsupported ceiling in England, while the box pews each have an extra folding seat tucked away at the end. Around the edge of the gallery is the repeated motif of a dove and a snake, representing deliverance and healing respectively, and designed by Wesley. The jasper columns were donated by Methodist churches both here and abroad, and were installed in 1891 to replace the original ones made out of warships' masts. The communion windows were donated by various branches of Methodism. The crypt below Wesley's Chapel contains the Museum of Methodism, opened in 1984, a bookstall and a refreshment area.

On Sundays, a congregation of around 120 in winter and up to 400 in summer attends the main service in this historic setting. Apart from the main chapel there is the smaller Foundry Chapel, named in memory of that earlier place of worship. It seats 25 to 30 people and contains benches and lectern from the original, and also the organ from John Wesley's house. Many parties of visitors, especially Americans, attend the daily offices or use the chapel for private prayer.

There are a number of groups and organisations attached to the regular congregation; these include a Sunday evening Bible study group, various house groups and a branch of the Wesley Guild. The congregation also involves itself in charitable projects and collects for the National Childrens Home. Community outreach is also important to the life of the chapel. The minister and his colleagues are available for individual counselling and involve themselves in the life of the local community. In particular, during Lent they visit all of the nearby block of flats.

Services: Sunday 11am Service with Eucharist, 6pm Prayer and Praise; Thursday 12.45pm (Offices said 8am and 6pm daily in Foundry Chapel) □ Facilities: amplification; some large print service books □ Children: Sunday school and creche, 10am □ Wheelchair: easy access □ Other details: hall □ Visiting: Chapel open 9am–6pm daily; Museum of Methodism and John Wesley's House open 10am–4pm Monday to Saturday (entrance fee)

West London Mission and Hinde Street Chapel

19 Thayer Street, W1 □ Telephone: 935 6179 □ Bus: 1, 6, 7, 8, 12, 13, 15, 16, 30, 73, 74, 88 (Oxford Street); 1, 2, 13, 18, 27, 30, 74 (Baker Street) □ Tube: Bond Street, Baker Street □ Parking: on street □ Contact: Superintendent Minister □ Available: all day by appointment

Methodism in this part of London has existed since the early days of the movement. Half a dozen buildings had been successively used for preaching, including a room above a slaughter-house in Davis Street. A piece of swamp beside the Tyburn stream, which ran down the present route of Marylebone Lane, was bought in 1808, and the Hinde Street Chapel was opened two years later. Described as 'ugly to a degree that was positively fascinating', it was rebuilt in 1887 by James Weir in the Classical style, with a two-storeyed portico. Alterations have been made since, most recently to accommodate the West London Mission offices.

Despite now being in the middle of a thriving business, retail and cultural area of the West End, and also despite the decline of the St Marylebone residential community, Hinde Street is regarded as a neighbourhood church. The congregation is drawn from a wide area, with students and young people forming a substantial proportion. The church is the centre for the Methodist Chaplaincy to London University. Hinde Street is also an important ministry to the several large hospitals nearby.

The Methodist Missions are the practical arm of the Church, complementing the spiritual healing of the Gospels. The West London Mission, now amalgamated with the Hinde Street congregation, started in 1887 in Piccadilly and was mainly concerned with alleviating poverty and destitution. The Mission moved to Kingsway Hall in 1912, and finally to Hinde Street in 1982. The work of the Mission continues with projects such as day centres for the homeless and alcoholics, and the Katherine Price Hughes House for men and women on probation.

Preaching, as exemplified by Lord Soper, has always been central to the worship at the chapel. The morning services are liturgical, with the Methodist Service Book of 1936 and the revised 1975 texts used at the 10am and 11am services respectively. The evening service is more informal, with mainly a young congregation. Guitars sometimes lead the music and the Taize form of service is sometimes used.

Services: 1st, 3rd & 5th Sundays 10am Holy Communion, 2nd & 4th Sundays 11am Holy Communion □ Facilities: amplification; Braille hymnbooks; large print Bible □ Children: Sunday school and creche at above times □ Wheelchair: steps, help required □ Other details: hall and other rooms (available for hire); quiet room for prayer and meditation □ Visiting: open most days

Westminster Central Hall

Storey's Gate, SW1 □ Telephone: 222 8010 □ Bus: 11, 24, 29, 78, 88 □ Tube: Westminster, St James Park □ Parking: difficult, on street □ Contact: Superintendent Minister □ Available: most days by telephone □ Other staff: Assistant Minister, musical directors, etc

The imposing dome structure of the Methodist Central Hall, facing Westminster Abbey, is quite a landmark. It was built in 1912 on the site of the Westminster Aquarium, as a belated Wesley Centenary Memorial. In recent years, a major refurbishment has taken place. The building's exterior is in the Viennese Baroque style, with Romanesque decoration. Inside, it is spacious and elegant, with an impressive foyer and a grand staircase, much in demand as a location by film companies. The spectacular domed Great Hall seats up to 2,600 people and is

Westminster Central Hall, SW1

quite magnificent with its three balconies, each with panelled ceilings. There is also a smaller chapel, used for prayer and communion services.

The Hall attracts a large congregation, not only from London but from all over the world. All are made welcome on Sundays, regardless of denomination, and there is a welcoming committee to greet newcomers. The standard of preaching is high, and clerical gowns and hoods are worn by the ministers. The strong musical tradition of Methodism is evidenced by the fine choir and, of course, the superb Grand Organ, which is often used for recitals.

There are numerous groups which use the Hall's facilities and strengthen the life of the church, including a Women's Guild, Bible study groups and youth and senior citizens clubs. Those wishing to keep in touch with all the events can join the Friends of Westminster; for a small subscription, Friends are informed by mail about forthcoming activities.

The work of the ministers, in addition to the running of the church as a whole, also includes their own personal ministry, involving visits to hospitals and to the housebound, as well as individual counselling. All in all, the many facets of Westminster Central Hall, both sacred and secular, go towards making it a busy and caring place of worship.

Services: Sunday 10am Prayer Fellowship, 11am Morning Praise, 6pm Private Prayers, 6.30pm Worship Service; Holy Communion 1st Sun 8pm, 3rd Sun 12.15pm (Order of services may vary) □ Facilities: amplification □ Children: Sunday school and creche, 11am □ Wheelchair: lifts, help available, toilets for disabled □ Other details: halls and rooms (available for hire), coffee bar, games room, etc □ Visiting: generally open during the day; bookstall open after Sunday services

Whitechapel Mission

212 Whitechapel Road, E1 □ Telephone: 247 8280 □ Bus: 10, 25, 225 □ Tube: Whitechapel □ Parking: on street □ Contact: Superintendent Minister □ Available: most times, except Saturday □ Other clergy: Rev Susan Featherstone (Assistant Minister)

The Whitechapel Mission specialises in helping the homeless and roofless. The Minister at the time of writing, Rev Peter Jennings, explains that 'our ministry begins with skin—we clean it, cover it, feed it, listen to it, and try to help the socially isolated and most vulnerable of God's children find security, dignity, warmth and acceptance in a family community. Our theology is instinctive rather than orthodox. We try to listen twice as much as we talk'.

Sundays are particularly busy. At 11am there is the service for local residents. Half of this congregation are African and the other half are young professionals and teachers from the area—mainly single adults. This is a traditional Free Church service. Activities of this congregation include a mums and babies group on Fridays, and a fortnightly religious fellowship. At 2pm, preparation begins for the influx of homeless people who will attend later in the day. The Mission is reopened at 4pm and around 200 people, mainly men, come in to wash, receive fresh clothes and be fed by Care Unit staff. A team of befrienders and listeners, plus a doctor, are on hand. The 6.30pm service is very informal indeed. As many as eighty attend, most of them male, and all are battered and vulnerable people, who are not afraid to answer back. The service has a radical message.

A Day Centre on Tuesday, Wednesday and Thursday offers meals and many forms of help. Wednesday is exclusively Ladies Day, with a religious meeting as well as numerous activities and use of the showers, while on Thursday a clothing store is open and staff spend the afternoon arguing individual cases with hospitals and the DHSS.

The present Mission was erected in 1970 on the site of the earlier Brunswick Chapel, opened in 1895. The church itself is on the first floor, and is modern and functional in design. It seats ninety, with an area screened off at the back where people can sit who do not wish to take part in the service. A striking feature is the set of Stations of the Cross, unusual in a Methodist church. (There are even two extra Stations not normally found, 'The Resurrection' and 'Jesus Speaks to Mary and John'). The multi-denominational Sunday evening congregation often contains Catholic members.

On the right-hand side of the altar is the Memory Table, upon which is a black book where names of deceased street people are recorded. Since most of the homeless have been forgotten by society at large, their deaths often go unrecorded, and the Memory Table is a way of these people can be commemorated by their friends.

The Mission contributes to many charities, including Crisis at Christmas. Last century, the Mission ran the Working Lads' Institute on the Whitechapel Road, an early rehabilitation centre for young offenders; although this closed some time ago, its work is continued through the Mission's involvement in Windy Ridge, near Colchester. This is both a farm and an approved probationary hostel, where youngsters can learn new skills.

Services: Sunday 11am, 6.30pm □ Children: creche can be arranged □ Wheelchair: no access to chapel, only to ground floor; toilets for disabled □ Other details: hall, meeting rooms, library, etc □ Visiting: open 9am–5pm daily

---

The New Church (Swedenborgians)

The New Church worships Jesus Christ as God and Saviour. It accepts the Bible as the inspired word of God whose meaning, however, is 'opened up' by means of 'the knowledge of correspondences which show the relationship of the spirit and letter'. Where it differs most from other churches is that it draws its theology from the writings of Emanuel Swedenborg (1688–1772)—a Swedish scientist, philosopher and 'servant of the Lord'. Swedenborg claimed that his spiritual senses were opened up so he could experience the state of the departed, giving him unique insight.

Swedenborg relates his experiences in his works, notably *Heaven and Hell*. Another book, *The True Christian Religion* contains the entire theology of the New Church, said to be the rational Christian doctrine of the New Age, the doctrine that 'makes sense'. When one attends a service at a New Church then, one will hear not only readings from the Old and New Testaments, but also from one of Swedenborgs many volumes. They have their own liturgy and hymn books adapted to portray the mysteries of Swedenborg's teachings on the Bible.

As a spiritual communion, the New Church is named both from St John's vision: 'And I, John, saw the Holy City, New Jerusalem, coming down from God out of Heaven',—and the promise: 'Behold I make all things new'.

For further information: Swedenborg House, 20–21 Bloomsbury Way, WC1

Michael Church (General Church of the New Jerusalem)

131 Burton Road, SW9 □ Bus: 3, 59, 95, 109, 133, 159, 196 □ Tube/BR: Brixton, Oval □ Parking: on street □ Minister: Rev Fred Elphick □ Address: Swedenborg Enquiry Centre, 21b Hayne Road, Beckenham, Kent □ Telephone 658 6320

Michael Church is a small, late Victorian (1898) brick church built specifically for the New Church congregation. At one time this area of Brixton was well populated by New Churchmen, but today only one or two members live in the locality. This has made it necessary for the church to organise weekday functions—such as evening classes—in members' homes (eg North and South London, Chadwell Heath and Guildford area). Newcomers are always welcome.

The principal activity takes place at the Sunday morning service, which includes a talk for children. Here thirty or so people gather to celebrate the message of the Bible as interpreted in the inspirational writings of Emanuel Swedenborg. Many hymns are sung by the congregation, and there are readings from the Old and New Testaments and from the writings of Swedenborg. The church is warm, the atmosphere is friendly and during the refreshments afterwards newcomers are rapidly made to feel part of the community.

The church is in a quiet residential area of Brixton and has a small garden which the present caretaker is turning into a 'Biblical Garden'—planting fig trees, olives, vines, cedar of Lebanon, etc.

Services: Sunday 11am □ Children: Sunday school during service □ Wheelchair: access difficult □ Other details: schoolroom □ Visiting: open at service times only; leaflets available

New Church Centre

5 Pembridge Villas, W11 □ Bus: 7, 12, 15, 15a, 27, 28, 31, 52, 52a, 88 □ Tube: Notting Hill Gate □ Parking: difficult □ Minister: Rev CVA Hasler □ Address: 112 Kensington Road, Southend, Essex □ Telephone: 0702 614929 □ Church Manager: Howard Turner □ Available: someone usually at church

The first thing that may catch one's attention about the New Church Centre is the 'shop window' facing onto the street. On display are the works of Swedenborg and other texts which leave no doubt as to the church's theology. Anyone interested further is welcome to drop in—the shop staff are only too pleased to answer any queries.

The most interesting feature of the interior is the wooden panelling around the chancel which, remarkably enough, formerly adorned the Cunard ocean liner, *The Mauretania* and was salvaged when she was broken up in 1936. The rest of the interior is brick-lined under a wooden ceiling, lit by a rainbow pattern stained-glass window.

At present services attract around twenty people who come from all over London, but it is hoped that the new bookstall and the 'open door' policy will arouse the interest of more people who live and work in the area.

Services: Sunday 11am (Communion once a month) □ *Wheelchair: easy access, toilet for disabled* □ *Other details: hall used as nursery; church used for recitals and concerts; bookstall* □ *Visiting: 'open door' policy; visitors most welcome*

The Oriental Orthodox Church

For 1,500 years until the present day the Western world has known next to nothing about this group of churches. It is a communion of five Churches of the ancient East: the Armenians, Copts, Ethiopians, the Syrians known as Jacobites or West Syrians, and the Christians of the Malabar Coast in India who probably came from Syria in the 5th century, though there is a tradition that their Church was founded by St Thomas the Apostle.

Their break with the rest of Christendom came about as long ago as 451 AD when the Council of Chalcedon condemned the Coptic Patriarch for his 'Monophysite' definition of the nature of Christ. This position, which all these Churches adopt though may prefer to term 'Henophysite', is that the two natures of Christ, divine and human, are perfectly united and fused together; this is in contrast to the Chalcedonian position that the incarnate Christ existed *in two natures*, which makes a slight distinction between the two. It may be interesting to note that the Assyrian Church of the East which is *not* in communion with these Churches, had already split with mainstream theology at the Council of Ephesus in 431 AD by adopting a Nestorian position, drawing a sharp distinction between these human and divine natures.

To a large extent we owe the presence of these Churches in Britain to the hardship and persecution members have faced in their native lands. They are keen to get to know other Christian denominations in London and to enable interested visitors to learn about their own traditions. Moreover, recent informal theological discussions over Chalcedon have been so successful that the 1,500 year old rift with the rest of Christianity is virtually healed. Their services have a unique atmosphere and it is only in comparatively recent years that we in the West have been able to experience them. An increasing number of Westerners are attending for worship and, generally, visitors are most welcome.

Armenian Church of St Peter

Cranley Gardens, SW7 □ *Bus: 14, 30, 45* □ *Tube: Gloucester Road* □ *Parking: on street* □ *Vicar: Rev Nerses Nersessian* □ *Address: 32 Beechwood Avenue, South Harrow* □ *Telephone: 422 2962* □ *Available: weekends*

St Peter's is a former Anglican church and very large it is too, with a seating capacity of 2,000. The vicar, Fr Nerses Nersessian, is also an ecumenical chaplain at St Alban's Cathedral where he gives a series of talks on the history of the Armenian church and its theology and spirituality. He is active in 'mending fences' between the Oriental Churches and the West, and so the interested visitor is assured of a warm reception.

The Armenian Church is pre-eminently a national Church, through which all their cultural activities are channelled. Faith helps to keep the morale of the people high through all the troubles of its post-First World War dispersal to every corner of the globe. The Church is seen as that which unites all Armenians, whether or not they go to services. The mother country is now split up between Turkey, Iran, and Soviet Armenia. Mount Ararat, the landing stage for Noah's Ark, stood at the heart of this nation, which adopted Christianity before any other, in 301 under King Todat. The cathedral at Etchmiatzin, built of Ararat granite, has stood for 1,600 years.

There are no icons or statues in Armemian churches. Murals, altar paintings, or stained glass are fine, but the Cross, such as that at St Peter's, must be plain with no representation of the human form like a western crucifix. At the altar twelve candles are set burning, representing the twelve apostles, and beside the huge Cross at St Peter's is a large picture of the Virgin and Child. The sacrament is given in front of the altar to the communicant who is barefoot or slippered.

Armenian chants and hymns are most impressive, some dating from the 3rd century. They bear some relationship to Gregorian chants. St Peter's has a sixteen-voice choir, strengthened with additional voices on high Holy Days. The church also possesses an immense organ, the second largest in the country. The word for the Armenian hymnal is the *Sharakan*, which translates as 'row of gems'.

Almost 150 people attend services regularly now that the London Armenian community has been strengthened by recent arrivals. Fr Nerses has recently started to give lectures in London and he is happy to give explanations to visitors to St Peter's. He is able to arrange guided visits to St Sarkis (see below) as well, and since he is also Curator of Oriental Manuscripts at the British Library his talks are both scholarly and full of interest on Armenian history, culture and art.

Services: Sunday 11am–1.30pm Divine Liturgy (followed by memorial service alternate Sundays); Feast Days & Saints' Days—check with church (All services in Armenian) □ Wheelchair: easy access □ Other details: hall available for hire □ Visiting: visitors welcome to services

Armenian Church of St Sarkis

Iverna Gardens, W8 □ Bus: 9, 27, 28, 31, 33, 49, 73 □ Tube: High Street Kensington □ Parking: on street □ Clergy: Bishop Y Gizirian □ Telephone: 937 0152 □ Available: phone for appointment □ Other clergy: Rev Nersessian (see St Peter's)

Set in a quiet square off Kensington High Street, St Sarkis is a most unusual church. It stands tall and proud, and is unique in London for its design which is based on that of the 7th century church of Haghbad. This site was bought in 1919 by the small Armenian community of the time, who then found they were unable to finance any building. Approaches were made to the philanthropist Caloust Gulbenkian and the money was made available. The church is still run by trustees appointed by Gulbenkian.

The exterior of the church is recognisably oriental, with some elaborate work on the niches, for example. The material used is a white stone which looks rather severe—perhaps because one feels it should look older. The church is square and

Armenian Church of St Sarkis, W8

quite small, little more than a chapel, with seating for around 100; the surprise is its height, of around 150 feet. It is topped by a splendid conical belfry, supported on a ring of plain Doric columns. On each side the windows are high up, just below the level of the triangular gables. The doors are decorated with line tracery, characteristic of Armenian art. The most eye-catching features of the church interior is the lavish spread of oriental carpets. Attached to the church, which has been extended and enlarged, is the new church hall, used by the twelve or so social groups of the Armenian community here, ranging from the General Benevolent Union to the youth club,which runs regular high-energy discos. Next door is the Bishop's residence, and it is he who conducts services here every Sunday. Though the service is in the Armenian language, translations are available.

Services: Sunday 11am–1.30pm Divine Liturgy (followed by memorial service alternate Sundays); Feast Days & Saints' Days—check with church (All services in Armenian) □ Facilities: texts available in English □ Children: Sunday school 9am–2.30pm □ Wheelchair: 4 steps, help required □ Other details: hall available for hire □ Visiting: visitors welcome, times by arrangement

Coptic Orthodox Patriarchal Church of St Mark

Scarsdale Villas, W8 □ Telephone: 937 5782 □ Bus: 9, 27, 28, 31, 33, 49, 73, 74, 264 □ Tube: High Street Kensington, Earls Court □ Parking: difficult □ Clergy: Fr Antonius Farag (937 0367), Fr Antonius Thabit (385 1991), Fr Bishoy Markor (603 6701) □ Available: anytime at church or home □ Archdeacon: Monir Naaman (204 1788) □ Deacon: TS Roufail (560 7962)

The word 'Copt' means simply 'Egyptian', but today it is generally understood to refer to a member of the Christian Church of Egypt. The Coptic Church, which has about ten million members, is considered to be the 'native' church which has survived from the 1st century, and stems from its founder St Mark, who to the Egyptians is not only the author of one of the canonical Gospels but also the first Evangelist and the first Patriarch of Alexandria. His remains, to this day, rest in the Cathedral of St Mark in Abbassaya, Cairo. The Copts themselves are proud to have been faithful to the living tradition of Orthodox Christianity for nearly two millenia in unbroken succession, from the time of the martyrdom of St Mark (c 68 AD) to the present day, and if one attends this beautiful and fascinating church in Kensington one will perhaps be able to experience some of the flavour of early Christianity.

The Liturgy is chanted in Coptic, English and Arabic, accompanied by the enchanting rhythm of hand cymbals. Services can last for up to four hours and the liturgies of St Basil, St Gregory and St Cyril are the most commonly used. Also included are readings from the Bible and from the *Agpeya*, the Coptic Orthodox Book of Prayer Hours. The congregation, with men sitting on the left of the nave aisle and women on the right, is a mixture of Egyptian and British people. An illuminated display in the English language has recently been installed to help members of the congregation, especially visitors and newcomers, follow the appropriate liturgy and prayers. The atmosphere is very friendly and worship culminates with Communion, considered by the Copts to be the sacrament of sacraments and the 'mystery of mysteries'. During Communion the congregation sing Psalm 150 and the service ends with Benediction, when one can witness the excitement of the children as they are sprinkled with the Holy Water.

The Coptic Church has a history of persecution, a recent example of this being the arrest on September 5th, 1981 of His Holiness Pope Shenouda III, the 117th successor to St Mark. He was released on January 1st, 1985. It was Pope Shenouda who consecrated this former Presbyterian church in Kensington for Orthodox worship, in 1979. The ceremony was witnessed by the leaders and dignitaries of many Churches including the Russian and Armenian Orthodox Churches, the Church of Scotland and the Anglican Church.

The present church has a large collection of Egyptian icons and a screen resembling the Veil of the Temple in the Old Testament. It can seat many people but the increasing congregations of up to 400 are proving a little difficult to contain. It is hoped to secure large premises soon which will enable them to develop plans for a Coptic Cultural and Educational Centre.

Mass: Sunday 8am–12noon; Monday & Thursday 7–9am; Tuesday 6–8am; Wednesday & Friday 9–11am; Saturday 8–10am (except 1st Saturday 10am–12noon) (All services in Coptic, Arabic and English except 1st Saturday which is English only) □ Facilities: amplification □ Children: Sunday school after Mass; Christian and Arabic language classes □ Wheelchair: several steps; help required □ Other details: hall (not for hire) □ Visiting: open for services only, or by arrangement

Ethiopian Congregation of St Mary of Zion

Worshipping at: St Matthew's, St Petersburgh Place, W2 □ Bus: 12, 88, (A2) □ Tube: Queensway, Bayswater □ Parking: on street □ Priest: V Rev Aregawi Wolde Gabriel □ Address: 253b Ladbroke Grove, W10 □ Telephone: 960 3848 □ Available: most times

There are several thousand Ethiopians in this country and the Ethiopian Church is engaged in a great deal of pastoral work, for although some of its members have been settled here for some time, perhaps educated here, many have arrived only recently and most certainly need a helping hand.

Not the least of the Church's problems is explaining to Europeans that this is an Apostolic Church with a long history and rich traditions. Indeed, even before Christianity arrived in the region there was monotheistic worship, and, like the Jews, the Ethiopians used to go up to Jerusalem. It is said that Menilek, son of Solomon and the Queen of Sheba, smuggled the Ark of the Covenant out of the Temple and into his own land where it remains to this day.

Acts 8 tells the story of the conversion to Christianity of an Ethiopian envoy. Then, around 330 AD, the first bishop, St Frumentius, was appointed, and Christianity instituted in the whole region. The Ethiopian Church respects all seven Sacraments, those of baptism, confirmation, Holy Communion and penitence (confession) being the most important. In the home country there is an estimated number of 170,000 clergy, including a special order of confessional fathers who take responsibility for giving spiritual advice.

There is a bishop for the Western Hemisphere, Bishop Yesehaq, who is based in New York, and his representative in Great Britain is the Very Reverend

Aregawi Wolde Gabriel, who is addressed as Abba, the Hebrew word for father. Other churches are found in the Caribbean countries.

The liturgical language of the Church is Geez, though the vernacular, Amharic, is also used, and prayer books have a well set-out translation into English. At present Sunday services are held at St Matthew's church, Bayswater (qv) and take place at 9.30am. The average attendance is about 50 in a typical week, a bit low because the community is so spread out. Special services are held on the major Holy Days and Saints' Days. No less than 33 Holy Days in the calendar are devoted to St Mary, and the congregation bears the same name as that of the new church in the religious capital Aksum; this was a great trading city even in the earliest Christian period, having links with ancient Greece and Egypt.

Abba Gabriel does not only work with Ethiopians. He also instructs numbers of Caribbean people who are interested in discovering more about the honourable and independent traditions of African Christianity. He is concerned to combat the spread of the Rastafarian idea that anyone could owe worship to Emperor Haile Selassie, who is only a man, and he will teach only those candidates who are serious in preparation for baptism.

Perhaps European Christians could get to know a little more about their sister church and the African heritage that has been obscured for so long.

Services: Sunday 9.30am Holy Liturgy (All services in Geez & Amharic) □ Wheelchair: level access

Indian Orthodox Congregation of St Gregorious

Worshipping at: St Andrew-by-the-Wardrobe, Queen Victoria Street, EC4 □ Bus: 45, 59, 63, 76, 109, 141, 184 □ Tube/BR: Blackfriars □ Parking: NCP opposite □ Priest: Fr George Kurian □ Address: Indian YMCA, 41 Fitzroy Square, W1 □ Telephone: 387 0411 □ Available: phone for appointment

The long and fascinating history of this Church began around 52 AD when, according to tradition, St Thomas landed on the Malabar Coast of South India and began to spread the Gospel. Many early members were Syrians; the Church is in full communion with the Oriental Orthodox Churches and indeed used to be called the Syrian Church in India until the recent adoption of the present, less confusing name of Indian Orthodox. The London parish, along with other European parishes, is under His Eminence Dr Paulos mar Gregorios, the Metropolitan of Delhi and the North. Dr Paulos is also a president of the World Council of Churches.

The Church was first represented in Britain in the 1930s and it now ministers to members from Glasgow to Southampton. Since 1979, weekly services have been held in the church of St Andrew-by-the-Wardrobe. These services follow the St James Liturgy and feature a good deal of lay participation in the form of readings, responses and singing. In accordance with Indian tradition, no music is written down, but all the hymns can be sung to eight memorised tunes. Some festivals and particularly the marriage ceremony show clearly the influence of the Church's Indian origins. In England, as in India, the congregation is composed largely of people from the wealthy and professional classes.

Refreshments are provided after the services, thus creating a valuable opportunity for the members of a dispersed community to get together and keep in touch. In addition to the weekly services there are Fellowship meetings every weekend, held in private houses up and down the country. There are also youth and women's meetings.

Services: Sunday 9am Morning Prayer, 10am Liturgy (All services held in Malayam) □ *Children: Sunday school* □ *Wheelchair: access via St Andrews Hill entrance*

The Orthodox Church

Many of us in the West are aware of the Greek and the Russian Orthodox Churches, but are uncertain as to their beliefs and origins. Perhaps the first thing that should be made clear then is that no matter what nationality the worshippers may be—Greek, Russian, Romanian, Serb, or whatever—there is only one Orthodox Church. Different languages may be used, but the same liturgy and the same church calendar are followed in every land.

A brief historical account will show that Orthodoxy is not some strange, alien Church but the Eastern tradition of Christianity regarding itself as true to the beliefs and practices of the early Church. Originally, Christendom was united in one Church presided over by the five Patriarchs of Rome, Jerusalem, Antioch, Alexandria and Constantinople. The Bishop of Rome was granted the honour of being first among equals, but he had no actual supremacy over the other Patriarchs. However, Rome grew to regard itself as dominant for a variety of reasons, political as well as ecclesiastical; further, Rome was cut off from the East by barbarian invasions and so the two traditions of Christianity, Latin and Byzantine, developed in isolation. The so-called Great Schism eventually came in 1054.

Another important factor in the history of Orthodoxy was the conversion of the Russians to Christianity. With the decline of Constantinople, the centre of Orthodoxy came to be based here and Moscow became a Patriarchate in 1598. Since then Orthodoxy has spread as far afield as Japan, the USA and Uganda.

In Britain, the Orthodox Church was first represented by Greek merchants who had a church on London Wall in 1677. However, it was only with the influx of refugees from both World Wars, from the Russian Revolution and from Cyprus that the number of Orthodox Christians in Britain became significant. Now, there are well over 100,000, the vast majority of them Greeks and Greek Cypriots, although there is an increasingly significant proportion of Western converts. This latter fact highlights an interesting situation now facing the Orthodox churches in Britain: while many stand as a symbol of the ethnic and cultural identity of their members, others are attracting broad-based congregations. Further, second and third generation youngsters may now be very British in terms of language and outlook, and this must begin to have an effect on the churches.

Orthodox churches, then—icons notwithstanding—are essentially similar to many familiar Western churches; accordingly, when visiting one should behave with the same decorum and respect. Dress restrictions may be a little tighter; many churches prefer women not to wear trousers or to have bare arms. The main service is the Liturgy, normally held according to the rite of St John Chrysostom. Lay worshippers may arrive at any time during this quite lengthy service, but this is far from being a sign of disrespect. After the final blessing, those present may go up to kiss the Cross which the priest holds and receive a piece of bread called the *antidoron,* which is blessed but not consecrated. In most churches, non-Orthodox are welcome and indeed encouraged to receive the *antidoron* as an expression of Christian fellowship and love.

For further information, contact the Secretary of the Fellowship of St Alban and St Sergius, 52 Landbroke Grove, W11 (Tel: 727 7713).

Arabic Orthodox Congregation

Worshipping at: The Chapel of the Annunciation, 5 Craven Hill, W2 □ Bus: 7, 12, 15, 15a, 27, 36, 88 □ Tube: Lancaster Gate □ Parking: on street □ Clergy: Fr Samir Gholham □ Address: 13 Kenwyn Road, SW20 □ Telephone: 879 3046 □ Available: most times

At present the Arabic-speaking Orthodox congregation, the Parish of the Patriarchate of Antioch in London, holds services at this attractive chapel in Bayswater. Normally it is the private chapel of the Headquarters of the Archdiocese of Thyateira and Great Britain headed by His Eminence Archbishop Methodius. The Arabic-speaking worshippers hope to acquire their own premises soon.

There are usually around 75 regular worshippers, and up to 200 at Feast Days, with most Middle Eastern nationalities represented. The congregation was set up only in the early 1980s but has grown steadily, generally amongst newcomers to London and their families, all of whom speak Arabic. The congregation is aware that language difficulties may arise with succeeding generations, and steps have already been taken to provide Arabic classes. At services, English translations of the Arabic liturgy are available.

Services: Sunday 11am Holy Liturgy (Services normally in Arabic) □ Children: Religion classes □ Wheelchair: help required □ Visiting: service times only; this is a private chapel

Byelorussian Parish of All Saints

Worshipping at: St Silas, Penton Road, N1 □ Telephone: 607 2865 □ Bus: 30, 73, 214 □ Tube/BR: Angel, Kings Cross □ Parking: on street □ Priest-in-Charge: V Rev J Pierkarski □ Address: 7 Haycroft Road, Stevenage, Herts □ Telephone: (0438) 358916 □ Available: at service or at home □ Other staff: Mr Jaswitowicz, 868 4554, (Chairman of Community)

Once a month St Silas' Church in Islington draws a small and dispersed community to its doors for Orthodox worship. The 1½ hour service, the Divine Liturgy, is conducted entirely in the Slavonic and Byelorussian languages. All ages come, from 2 to 71, as it also provides an opportunity for Byelorussians from all over London to meet together. Refreshments are served after the service. The service is held monthly because the priest serves other parishes and communities as far afield as Cambridge, Birmingham and Wolverhampton.

Services: Sunday 12.30pm Divine Liturgy (once a month) □ Wheelchair: level access through firedoors

Greek Cathedral of All Saints

Pratt Street, NW1 (Corner of Camden Street) □ Telephone: 485 2149 □ Bus: 29, 46, 214, 253 □ Tube/BR: Camden Town, Camden Road □ Parking: car park next to church □ Clergy: Fr George Zaphirakos (205 5358), Archimandrite Nikiphoros, Deacon Andreas □ Available: 9.30am–7pm at church

Every Easter, the Orthodox calendar reaches its climax with the procession of the *Epitaphios* (the figure of Christ taken down from the Cross) through the streets on Good Friday. In Camden Town, with its large Greek population, some ten or twelve thousand people join in the procession, making it a lively and spectacular local event. Many will later attend All Saints Cathedral for the exultant service of the Resurrection, held at midnight on Easter Day.

From the outside, All Saints is a fairly austere 1820s neo-Classical building, of regular proportions with tall Regency windows. The interior is also symmetrical, with fluted Corinthian columns supporting the roomy gallery, and yet, all these spare Classical harmonies are scarcely noticeable among the flowers, candles, the chandeliers from Greece that light the nave and aisles, and above all, the icons. On the altar screen are copies of four small icons from a Russian Orthodox monastery in France, and the originals are also displayed in the church. There are numerous other icons, side-altar paintings, and a Byzantine tapestry from the Church of the Holy Cross in old Constantinople. The iconostasis, the three thrones and the communion table are carved out of fine Cyprus walnut.

All Saints has been used for Orthodox worship since 1948 and has always been a popular church for weedings. Over 120 are held here every year and Father Zaphirakos remarks that the figure was even higher before the more recent Greek churches became available. Funds are currently being raised to clean and restore this splendid church.

Services: Sunday 9.30am–1pm Matins & Liturgy; Saturday 5.30–6.15pm Vespers; on eve of Feasts & Feast Days, check with church (Services normally held in Greek) □ Facilities: 2 prayer books for the Blind □ Children: teaching for 6–12 year olds, Mon & Wed evenings □ Wheelchair: several steps □ Other details: coffee room □ Visiting: open 10am–7pm, visitors welcome; guide book available (in Greek)

Greek Cathedral of the Holy Wisdom (St Sophia)

Moscow Road, W2 □ Telepone: 229 4643 □ Bus: 7, 12, 15, 15a, 27, 28, 31, 36, 36b, 88 □ Tube: Bayswater, Queensway □ Parking: easy, on street □ Clergy: Bishop Timotheos of Melitoupolis, Fr Panteleimon, Fr George □ Available: generally at church

The Greek inscription over the doorway of this church translates as follows: 'The Greek Colony in this seagirt island built this church far from their dear country,

Greek Cathedral of the Holy Wisdom, W2

dedicating it to the Holy Wisdom of God, during the reign of the great and illustrious Queen Victoria. London 1878'. This raises an interesting point that, unlike nearly all Greek churches in Britain, the cathedral was built specifically for Orthodox worship and was not acquired from some other denomination. It was financed by the growing Greek community to replace the previous church in London Wall which was no longer convenient as few worshippers still lived in the City.

The cathedral is in the form of a Greek Cross with a dome over the centre. The exterior has brickwork alternating with stone but is rather plain, and it is only upon entering that the true splendour of the building can be seen. One is first struck by the huge iconostasis, carved from walnut, and the exquisitely worked floor. There is a large silver cross with ruby lamps suspended from the arch over the central aisle, and the walls and pillars supporting the dome are clad in a rich variety of marbles.

The two styles of mosaic work form an interesting contrast. The decoration of the dome for example, showing the *Pantokrator* and the Apostles, was done in the 1880s by A G Walker. Much influenced by the pre-Raphaelites, he produced work that is rounded, bright and of a rather Latin character. On the other hand, the later mosaics by Boris Anrep, such as those on the transept arches, revert to the darker tones and the angular, flat style that is distinctly Byzantine.

This was not always a cathedral, but only became one in 1922. The Holy Synod of Constantinople decided to establish a Bishopric for those Orthodox communities lying outside its jurisdiction, to be based in London. This was to become the see of the Holy Metropolis of Thyateira, and the new Cathedral of the Holy Wisdom the seat of the bishop.

The cathedral attracts worshippers from all over London. Around 400 people attend the Sunday service, when a mixed youth choir sings. The Bishop, who has written several books about the Greek community in London, is well aware of the Church's social position, and says 'If the Greeks live, then we live'. The cathedral can help those facing homelessness, or with language difficulties, and the church hall is used for various social and cultural events for the Greek community to enjoy.

Services: Sunday 9.30am–12.30pm Matins & Liturgy; Saturday 5.30–6.30pm Vespers; on eve of Feasts & Feast Days, check with church (Services are normally in Greek, but Confessions are available in English, French & Greek) □ Facilities: amplification □ Children: Saturday school □ Wheelchair: help required □ Other details: hall can be hired for Greek wedding receptions, etc; hall is used for dance lessons, lectures, community centre □ Visiting: visitors are welcome to services

Greek Cathedral of the Nativity of the Mother of God

305 Camberwell New Road, SE5 □ Bus: 12, 35, 36, 36a, 36b, 40, 42, 45, 68, 171, 176, 184, 185, 185a □ Tube: Oval, then catch a bus □ Parking: by side of church □ Clergy: Bishop Christopher of Telmessos, Fr Athen Agoras, Deacon Vasileos Yianni, (703 0137) □ Available: nearly always at church

The Byzantine style of the interior evokes the flavour of churches in the East, and helps the Greek and Cypriot worshippers preserve their faith and traditions.

Bishop Christopher comments that 'without the church, soon the people would no longer be Orthodox', and he feels fortunate to have acquired the cathedral which the congregation have come to cherish.

The cathedral was bought from the Catholic Apostolic Church in 1963 and immediately altered to suit Orthodox worship. The iconostasis was installed, along with various icons from Greece and Cyprus. The walls are of bare stone but do not make the place feel cold; indeed, the soft light provided by the many lamps and candles creates an attractive atmosphere.

The principal Sunday service, conducted in Greek and lasting for up to four hours, is attended by around 200 worshippers. Most age groups are represented, though it is recognised that it is getting more difficult to attract the younger British-born generation.

Bishop Christopher has been at the cathedral from the first; he now leads a quiet, monastic life and has quarters at the rear of the building.

Services: Sunday 9am–1pm Matins & Liturgy; Saturday 6pm Vespers; Thursday 6pm Special Litany to Mother of God; on eve of Feasts & Feast Days, check with church (Services normally held in Greek) □ Facilities: amplification □ Children: Saturday school □ Wheelchair: easy access □ Other details: hall (available for hire), teaching rooms □ Visiting: open only at service times; few visitors

Greek Cathedral of St Andrew

Kentish Town Road, NW1 □ Telephone: 485 6385 □ Bus: 27, 53, 134, 137, 214 □ Tube/BR: Kentish Town, Camden Road, Kentish Town West □ Parking: on side streets □ Clergy: Bishop Chrysostomos of Kyanea, Fr Andreas Garivalinos (202 7987), Deacon Constantinos Garivalinos (889 7013) □ Available: generally at church

The Cathedral of St Andrew has one of the largest Orthodox congregations in London: around 500 Greeks and Cypriots regularly attend the Sunday service. Visitors are welcome, but are not able to take Communion of course, unless they are Orthodox themselves. The services lasts for three hours and includes a sermon by the Bishop.

The church is a Victorian basilica bought from the Anglican Church in late 1957 and altered to meet Orthodox requirements. It is generally open all day for people to see the interior, with its icons and an attractive iconostasis carved by a Greek craftsman from gentle limewood.

Services: Sunday 9.45am–12.45pm Matins & Liturgy; on eve of Feasts & Feast Days, check with church (Services normally held in Greek) □ Facilities: amplification □ Children: Saturday & evening teaching □ Wheelchair: difficult, one large step □ Other details: school building next door; hall for use by Greek community □ Visiting: open 8.30am–7pm; few visitors; 'dress must be appropriate to the holiness of the place'

Romanian Congregation of St Dunstan-in-the-West

Worshipping at: St Dunstan-in-the-West, Fleet Street, EC4 □ Telephone: 242 6037 (office) □ Bus: 4, 6, 9, 11, 15, 15a, 17, 45 □ Tube: Aldwych □ Parking: very difficult except Sundays □ Priest: Fr Peter Pufulete □ Address: 250 Clapham Road, SW9 □ Telephone: 735 9515 □ Available: any time □ Other contacts: Mr Harry McCormick (Chorleywood 2577)

The Romanian Orthodox congregation has its own altar in St Dunstan-in-the-West (qv), the Anglican ecumenical church in the City. The Romanians have worshipped there since 1965. The altar screen, over 250 years old, is delicately hand-carved out of walnut and painted in fine detail. It was brought here in 1966 from the monastery of Antim in Bucharest, the seat of the Romanian Patriarch. Regrettably, the altar has twice been the target of vandalism in recent years, and valuable items have been stolen and smashed.

The small congregation is used to adversity: many are exiles or refugees (several members arrived by jumping ship when their vessel docked here). However, some have married British people, and out of all the Orthodox congregations the Romanians have one of the highest proportions of young people—around 60% of regular worshippers. They all have a strong attachment to Romania, and many have chosen to go there to hold their wedding celebrations. There are holiday visits too, arranged by Fr Peter Pufulete, the priest in charge since 1980. Fr Peter represents the Romanian Church to the see of Canterbury.

The services here are melodic in the southern rather than the Slav tradition; there is a fine choir which has made several recordings, available from the church. There is a special service on the day of the patron saint of Romania, who is none other than our own St George!

Services: Sunday & Feast days 11am Liturgy (Services held in Romanian; lesson in English) □ Facilities: amplification □ Wheelchair: 2 steps

Russian Patriarchal Cathedral of the Dormition and All Saints

67 Ennismore Gardens, SW7 □ Telephone: 584 0096 □ Bus: 9, 14, 19, 22, 30, 52, 73, 74, 137 □ Tube: Knightsbridge, South Kensington □ Parking: in the square □ Clergy: Metropolitan Anthony of Sourozh, Fr Michael Fortounatto (603 5200), Fr John Lee (876 7993), Fr Alexander Fostiropoulos (c/o 836 5454) □ Available: someone usually at church

This Byzantine-style cathedral is readily reminiscent of the ancient churches of the East. The frontage is in honey-coloured sandstone, with a rose window that is stern rather than elaborate but no less effective for that. The porch has marble columns behind the front two corkscrew columns which are of stone. The rest of the facade is broken up by pilasters to form shallow niches, and a bell tower, rising to an impressive height, completes the picture.

There is neither pomp nor circumstance about the interior. The stained glass is a feature of this former Anglican church and it harmonises well with the icons on the screen and at the base of each pillar. The half-domed altar area is splendid,

Russian Patriarchal Cathedral of the Dormition and All Saints, SW7

and the iconostasis is simple yet effective in white and gold. On the spandrels of the large round arches are new mosaics, which are restrained in sympathy with the quiet colours of the surroundings.

A strong sense of quiet is also characteristic of Russian Orthodox services. Incense is used, there are many candles, and the liturgy is indeed strong on ritual, but the service is meditative as well as being dramatic. The cathedral has 2,000 members, and at Easter it is packed full, with crowds forming out on the square. Some are old Russians who remember the Revolution, but now most were born in this country and there are also a good few converts.

Metropolitan Anthony Bloom is the Bishop and Head of the Church (the Patriarchate of Moscow) in Great Britain. He has a reputation as a great teacher and is highly respected by people of all denominations. Through him and the parish priests, the cathedral runs study groups, often held at the nearby Parish House. There is a bookstall at the cathedral which stocks titles on Orthodoxy to suit all from the mildly curious to the serious student. Many books have been specially imported and are unavailable elsewhere in Britain.

Services: Sunday 10.30am Liturgy, 5.30pm Vespers; Saturday 5.30pm Vespers; on eve of Feasts & Feast Days, check with church (Services held in Church Slavonic & English) □ *Children: Sunday school, once a month* □ *Wheelchair: level access* □ *Other details: bookstall* □ *Visiting: open half an hour before services*

Russian Synodal Cathedral of the Dormition of the Mother of God

Emperor's Gate, SW7 □ *Bus: 30, 49, 52, 74, 264* □ *Tube: Gloucester Road* □ *Parking: difficult except on Sunday* □ *Clergy: Fr John Suscenko (743 8886), Deacon Seraphim (742 8875)* □ *Available: Contact Fr John by phone*

The divisions in the Russian Orthodox Church lie in the events of 1917. Following the takeover by the Bolsheviks, with whom he refused to have any dealings whatsoever, the Patriarch Tikhon ordered the Church out of the country. Members of the Church in Exile (or the Church outside Russia, as it is now less dramatically called) remain faithful to that declaration. Accordingly, they have a separate organisation from that of the Church led in this country by Metropolitan Anthony of Sourozh, although both are Orthodox Churches and hence use the same rite. This parish is parallel with that of the church in Ennismore Gardens.

The Russians have been worshipping in this cathedral since 1954, and members come from all parts of London and the South. They range in age from surviving opponents of the Revolution to young children; many are emigrés from the time of the Second World War.

The building itself is a Victorian church with a high roof above ten double lancet windows. Upon entering one is struck—perhaps through the absence of pews—by a feeling of space. Worshippers will usually first approach the icons of Christ, Mary and the saints to venerate them before taking up positions in the central area of the church. All members, both young and old, show great reverence, making the Sign of the Cross and bowing to the ground.

Services are held in a deeply devotional atmosphere. The choir sings well from the gallery, and the liturgy in Church Slavonic is dignified and recited with feeling. For a visitor, it may be difficult to follow the service in detail, but the lesson is usually read in English.

Services: Sunday 10.30am Holy Liturgy; on eve of Feasts & Feast Days, check with church (Services held in Church Slavonic with some English) □ Facilities: amplification (used for very large congregations, eg Easter) □ Children: Saturday school at the Convent of the Annunciation, 26 Brondesbury Park, NW6 □ Wheelchair: no access □ Other details: hall downstairs □ Visiting: open only during services

St Basil's Chapel

St Basil's House, 52 Ladbroke Grove, W11 □ Bus: 12, 52, 88 □ Tube: Notting Hill, Holland Park □ Parking: difficult □ Priest: Fr Natanael Kalaydjev □ Address: 37 Queensborough Terrace, W2 □ Telephone: 221 7599 □ Secretary, Fellowship of St Alban and St Sergius: Elizabeth Briere (727 7713)

The Bulgarians in London hold services in St Basil's Chapel, where between 12 and 20 worshippers attend services led by Father Natanael. Most arrived here since the War and many married English people, so although the community is small there are a number of young families.

The chapel, which contains an Orthodox and an Anglican altar, is also used for prayers by members of the Fellowship of St Alban and St Sergius. This Fellowship, based at St Basil's House, works to improve understanding between the Eastern and Western Churches, and prays 'for the peace of the whole world, for the good estate of the holy Churches of God, and for the union of all' (from the Liturgy of St John Chrysostom).

The Fellowship organises an annual retreat and a pilgrimage to St Albans Cathedral, and members can enjoy the library and the hospitality of St Basil's House. Enquiries are welcome from anyone wishing to know more about the relationship between the Churches, and the bookstall is open to all.

Services: 1st & 3rd Sundays 11am Liturgy; on eve of Feasts & Feast Days, check with chapel □ Wheelchair: no access □ Other details: library (used as meeting room after Liturgy), bookshop □ Visiting: at reasonable hours, by arrangement

Serbian Church of St Sava

89 Lancaster Road, W11 □ Bus: 7, 15, 52, 295 □ Tube: Ladbroke Grove □ Parking: in car park □ Priest: Fr Milun Kostić (727 8367) □ Available: generally at church

St Sava is the patron saint of all the Serbs, the largest population in Yugoslavia. A royal prince of the ancient Nemanyed dynasty, Sava renounced his title in order to become first a monk and then a popular preacher. The Patriarch of Constantinople name him head of the Church and its first Archbishop, and he was later canonised. The future of the Serbian Orthodox Church was assured.

In Britain there are several Serbian churches under the jurisdiction of the Bishop for Western Europe and his Episcopal Vicar. The Serbian community in London, mostly settled here since the Second World War, numbers several thousand, and at festivals, some 500 of these worship at St Sava's church. Formerly an Anglican church, St Sava's was consecrated for Orthodox worship in

1952. It is spacious, with a plain brick exterior and windows showing Serbian flags of red, blue and white.

The inconostasis is particularly noteworthy, carved in Yugoslavian walnut and frescoed with icons copied from a 13th century Serbian monastery. As well as the customary figures of Christ and the Virgin, there are icons of St Sava and his father Simeon, who was also canonised. Also carved in walnut are the beautiful thrones, one for royalty and one for the Bishop. The royal throne was used by Queen Elizabeth II one Saturday in 1956 when she attended a Vespers service here. It was an important event: the son of Prince Andrew of Serbia was being baptised, and the Queen was acting as godmother.

This is an admittedly unusual example of the strong ties between the Serbian and British peoples. St Sava's has built up excellent neighbourhood relations. Local schools regularly visit the church and the flourishing community centre next door to learn more about Serbian culture and Orthodox worship. A programme of working holidays has been organised to help restore an ancient monastery in Serbia . . . any volunteers?

Services: Sunday 10.30am Liturgy; on eve of Feasts & Feast Days, check with church (Services normally held in Church Slavonic) □ *Facilities: amplification* □ *Children: Sunday school run by voluntary teachers* □ *Wheelchair: steps, but access possible* □ *Other details: Community Centre with halls, bar, library, classrooms, flats, etc* □ *Visiting: open at all times, all welcome; bookstall; tours can be arranged*

Pentecostal Churches

Pentecostalism refers to the descent of the Holy Spirit on the Apostles at Pentecost (Acts, ch 2). Modern manifestations of this were first recorded at Los Angeles in 1906 and the movement has since spread worldwide. It is characterised by enthusiastic preaching and by 'speaking in tongues', ecstatic utterances either unintelligible or echoing languages not known to the speaker.

The first British meeting took place in All Saints Church, Sunderland, in 1907, though the movement really took off between 1915 and 1935 when the Welsh evangelists Stephen and George Jeffreys, with their nephew Edward, preached fervently to packed halls throughout the land. The crusade was followed by increased membership of existing Pentecostal groups and the formation of the Elim Foursquare Gospel Alliance (now the Elim Church) in 1915. This and the Assemblies of God (founded 1924) represent the two major strands of Pentecostalism in Britain today. There are also many smaller groups originating either in Africa, North America or the West Indies, many of whom, with flourishing congregations but no place of worship of their own, meet in churches of other denominations throughout Britain.

A large proportion of members of Pentecostal churches are Black people who are continuing the style of worship they practised in the West Indies, where Pentecostalism is a well-established tradition. Services are often several hours long and are marked by an exuberance seldom found in other Churches. Musical accompaniment is often provided by a small band rather than just a piano or organ, and lay participation is extensive—through singing, extempore testimony, shouts of 'hallelujah', even dancing and speaking in tongues. Visitors are always made to feel welcome and, as often as not, are invited to share in food prepared by members of the congregation.

All Souls Pentecostal Church

Worshipping at: URC Claremont, Whitelion Street, N1 □ Bus: 4, 19, 30, 43, 73, 171, 214, 279 □ Tube: Angel □ Parking: difficult □ Pastor: Rev James Brako □ Address: 31 Norfolk Street, E7 □ Telephone: 555 9060 □ Available: at all times □ Other staff: The Secretary, Mr Asare (555 6720); Elder Ernest (624 6728)

Every Sunday, Islington Claremont URC rings to the sound of 200 or so enthusiastic worshippers of the All Souls Pentecostal Church. Services are long and lively. The whole congregation is involved in clapping, dancing and singing along to music from a band with drums, saxophone and tambourines. Hymns are taken from the Methodist Hymn Book. Communion, preaching of the Gospels and healing of the sick are also performed. The congregation is mixed, though with the majority Ghanaian, from all over London and all ages. All newcomers are most welcome.

Services: Sunday 2pm–5.30pm; Friday 8pm–10pm □ Wheelchair: several steps into the hall but level access into the building

Apostolic Church

St Oswalds Place, SE11 □ Bus: 2, 2b, 3, 109, 159 □ Tube: Vauxhall □ Parking: easy, on street □ Pastor: Rev Leo Isaac □ Address: 8 Culverhouse Gardens, Streatham, SW16 □ Telephone: 769 8389 □ Available: service times

The Aspostolic Church developed out of the Welsh revival early this century when DP Williams, who gained a wide reputation as a charismatic preacher, founded the first church. Soon, other independent churches, finding themselves in agreement with the style and teachings of the new church (the theology is based around Ephesians 4.11–12) joined the movement. With its emphasis on missionary work the church not only grew but spread, and now has representatives as far afield as Brazil, Australia, America and many parts of Africa. Prayers are regularly held for members abroad; the previous incumbent of Vauxhall is now working in Brazil.

The church itself is a large modern building built in the 1960s. Its large hall is of simple design which, apart from a large crucifix above the altar stage, has no decoration at all. There is a small creche upstairs overlooking the hall and the service is relayed there over a speaker system. Participation is encouraged at services through readings and testimonies of faith. A large choir is also an important feature. Baptisms (adults only) are a regular occurrence and take place in the large pool that stretches across the front of the hall.

Next door to the church is a new community centre and although there is no official affiliation, the members of the church and the minister are very involved in its activities, from jumble sales to the youth club. The minister also visits local schools to take assemblies and to teach on relevant subjects such as the dangers of drugs.

Assembly of God, Harrow Road, W2

Services: Sunday 11am–1pm, 6pm Gospel service, 4pm Young peoples (every 2nd Sun) □ Facilities: amplification, overhead projector □ Children: creche □ Wheelchair: 1 shallow step □ Visiting: open only for services

Assembly of God

141 Harrow Road, Paddington, W2 □ Telephone: 286 9261 □ Bus: 18, 36, 36b □ Tube: Royal Oak □ Parking: on street □ Pastor: Rev G Thomas □ Address: 29 Sedgmoor Gardens, Flackwell Heath, Bucks □ Telephone: (23303) 06285 □ Available: evenings □ Other contacts: Caretaker lives at church

Between 50 and 60 people regularly attend Sunday services in this small church, converted from a public house, which can seat only 100 at the most. Thus the meetings have an intimacy to begin with, and services soon taken on an exuberant nature. Spontaneous testimonies of faith may be given, and there is a strong emphasis on music. Not only is there an organ and guitars, but tambourines are provided to those who wish to participate in the music-making. There is no choir, but members of the congregation sing harmonies to the hymns expertly. Many worshippers have an African background, though all are welcome. The minister Rev Thomas states that 'we hope this church stands as a lighthouse in this city of sin, preaching the gospel of light, and dispelling darkness'.

On Wednesdays the chairs are arranged in a circle for the smaller evening prayer and Bible study meetings, while on Saturday afternoons the 15 or so worshippers attending will go out into the Edgware Road after the service to sing hymns and distribute leaflets. There are no other organised activities, but Rev Thomas feels that the services themselves have an important social role, bringing people together in worship. Christmas and special birthdays are celebrated after the service with a 'bring-and-share' lunch or supper.

Services: Sunday 11am and 6.30pm; Wednesday 7.30pm Prayer meeting and Bible study □ Facilities: amplification □ Children: Sunday school on first floor □ Wheelchair: level access □ Other details: room above church □ Visiting: open at service times only; leaflets available

Assembly of God, Peniel Chapel

Kensington Park Road, W11 □ Telephone: 727 0339 □ Bus: 7, 12, 15, 15a, 27, 28, 31, 52, 52a, 88 □ Tube: Ladbroke Grove, Notting Hill Gate □ Parking: on street □ Pastor: Rev Raymond Westbrook □ Address: 77 Highlever Road, W10 □ Telephone: 969 7127 □ Available: when at home □ Other staff: Pastor Miles (633 7765)

Peniel Chapel is situated just off Portobello Road, famous for its busy weekend markets. Built originally for Anglican use in the 1850s, the church was soon after sold to the Presbyterians, and The Assembly of God congregation began worship there in 1922, buying the property in 1924. The church is presently undergoing an almost complete rebuilding, during which time services will be held in a nearby hall. The interim venue had not been selected at the time of writing, but an enquiry by telephone will confirm the address.

The present congregation, unlike many Pentecostal churches, contains a mixture of ethnic groups and social classes. An average of 30–40 adults attend the Sunday morning service with about the same number of children. The services are evangelical in nature. There is at least one traditional hymn, but on the whole, modern songs are preferred. An overhead projector displays the words of the songs on the wall behind the platform, while books are used for hymns.

While the adult members of the congregation meet for coffee and a chat after the service, the children stay behind for an hour or so of Junior Church. A well attended mothers and toddlers group meets twice a week. Pastor Westbrook say that the work of the church is not based on social activities. Rather, the church tries to help the whole person 'by bringing them into contact with Christ'.

Services: Sunday 10.30am, 6pm Communion; Tuesday 7.30pm Prayer meeting; Friday 7.30pm Family service □ Facilities: amplification, pool for baptism, overhead projector for songs □ Children: Junior Church, Sunday 12.15pm–1.15pm □ Wheelchair: level access □ Visiting: open at service times only

Beaulah United Church of God

Worshipping at: St John with St Andrew, Waterloo Road, SE1 □ Bus: 1, 68, 131, 171, 176, 177 □ Tube/BR: Waterloo □ Parking: difficult □ Minister: Pastor Willie □ Address: 37 Wordsworth Road, SE20 □ Telephone: 659 5903

The Beaulah United Church of God is a small group that meets at the Anglican Church of St John with St Andrew in Waterloo. The Church was founded by Pastor Willie in 1969, though it has been worshipping here only since 1985.

The Beaulah Church is going through a quiet period at the moment with an attendance of between 6 and 12 at the two services on Sundays. There are no activities although at certain times in the year the Beaulah Church invites several other church groups from around the country to join in a big evening that is both a religious and social occasion.

The services, Pentecostal in style, have a set time in the afternoon, but in the evening the service ends at any time around 10pm depending on the spirit of the meeting. Services are usually led by Pastor Willie and augmented with readings by members of the congregation. Other preachers may be invited to lead services at Pastor Willie's discretion.

Members of the Church are mainly of Jamaican origin, yet as Pastor Willie says 'The door is open to anyone that may come; it is a Church of God'.

Services: Sunday 12.30pm-2.45pm, 6.30pm-10pm(ish) □ Wheelchair: several steps

Bible Truth Church of God

16a Hetherington Road, SW4 □ Bus: 45, 88, 155 □ Tube: Clapham North □ Parking: on street □ Minister: Rev E Crichlow □ Telephone: 733 9265 □ Available: phone in evenings

At the corner of Hetherington Road and Kepler Road is a small, blue, corrugated iron building that houses the Bible Truth Church of God. Acquired from the Methodists in 1962, the building is now the venue for a full week of activities and worship.

On Tuesdays, for example, there is a prayer meeting, while Wednesdays are both 'missionary days', when members meet to discuss and plan their evangelising work in local streets, and also days when the older church members can get together in the afternoon. On Thursdays there is Bible Class; Friday evening is given over to the young people, while on Saturdays the church is often hired out to other Pentecostal groups who have no baptism facilities of their own.

The week culminates in the two Sunday services, each attended by between 40 and 50 worshippers. Often over 2½ hours long, the services include hymns (accompanied by guitars and drums in the evening), and a sermon given by the minister. Deacons and elders also help run the services. The congregation contains people of all ages, most of whom are of Afro-Caribbean origin. There are many Bible Truth churches in the West Indies and in North America, and this particular church is the headquarters of the London branch.

Services: Sunday 12noon & 6.30pm (Communion each 2nd Sunday); Tuesday 8pm Prayer meeting □ Facilities: baptismal pool □ Children: Sunday school □ Visiting: open at service times only

The Bibleway Church

The Good Shepherd Mission, 17 Three Colts Lane, Bethnal Green, E2 □ Telephone: 739 3822 □ Bus: 8, 8a, 106, 253 □ Tube: Bethnal Green □ Parking: on street □ Contact: Rev HC McFarlane □ Address: 123 Balls Pond Road, N1 □ Telephone: 254 2727 □ Available: most times

The Bibleway Church has been worshipping at the Good Shepherd Mission since 1984, the third venue since their origins in 1978. The present building is owned by the Shaftesbury Society and the work of the Mission and the Bibleway Church is closely linked. The Mission dates back to 1855 when several teachers began to educate poor children and their successors have continued to provide a place where young people can meet to enjoy themselves and hear the Gospel. In 1980 Ronald Willcox, a senior member of the Shaftesbury Society and of St Helen's Bishopsgate, started this latest youth project in Bethnal Green which now provides four nights a week of youth club activities for local youngsters.

Many other activities take place at the Mission including a lunchtime drop-in for young unemployed people, a football team and a mid-week ladies' Bible study. The Bibleway Church is involved in much of this work, especially the welfare of the lonely and isolated local elderly people; Rev McFarlane spends a great deal of his time working amongst Afro-Caribbean OAP's and has helped organise an Elderly Care Project.

On Sundays the building is used for worship by the Bibleway Church who utilise the premises continuously from midday to 10pm. Following a Sunday school the Divine Worship Service is in true Pentecostal style with much music from guitars and drums, and preaching. Sunday afternoons at the Mission are spent in Bible study and the occasional football match. The evenings are again a time for prayer and worship with the Evangelistic Service. The church at present has about 50 people attending throughout the Sunday and membership is rapidly growing—indeed the church 'has steadily been climbing Jacob's ladder to higher blessings in the Lord', and continuously strives to bring hope to people who are present living without such hope.

The church building itself used to be a school and is ideally suited for the range of activities which take place here. It is basically one large hall with a number of rooms for other activities.

Services: Sunday 1.30-2.45pm Divine Worship, 7.30-8.30pm Evangelistic Service □ *Facilities: amplification* □ *Children: Sunday school 12.30–1.30pm* □ *Wheelchair: 1 step only* □ *Other details: multi-purpose building for a wide range of activities*

Calvary Church of God in Christ

Worshipping at: Congregational Church, Kelly Street, NW5 □ *Bus: 27, 46, 53, 134, 137, 214* □ *Tube/BR: Camden Town, Kentish Town West* □ *Parking: on street* □ *Pastor: Rev Gill* □ *Address: 41 Esmond Road, NW6* □ *Telephone: 328 5088* □ *Available: telephone for appointment*

The Calvary Church of God in Christ is an international Afro-Caribbean denomination with its headquarters in Memphis, Tennessee. It has several congregations within London, including Kentish Town, where services are held at the old Kelly Street Congregational Church. This particular congregation started in the 1960s, and membership remains strong; attendance at services is good, and draws people from afar as well as local people.

Sundays are very active. At 10.30am is Sunday school for young children; there is also an adult Bible study group which meets before the service. The morning service itself actually begins at noon, and lasts for two hours or more. The service is lively, with plenty of music and singing (with tambourines and an electric guitar providing the accompaniment) and emphasis on prayer and preaching, based on the Scriptures. Participation by the congregation is total, in both prayer and praise. Everyone is welcome at any service, and will be sure of a warm greeting, regardless of nationality.

After the Sunday service there is a meal, and people can stay to talk with friends or to meet other people. Following the meal, the pastor and other members of the congregation will take their fellowship to others, such as older people, who cannot make it to the services. The church remains open, however, and people are welcome to stay to attend the evening service.

Activities continue through the week. On Wednesday is a prayer meeting, while Thursday has a meeting called YPWW (Young People Willing Workers) when young committed church members come to share fellowship and study the Bible. Once a month there is an Activities Night, where the young people's various skills are brought into the use to serve God and the community.

The Kelly Street church building is shortly to close; it will be demolished and a new church, shared by the Congregationalist Church and the Calvary Church, is to be erected. While this takes place, the services will still continue, but in the church hall rather than the old church itself.

Services: Sunday 12noon–2.30pm, 6pm–8pm (Holy Communion, 1st & 3rd Sundays); Wednesday 7.30–9pm Prayer meeting □ *Children: Sunday school 10.30–12noon* □ *Wheelchair: impossible; long narrow staircase*

Church of God

Worshipping at: St Andrew's Methodist Church, 240 Lancaster Road, W11 □ Telephone: 229 7728 □ Bus: 7, 15, 15a, 52, 52a, 295 □ Tube: Ladbroke Grove □ Parking: on street □ Contact: Mrs Campbell □ Address: 129 Sulgrave Road, W6 □ Telephone: 603 5005 □ Available: ring for appointment □ Other contacts: Mrs Williams, Evangelist, 32 Willcott Road, W3, (992 6402)

The England branch of the Church of God was founded in the early 1970s by Bishop Campbell who, having previously worked with an Evangelical church as a minister, felt a need to 'launch out into the Gospel'. At first Bishop Campbell held meetings in his home, but numbers soon increased and a hall was hired. He went briefly to America, where he had a chance to experience American evangelism, and where he was ordained a Bishop by the American Church of God. The Church of God has shared St Andrew's Methodist Church for 13 years, and is the head church of six other groups worshipping in the Greater London area. Bishop Campbell's wife is pastor-in-charge at St Andrew's.

Sunday services, consisting of readings from the Gospel, hymns and songs and individual testimonies, are lively and moving. The congregation is of predominantly African and Caribbean origin. Special attention is given to children at the afternoon service, being more of a 'teaching' service. Each Sunday of the month is dedicated as follows; the first Sunday of the month is known as the Lord's Supper and Communion, when the early part of the day is spent in fasting and prayer; services are dedicated to the Men's Fellowship on the second Sunday, to the Ladies' Auxiliary on the third Sunday, and to young people on the fourth. If there is a fifth Sunday, then services are dedicated to all groups. Although services are given over to a group in this way, all members are invited to attend each one.

Services: Sunday 1.30pm and 7.30pm; Tuesday 7pm Gospel reading and study □ Facilities: amplification, deaf loop □ Children: encouraged to attend afternoon service □ Wheelchair: access difficult, many steps to chapel □ Other details: hall

Church of the Nazarene

Grant Road, SW16 □ Bus: 19, 45, 77 □ BR: Clapham Junction □ Parking: on street □ Minister: Rev Joe Bentham □ Telephone: 0923 36213 □ Available: ring in evenings □ Other contacts: Mrs Packard (HQ: 061-702 9444)

The Church of the Nazarene attracts a small but commited community of regular churchgoers. Situated in the middle of a council estate directly opposite Clapham Junction station, it is a small brick church built in the 1950s. The church's evangelism is denoted by the phrase inscribed in large letters on the roof, immediately visible to the passer-by: 'Jesus says—I am the way, the truth and the life'.

The congregation is mostly middle-aged with families, who immigrated from the Caribbean in the 1950s. Recently, more white people have been attending. Services are open to all. About 75 people attend the Sunday morning family worship, and about 40 come for evening prayer. Children take part in the morning service, such as readings, before Sunday school. There are prayer and Bible study meetings on Wednesdays and Fridays.

Services: Sunday 11am and 6.30pm □ Children: Sunday school, 12.15pm for ages 5 to 12. Youth programme Friday evening □ Wheelchair: easy access □ Other details: two study rooms, reading room, etc □ Visiting: open at service and activity times only

Elim Central Pentecostal Church

Clapham Crescent, SW4 □ Telephone: 622 2910 □ Bus: 35, 37, 88, 118, 131, 155, 189 □ Tube: Clapham Common □ Parking: on street □ Pastor: Rev R Morell □ Address: 18 Twymount Road, SE27 □ Telephone: 670 1864 □ Available: mornings by 'phone and at church Weds. 2.30–3.45pm (Pastor's Hour)

The Elim Central Church shares prominence on Clapham Crescent with the William Bonney Estate; the church's name is displayed in large letters on the frontage. A large brick building of the 1950s, it replaced the original building in which the South West London Elim congregation started worshipping seventy years ago.

Three sets of glass front doors lead into a roomy and attractive interior, with tip-up seating, a large balcony and a new suspended ceiling. Services are conducted from a split-level platform at the front.

Elim services are all about rejoicing in praise and open participation. There is no set liturgy and little formality, except for the Breaking of Bread and the Ministry of the Word at the Sunday morning service. There is a Gospel Service in the evening. Both services are preceded by a half-hour prayer session. The congregation is mainly West Indian, and most live in the area, although some come from as far afield as Croydon. There are mainly adults over thirty years, with some teenagers and around thirty children. A Junior Choir participates and an organ is played at most services. An overhead projector and screen is used on the front platform as a visual aid for the congregation.

The church remains in use during the week. There is a lively Tuesday evening prayer meeting, with much singing and participation from the congregation. The first Tuesday in the month is a day of prayer and fasting, and there are three prayer meetings that day. Youth activities include Fellowship meetings, visits to old people's homes and an activity group. A 'Praise and Power' meeting is held on Saturday afternoons. Also, house groups are being set up and in summer there is a community outreach programme.

Services: Sunday 11am Communion and Worship, 6.30pm Gospel service, (reversed on first Sunday of the month); Tuesday 7.30pm Prayer meeting □ Facilities: amplification, deaf loop, overhead projector □ Children: Sunday school 12.45pm □ Wheelchair: two small steps to entrance; toilets for disabled □ Other details: hall used for prayer meetings and activities □ Visiting: open at service and activity times only

The Latter Rain Outpouring Revival Church

234 Hoxton Street, N1 □ Telephone: 739 5389 □ Bus: 22, 22a, 48, 67, 243, 243a □ Tube/BR: Old Street □ Parking: on street □ Minister: Bishop Parris □ Address: 242 Hoxton Street, N1 □ Available: ring church for appointment

The Latter Rain Outpouring Revival Church is based in Hackney, not far from Hoxton Street Market. Founded by Bishop OV Parris, membership has reached

200 since meetings started here in the early 1970s. Bishop Parris is minister for three other branches of the Church, one of which is based in America. In her absence, Sister Baker conducts the services.

The main service consists of singing, reading Scriptures from the New Testament Bible, and prayers made by members of the congregation. Although attended by a majority of Black Pentecostalists from the East End, regular members also come from all over London. Members are of all ages and include young families. Women are asked not to wear make-up, jewellery or trousers to the service, but a hat appears to be essential.

The church is equipped with movable seating that faces the large stage platform and altar, a choir stall and an organ gallery; the interior is quite plain. Fresh flowers decorate the altarpiece each Sunday.

The services feature music from an electric organ and a six-strong women's choir. Members of the congregation are also free to express their rejoicing through handclapping, tambourine tapping and even dancing. At the conclusion of the two-hour service, any member of the congregation who wishes to accept God into his or her life is invited to come forward while the other members pray for that person.

During the week, members meet for prayer meetings, Bible studies and occasional functions at a private home in Evering Road.

Services: Sunday 10.30am–2.30pm, 6.30pm–9.30pm □ Facilities: amplification □ Children: nursery □ Wheelchair: steps, help required □ Other details: utility rooms □ Visiting: open at service times only

Mount Calvary Spiritual Baptist Church

Worshipping at: All Saints & St Columb, Powis Gardens, W11 □ Bus: 7, 15, 15a, 52, 52a □ Tube: Ladbroke Grove, Westbourne Park □ Parking: on street □ Minister: Rev Mother PA Noel (Mother of Israel) □ Address: 31a Hazel Road, NW10 □ Telephone: 960 5985 □ Available: weekday mornings □ Other staff: Ann Dick (teacher)

Meeting at the Anglican Church of All Saints and St Columb, the Mount Calvary Spiritual Baptists are a small but committed Afro-Caribbean congregation, led by the Reverend Mother of Israel. Members are mainly adult, young to middle aged. Worship takes place on Sunday afternoons, with twenty or more people attending. These services are long, beginning at 1pm and lasting until 4pm or later, and are of a devotional nature; women wear white scarves around their heads during worship.

A chosen Biblical text is used as a starting point for the preaching, and its meaning and relevance is considered in depth. One section of the service gives an opportunity for members to stand up and give testimony to their love of God, or to talk about the Biblical text and relate what it means to them. An important aspect of praise is the singing of hymns; here, the Redemption Hymnal is used, and the singing itself is unaccompanied.

In the latter part of the service is a time set aside for healing and prayer; members can go to the front, where the Reverend Mother of Israel will lay on her hands, either to heal sickness or purge evil spirits. Some of the worshippers undergo a particularly intense religious experience, even to the point of collapse.

Services: Sunday 1pm–4pm □ *Wheelchair: full facilities at church (including toilets for disabled)*

Musama Disco Christo Church

Worshipping at: St Andrew's, Short Street, SE1 □ *Bus: 45, 59, 63, 109, 141* □ *Tube/BR: Waterloo* □ *Parking: on street* □ *Minister: Rev Jeri H Jehu-Appiah* □ *Address: 42 Brixton Water Lane, SW2* □ *Telephone: 259 0833* □ *Available: when in* □ *Other clergy: Pastor Edna Tait*

The Musama Disco Christo Church, founded in Ghana in 1922, has three branches in London, as well as in several West African countries and in the United States. The Waterloo branch was the first to be established in England, in 1983, although the seeds of the Church were sown in 1978 when a group of ministers visited and started prayer groups. A year later, a new team, including Rev Jeri Jehu-Appiah, the grandson of the founder of the Church, started meetings at St John the Divine, in Vassal Road. Today, the Waterloo branch has a congregation of around 45, mainly West Indian, people.

The name of the church means 'The Army of the Cross of Christ' in an unknown heavenly language. Pentecostal in nature, the Church advocates the revival of prophetism in Christianity. Members are taught how to receive from God, through the Holy Spirit, instructions on how to live in the glory of God. Prayer is thus used to discover the will of God, rather than as a means of talking to God. Other ways of communication from God may be through dreams, visions, signs, prophesies and the formation of thoughts. Unlike other Pentecostalists' teaching, salvation is regarded as ongoing; the 'I am saved' theory is rejected.

Sunday services are energetic, with dancing and hand-clapping to hymns. After the sermon, individual testimonies are given. Occasionally healing and spiritual revival is practised. At the beginning of each month a thanksgiving service is held, which usually includes a large number of testimonies and affirmation of faith. The whole family is encouraged to attend all services as there is no Sunday school for the children.

During the week, prayer meetings and Bible study groups are held at the minister's house. An annual trip to the south coast is organised for baptismal purposes.

Services: Sunday 2pm; Prayer meetings, Tuesday 8–9.30pm, Thursday 9–10.30pm, Friday 8–9.30pm □ *Wheelchair: level access*

New Testament Church of God

Lambert Road, Brixton Hill, SW2 □ *Telephone: 737 0963* □ *Bus: 2, 2b, 3, 45, 95, 133, 196* □ *Tube/BR: Brixton* □ *Parking: on street* □ *Minister: Rev VN Nelson* □ *Address: 38 Earlsthorpe Road, SE26* □ *Telephone: 778 4921* □ *Available: phone for appointment*

The New Testament Church of God in Brixton is a hive of activity. Even though they have only been in the building since the late 1970s, members have managed to build up a congregation of 250 and have completely renovated this formerly redundant, pigeon-infested Anglican church. It has been scrubbed both inside and out, the pews have been restored and the interior has been radically altered. What was a high, echoing nave has been divided into a worship area with church hall above accessible by iron staircases and a lift. In this way they have made maximum use of the available space while retaining a large and attractive place for worship, the low ceiling having been cleverly incorporated into the design of the church.

The interior is crammed full of pews and is lit by some stained-glass windows. A total-immersion baptism pool sits to the right of the chancel area; it is normally covered over to provide a stage for the band of young people who play guitars, drums and saxophones at the jubilant services. There is also a senior choir. Everyone has a chance to participate in a service if they so wish—for example, on Youth Sunday the youngsters take over completely, preaching, singing and entertaining throughout the service. Many people speak in tongues—considered to be evidence of the 'Spirit giving utterance'—and the messages they receive are translated for all to hear.

The church is the biggest Pentecostal church in Brixton and attracts worshippers from all over London. The congregation is almost entirely made up of people of Afro-Caribbean origin. The church runs various different groups throughout the week including a non-smoking pensioners group and a youth group. After services coffee and tea are available.

The Church of God is the oldest Pentecostal Church in the world, having been founded in the USA in 1886. In the UK where it is known as the New Testament Church of God there are over 100 branches.

Services: Sunday 12noon Divine Worship, 6.30pm Evangelistic Service, 1st Sunday Healing and Deliverance Service; Monday 11am Fasting and Prayer Service, Wednesday 7.30pm Prayer and Testimony Service □ Children: Sunday school 10.30am □ Wheelchair: help required, lift to hall □ Other details: hall (available for hire) □ Visiting: open at service times only

---

The Presbyterian Church of Wales

As the Welsh population in London has declined, so has this denomination. Now there are only three ministers serving all eleven churches in the Greater London area; thus it is not uncommon to see lay preachers leading services. It is sadly indicative of the present position that the best known Welsh Presbyterian church in London, the striking Gothic structure on Charing Cross Road near Cambridge Circus, is no longer a church at all, but a nightclub.

Formerly known as the Calvinistic Methodist Church, this is the largest Free Church in Wales and dates back to the revivalist preaching of Griffith Jones of Llanddowror (1684–1761). They broke with the established Church later than did the English Methodists, not ordaining their own ministers until 1811. The Church has a great tradition of hymn-singing and expository preaching, though the theology is no longer rigidly Calvinistic. All services are held in Welsh.

Jewin Welsh Church

Fann Street, EC1 □ Telephone: 628 8370 □ Bus: 4, 297a □ Tube/BR: Barbican □ Parking: difficult except Sunday □ Minister: Rev Elfed Williams □ Contact: Mr Evans, at church

This church began in a little back room in Cock Lane, Smithfield in 1774. Since then it has moved several times and in the mid-19th century was situated in Jewin Crescent in the City. In 1879 it moved to the present Fann Street site, but the name 'Jewin' was retained. The New Jewin Welsh Church was destroyed in the Second World War however, and it was not until 1961 that the present church was built, in traditional Welsh Chapel style.

The interior is attractively styled in wood with the pews arranged around three walls, and in galleries, directing attention onto the pulpit. Behind the pulpit is a tall organ, while at the rear of the church is a stained glass window—a memorial of both World Wars—containing scenes from the Book of Revelation.

The central part of the service is the sermon, which may well be given by a lay preacher. Before the war, many Welsh people, mostly dairymen and their families, lived in the area and one had to arrive early to be sure of getting a seat; now between 50 and 60 people can be expected for a Sunday service. These tend to travel from further afield and, in light of this, Jewin church activities have come to be concentrated on as few days as possible. Thus on Tuesday, for example, a devotional meeting precedes the 7.30pm literary society meeting, while a discussion group meets on Sunday afternoons before the evening service. A major event in the church's calendar is the Hymn Singing Festival held on the third Sunday in May

Services: Sunday 10.45am, 6pm (Communion 1st Sunday) □ Facilities: amplification □ Wheelchair: easy access □ Other details: hall used for church events □ Visiting: open only at service times

Shirland Road Presbyterian Church of Wales

Shirland Road, W9 □ Bus: 6, 48 □ Tube: Warwick Avenue □ Parking: not difficult □ Secretary: Sian Thomas □ Address: 3 Pooles Lane, SW10 □ Telephone: 351 0528 □ Available: evenings (telephone)

This Classical style church was completed in 1858 with seating for 300 people, but membership has now declined to the point where only twenty or so mainly elderly people now attend the single weekly service here. The exterior bear witness to the church's lack of funds though the interior, with its pews, large pulpit and fine old organ, is still in a good state of repair. The hall below the chapel is now used solely for congregational policy meetings.

Since the recent death of the longstanding minister, Rev Thomas, there has been no permanent replacement. Instead, either one of the three London ministers comes to take the service or Rev Thomas's daughter, Sian Thomas, who is also church secretary, will lead the service. For this reason, Communion is not on any specific Sunday but is subject to the availability of a minister.

Services: Sunday 6pm (Communion once a month) □ Wheelchair: 4 steps □ Other details: large and small hall □ Visiting: open for services only

The Religious Society of Friends (Quakers)

The term Quaker was originally rather derogatory but is now universally applied as an acceptable alternative to the full title of the Religious Society of Friends. The name refers to Friends' supposed tendency to 'quake' when moved to speak at meetings.

Unlike the Levellers, Muggletonians and other Dissenter groups that blossomed briefly in the 17th century, the Quakers have survived and flourished. This is no mean feat considering the initially hostile opposition to their uncompromising stand on such issues as non-violence and equality, and the fact that they have made no attempt at proselytising. Throughout years of changing moral and religious climates they have clung steadfastly to the simple faith exemplified by their founder, George Fox. Strong traditions of commitment to pacifism and social reform, on an individual level, have grown up.

Quakerism demands adherence to no creeds or dogma; their services involve no ritual. The inner light of Christ is the focus of Quaker worship and the meetings are held in silence unless anyone chooses to speak. There are elders and overseers and each meeting has its clerk, but there is no clergy. At meetings one may find people who regard themselves as agnostic or even Buddhist, and there are often newcomers or 'attenders' (people who go regularly but never formally join), but the Friends, affiliated to the British Council of Churches, is unquestionably a branch of Christianity, albeit a most liberal one. Along with the Salvation Army, Quakers are the only major denomination to uphold no Sacraments whatsoever.

The meeting rooms are generally plainly furnished and have a number of chairs around a table. On the table there will be a Bible, a vase of flowers, and a copy of the Quaker Work *Christian Faith and Practice* (revised every 25 years). The Bible is regarded as a supplement to, not a substitute for, the light of Christ within which is our only sure guide.

Further information is available from Friends House, Euston Road, NW1

Bunhill Fields Friends Meeting House

Quaker Court, Banner Street, EC1 □ Telephone: 253 4481 □ Bus: 43, 55, 76, 141, 243 □ Tube/BR: Old Street □ Parking: car park □ Clerk: Olive Yarrow □ Address: 62 Canarvon Road, South Woodford, E18 □ Available: most times at home □ Other contacts: Molly Porter, assistant clerk (254 4699); BIA (250 1193)

This society of Friends started meetings in 1874, in a tent that could seat 300 on an empty part of a Quaker burial ground. The area includes other burial grounds, and its name is derived from 'Bone Hill', so called because of the many cartloads of skulls and bones transported there in 1549 from Charnel House, near St Paul's. Many famous Quakers, including George Fox, are buried here, and the burial ground still attracts visitors.

By selling a strip of their section of the ground, the local Quakers replaced the tent with a building, which included classrooms, a coffee tavern and mission offices. Much of the building is now leased to the Bedford Institute Association which works with the elderly and homeless in the East End. Meetings of the Bunhill Friends are held in the basement. Access to this room is by a set of steep stairs, but this does not deter older members from attending.

Members are mostly professional people and include some Americans; there is a wide variety of ages. Membership is small but meetings are boosted by visitors from other groups. After meetings, members talk together over a cup of coffee. Discussion groups outside meeting times are organised, and members are involved in peace and community work.

Meetings: Sunday 11am □ Children: catered for during meeting if required □ Wheelchair: no access □ Visiting: open at meeting times only

Friends House

Euston Road, NW1 □ Telephone: 387 3601—for queries other than Meeting □ Bus: 14, 18, 30, 73 pass the door □ Tube/BR: Euston, also Euston Square □ Parking: very difficult, except Sundays □ Clerk: Sally Maxwell □ Address: 28 Wallace House, Caledonian Road, N7 □ Telephone: 609 5539—Sunday Meeting information

Friends House, a large, handsome building on Euston Road, exactly opposite the station, is a national rather than a local centre and the meeting for worship held on Sunday mornings is but one small element of the work and acitivities going on there. Built in 1926 to replace the original Headquarters in Liverpool Street, it was designed by Hubert Lidbetter. The central offices of the Society of Friends in Great Britain are housed here, its three main departments dealing with Quaker concerns on a national and international level, as well as providing information on the movement. Friends House also makes its facilities available to a host of other religious and political groups.

The Quaker meeting for worship, held in rooms 7, 8 and 9 once the partitions have been pulled back to make one large room, is well known for attracting a high percentage of visitors. As many as half of the 70–80 people sharing in the worship might be either from other Quaker meetings or attending a meeting for the first time. The majority are enthusiastic, single, educated people and verbal ministry is freely given, making this an interesting meeting to attend for the first time enquirer. Because of the non-residential location and lack of families, no children's class is available.

On other days a receptionist is stationed at the garden entrance, at the side of the building reached through a small public garden. Here, in the entrance hall, leaflets can be obtained both on the Quaker movement and on the variety of meetings and activities that take place in the building. There is also a bookshop with Quaker and other publications and a library which contains a wide range of religious books, and Quaker archives dating back to Fox's time. Lining the library walls are 17th century paintings from the Heemskerk school of Dutch painting showing Quaker groups and portraits.

It is estimated that over 100,000 people pass through this bustling, yet dignified building every year.

Meetings: Sunday 11am (Rooms 7, 8 and 9) □ Facilities: amplification □ Wheelchair: level access from Endsleigh Gardens through courtyard; lift inside □ Other details: enquiries about use/hire of Friends House facilities, contact Barbara Levelle on extension 25; for other departments ask at reception □ Visiting: open 9am–9.30pm Mon–Sat; Bookshop Mon–Fri 9.30am–5.30pm, except Tues 10am–5.30pm; Library Tues–Fri 10am–5pm

Hampstead Friends Meeting House

120 Heath Street, NW3 □ Telephone: 435 9473 □ Bus: 210, 268 □ Tube: Hampstead □ Parking: on street □ Clerk: Malcolm Stokes □ Address: 12 Southwood Park, N6 □ Telephone: 348 4452 □ Available: most times □ Other contacts: Sylvia Best, warden (435 9473)

The Meeting House, set back from the bustle of Heath Street, is entered through turn-of-the-century wooden gates and down a short tree-lined walk. Built around 1907, the building is white, with gables, and windows made up of small panes; an attractive feature is the green-domed porch with its dark, slender and simple columns. It is in a quiet residential neighbourhood, and the street slopes down to the Anglican church no more than one hundred yards away.

In an independently-minded community like Hampstead, it is not surprising to find this is one of the Quaker Meetings in London which is experiencing a growth in numbers. There are around 60 to 70 Friends who come each Sunday and in addition anything up to a third of those present will be 'attenders' with perhaps another ten who are newcomers. Another 70 or 80 Friends come less regularly. Coffee is served after meetings. The Meeting covers a wide area including most of Camden, and from Kilburn to Kentish Town.

The meeting room has a square floor plan and rises up through the two storeys; it is well-lit and overlooks the neighbouring gardens. There is another room on the ground floor where books are on sale each Sunday. In the upstairs library a Sunday group for children meets; this comfortable room is also used by various committees.

Hampstead Friends have organised an impressive array of special events. Successful concerts have been held in the meeting room, and art exhibitions take place regularly.

The aim has been to encourage aspiring artists and musicians who live locally, and to provide a forum for their talent. Book sales for CND and other organisations have also been arranged. A four-day fast and vigil for Hiroshima and Nagasaki Days on the nearby Heath has become an annual event. Joint activities with other East Hampstead churches also take place; these churches have formed an informal association since the demise of the local Council of Churches.

The library room is hired by a number of groups. During school term there is a daily playgroup which was started by members but is now community-run. A yoga class, other meditation groups and the Hampstead Photographic Society all meet here regularly. A healing group meets at the House every Saturday.

Meetings: Sunday 11am □ Facilities: amplification and deaf loop □ Children: class for older children during meeting □ Wheelchair: 4 steps; help available □ Other details: library, kitchen, other rooms □ Visiting: warden happy to show visitors around at any reasonable time

Ratcliff Society of Friends

Toynbee Hall, 28 Commercial Street, E1 □ Telephone: 247 3633 □ Bus: 5, 15, 15a, 40 □ Tube: Aldgate East □ Parking: on street □ Clerk: Pat Broadbent □ Address: 77 Murillo Road, SE13 □ Telephone: 318 1253 □ Available: ring for appointment □ Other contacts: Jeffrey Smith (739 2301)

The Ratcliff Society of Friends has existed for over 300 years. Originally based in a meeting house on the Ratcliff Highway, they have used the Toynbee Hall for the last 20 years. The original meeting house was destroyed during the last war, after which they continued worshipping at members' homes and hired halls.

Toynbee Hall was built at the turn of the century and is administered by University Settlements. Its most striking features are works of sculpture placed in the grounds, though perhaps another feature is the complexity of the arrangement of rooms inside, making it difficult to find the room used by the Friends. The financial burden of running the meetings at the hall is relieved by sharing the room with an old people's day centre.

At the Sunday meeting the room is arranged in the usual Quaker style, with chairs in a square and a table placed in the middle. The serenity of the silent worship is not unduly affected by noise from the busy Commercial Street. A children's class is arranged by a member and takes place at the same time as the meeting. Coffee is served after the meeting, when members can talk about their activities.

Over the last three years membership has grown, now numbering 26. Meetings regularly attract up to 20 people, with several visitors at most meetings. Members are mostly in the 25–35 age group; being moved around London by their jobs does not deter them from attending meetings. Discussion groups are held in homes, with members suggesting topics. Associations with peace and concern groups, characteristic of the Quaker movement, is not done as a group affiliation, but is left to the individual. Members also take part in community work.

Meetings: Sunday 11am □ Children: Sunday 11am class; contact Caroline Gregory (985 7422) □ Wheelchair: 1 step to room; toilets for disabled □ Visiting: open at meeting times only

Wandsworth Friends Meeting House

59 Wandsworth High Street, SW18 □ Telephone: 874 9758 □ Bus: 28, 44, 77a, 220, 280 □ BR: Wandsworth Town □ Parking: on street □ Clerk: Alan Philips □ Address: 3 Roseneath Road, SW11 □ Telephone: 228 6984 □ Assistant Clerk: Maureen Metcalfe

The Meeting House in Wandsworth is the oldest in London and the site has been used by Quakers as a place of worship for over 300 years. The first building on the site was little more than a shed, built in 1673, and was visited by the founder of the Religious Society of Friends, George Fox.

The 'shed' was used for nearly 100 years but proved more and more inadequate as a meeting place, so the present Meeting House was built in 1778. Over the years the building has been modified so that it now includes the room for worship, a library/meeting room, children's classrooms, a kitchen and a caretaker's flat. There is also a burial ground no longer used for burials, but regarded more as a

Wandsworth Friends Meeting House, SW18

garden. The interior of the Meeting House is very simple, with white painted walls and bare woodwork. For a number of years until 1979 the woodwork and benches were painted a dove grey. It is now all stripped to the natural wood and creates a calm effect to complement the Quaker style of worship.

Wandsworth Friends, a number of whom are social workers and teachers, uphold the Quaker traditions of community care, much of which is on a personal level such as the voluntary help given to a home for single parents. Members are presently discussing how their services and facilities might best be used to meet inner city issues. Also they follow Elizabeth Fry's famous example of work with prisoners and hold a Sunday meeting at the nearby Wandsworth Prison. Members also attend peace vigils held in London and are involved with a number of local community groups' such as Amnesty International and the Abbeyfield society.

The Wandsworth Friends have a meeting attendance of between 30 to 50 of all ages. Out of this number, the various committees are staffed to organise Quaker activities and the general running of the Meeting House.

Friends also participate in the Wandsworth Council for Community Relations and the Wandsworth inter-faith group, and support public Easter and Christmas services with other denominations. The Clerk is a member of the local fraternal group of Wandsworth Incumbents who meet to discuss religious and moral issus.

Meetings: Sunday 10.45am, (Every 2nd Sunday 2.15pm at Royal Hospital and Home for Incurables) □ Children: class during Sunday meeting, except 2nd Sunday of month □ Wheelchair: level access □ Other details: rooms may be hired, subject to clerk's approval □ Visiting: open for meetings; otherwise by arrangement

Westminster Friends Meeting House

52 St Martins Lane, WC2 □ Telephone: 836 7204 □ Bus: 1, 24, 29 □ Tube: Leicester Square □ Parking: difficult □ Clerk: Anne Goh □ Address: 54 Aldbourne Road, W12 □ Telephone: 743 2994 □ Other staff: Diana Galvin, Warden (contact at FMH) □ Available: telephone for appointment

Westminster meetings began in 1665, shortly after the rise of Quakerism in London. Their first Meeting House was in Little Almonry, close to Westminster Abbey, and it was while there that the 'Westminster Sufferings' took place, with Friends being made to pay heavy fines or thrown in prison if found worshipping. Today the little cul-de-sac no longer exists, and much more has changed besides. Now based in St Martins Lane, the Westminster Meeting is right in the centre of club and theatre land and so attracts many visiting actors and artists. It has the reputation of having an intellectual membership, and many non-Quakers also attend.

Dating from 1956, the present building is fourth in the Meeting history. Its predecessor, built in 1883, was the first erected by the group rather than leased. Like so many places of worship in London, it was all but destroyed in the Blitz, and until 1956 the only venue for meetings was the patched-up lobby.

Westminster holds four meetings a week, making it one of the busiest Meeting Houses in London. On Sundays, when around 45 attend, and on Tuesdays, the main meeting room (which can seat 150) is used while the smaller, more informal

Wednesday and Thursday meetings are held in the lobby. The Westminster Meeting is also responsible for organising the weekly Friday meeting at St Vedast's Church, Foster Lane and the monthly Sunday meeting at St Matthew's Church, St Petersburgh Place.

Four rooms here may be hired, including the meeting room and lobby. Regular hirers include a weekly meditation and yoga group and Oxfam. There is also a cellar used only by voluntary groups such as Alcoholics Anonymous and a young offenders club accompanied by Probation Officers. It should be noted that because of their work with and support for Alcoholic Anonymous, the premises are 'dry'—no alcohol allowed, even for weddings.

Meetings: Sunday 11am; Tuesday & Thursday 1–1.30pm; Wednesdays 6.15–7pm □ Facilities: deaf loop □ Children: class held in committee room during Sunday 11am service □ Wheelchair: level access □ Other details: 4 rooms for hire □ Visiting: open for meetings; otherwise by arrangement □ Other services organised by Westminster Friends: Friday 1–1.30pm at St Vedast's Church, Foster Lane (qv), 4th Sunday of every month 2.45–3.30pm at St Matthew's Church, St Petersburgh Place W2 (qv)

The Roman Catholic Church

Central to the Roman Catholic Church's definition of itself is the view that it is in perfect continuity with the first Christian community and can thus be regarded as having been established by Christ himself. The Church does not regard itself as one denomination among many, but as the one holy apostolic Catholic Church. The word Catholic simply means universal.

Any attempt to delve into Roman Catholic theology must be abandoned here in favour of a brief outline of the Church's history in Britain. Since the days of Henry VIII it has virtually been one of persecution and repression gradually abated by a series of relief measures passed by Parliament. For many years the only places where a Roman Mass could be said legally were a handful of chapels belonging to foreign embassies, and British Catholics would secretly assemble there for worship. British priests, having studied and been ordained on the Continent, would return to work in Britain, saying Mass in private homes, risking martyrdom and relying on the protection of the faithful.

It was not until 1778 that the first Emancipation Act was passed, and this proved sufficient fuel to incite the Gordon Riots of 1780 when Embassy chapels and homes of Catholics were looted and the mob roamed the streets swearing 'No Popery'. In 1791, Catholics were granted freedom of worship in Britain and it is from the following period that many of London's churches were built. By 1829 almost all disabilities had been removed and in 1850 the Hierarchy was restored. The following hundred years was a period of great expansion with many new Catholic communities—firstly Irish, then from the Continent—being established.

Another important event is the Second Vatican Council of 1962–65. The effect of this Council's recommendations can be clearly seen in Catholic churches and at services today. For example, the Mass is almost always said in the vernacular tongue, and only very rarely in the Latin of past centuries; further, the priest stands behind a forward altar, facing the worshippers and much nearer to them.

These are some of the most apparent signs of the Council's underlying principles of drawing priest and laity closer together, and opening up the Liturgy to greater understanding and increased lay participation.

In Catholic churches then, one will find a forward altar along with other regular features that have not changed, such as the Stations of the Cross, and statues of the saints and particularly the Blessed Virgin Mary. The centre of the liturgical life is the Mass, celebrated daily in most churches, and which Catholics should attend each Sunday and on all Feasts of Obligation. All are welcome to Mass but Communion, usually by wafer only, may not be taken by non-Catholics. The Catholic Church upholds the Seven Sacraments (Baptism, Confirmation, Holy Communion, Confession, Marriage, Holy Orders, and the Annointing of the Sick or Extreme Unction) but recognises Baptism as a special link with other Churches and denominations, almost all of whom perform this rite. The Catholic approach to the ecumenical movement is that God is present in varying degrees in other denominations, but, while Rome invites others to return to the fold, it clearly cannot compromise the truth or sacrifice the unique position of the Church.

Church of the Blessed Sacrament

Copenhagen Street, N1 □ Bus: 14, 17, 45, 221, 259 □ Tube/BR: Kings Cross, Caledonian Road □ Parking: on street □ Parish Priest: Rev Jim Kennedy □ Address: 165 Copenhagen Street, N1 □ Telephone: 837 4841 □ Available: most times

The Church of the Blessed Sacrament serves approximately 2,500 Roman Catholics within its parish boundaries, and attracts more than 500 people to Mass over an average Sunday. The Parish Diary is packed with a variety of activities, ranging from prayer meetings to Bingo sessions. There are outings in summer, plays performed at festive seasons, and an annual sports day.

For all this activity, it is recognised that the parish is a challenging one with an increasing Catholic population. The community consists largely of low-income and one-parent families, unemployed people and senior citizens. In the light of this, the Rt Rev Victor Guazzelli, Bishop of East London, set up a parish team in 1986 in order to discover 'how best the Catholic Church can serve the community'. The team comprises the two priests (Fr Kennedy and Fr Dermot), two Loreto sisters and Sister Katharine, the headteacher from the local primary school. As a result of this initiative many new groups have been formed, including a catechesis working party exploring various areas of sacramental life and a community development group looking after the welfare and needs of local people.

The church itself is nothing grand: a small, square, brick building with a discreet facade. The plainly decorated interior has wooden pews which can seat about 300 people. There is a small shop selling devotional items and cards which is open around the major Mass times. The Parish House, built beside the church in 1960, is available throughout the day for people to pop in and talk with the priests or fellow parishioners.

Mass: Sunday (Sat 7pm), 8.30am, 10.30am, 12noon, 6.30pm; Holy Days 8.30am, 9.15am, 1pm, 7pm; Weekdays as announced □ Confession: Saturday 12–12.30pm, 6–6.30pm □ Facilities: amplification □ Wheelchair: difficult, 8 steps □ Other details: hall available for hire; shop □ Visiting: open 7.30–11.30am except Mondays; if locked, apply at Parish House

Brompton Oratory (The London Oratory)

Brompton Road, SW7 □ Telephone: 589 4811, 581 1711/2 □ Bus: 14, 30, 74 □ Tube: South Kensington, Knightsbridge □ Parking: some spaces, otherwise meters □ Superior & Parish Priest: V Rev Richard Price □ Other clergy: many other priests in residence □ Available: duty priest always available

In no way could the London Oratory be described as 'another' Catholic church; possessing the proportions of a small cathedral, it stands as a major Knightsbridge landmark in Brompton Road, just up the road from Harrods and Hyde Park. Its overwhelming impression is one of spaciousness—the sanctuary alone is seventy feet deep, and the nave, one of the widest in England, is ten feet wider than that of St Paul's Cathedral, to which the church bears some resemblance. It has a similar dome area, crossed over by two chapels, with well proportioned arches to complete the picture. The original vision was to create an Italian-style design, and some most appropriate furnishings were acquired, including some very large statues of the Twelve Apostles by the sculptor Guiseppe Mazzuoli (1644–1725). However, there is an element of pastiche involved in re-creating an Italian church in London. The pulpit, for example—the work of Commendatore Formilli—was not designed until 1930. There were departures from architect Herbert Gribble's original design and it was 1895 before the dome was added, to the design of one George Sherrin.

The origins of the word 'oratory' lie with a Florentine man called Philip Neri (1515–95), a citizen of Rome for most of his life, passing from devout laymanship to a reluctant ordination at the age of thirty-five. He had a real gift with young people and regularly gathered them together for times of study and prayer. Eventually the venues for these meetings became known as the Oratory. In England, he was quite unknown until two men, John Henry Newman and Frederick William Faber brought him to the attention of the country. Newman and his followers took the lead, seeking instruction in Rome itself and becoming Oratorians after ordination in 1847. On their return to England, they were joined by Faber in 1848. But a country venue for such a large community was soon found to be impracticable and the group divided. Newman settled in Birmingham and Faber was sent to found an Oratory in London.

The London Oratorians found themselves in premises variously described as a whisky store, a gin shop, and a dance hall, in King William Street just off the Strand. After three years a property was found in Brompton, an area as much admired by Faber as disliked by Newman. It was decided to build a temporary house and church until funds became available for something more elaborate. The church remained until its demolition in 1880, with many of the fittings being re-used in the new building, which was consecrated on April 16, 1884.

Priests do not 'move on' after a few years at the Oratory, but remain within a permanent community although bound by no vows to do so. The twelve priests who live in the Oratory House next door take it in turn to act as duty priest, who is available for counselling and consultation of all kinds, as well as providing the usual confessional facilities. The Oratory is not an inward-looking body. It has a large congregation, a very fine musical tradition and a comprehensive social life. Midsummer fetes, thriving scout and brownie groups and even an Oratory Cadet Corps are just some of the activities on offer.

'Our work', says Fr Ignatius Harrison, 'is preaching, administrating the

Brompton Oratory, SW7

Sacraments of the Church and spiritual counselling of the faithful'. The rich ceremonial character of its worship, alongside some of the most inspired music-making in London, are offered as the 'best possible to God'.

Mass: Sunday (Sat 6pm), 7am, 8am, 9am, 10am (Family), 11am (Solemn, Latin), 12.30pm, 4.30pm, 7pm; Holy Days 7am, 8am, 10am, 12.15pm, 1.15pm, 4.30pm, 6pm (Solemn, Latin); Weekdays 7am, 8am, 10am, 12.30pm (not Sat), 6pm □ *Confession: at call (French, German, Italian & Spanish spoken)* □ *Facilities: deaf loop* □ *Wheelchair: ramp* □ *Visiting: open 6.30am–8pm daily; please do not disturb services*

Corpus Christi

Maiden Lane, WC2 □ *Bus: 1, 6, 9, 11, 13, 15, 77, 170* □ *Tube/BR: Covent Garden, Charing Cross* □ *Parking: difficult* □ *Parish Priest: Rev Henry W Dodd* □ *Address: The Presbytery, Maiden Lane, WC2* □ *Available: most times (not Thursday afternoons)*

Corpus Christi is the Roman Catholic parish church of Covent Garden. Sandwiched in Maiden Lane, its bell tower dominating the surrounding buildings, it is an imposing sight, although it is now grimed with age. It was built in 1874 under the direction of Canon Keynes, who also erected several other churches in the diocese. At that time, there were may Catholics living in the area, but in 1882, when the Royal Courts of Justice were built, a 5½ acre site was cleared, and thousands of families moved out. Even now, the local population is scarcely a hundred.

The church's interior has a charm all of its own, from the Sacred Heart which greets visitors as they descend the steps, to the fittings, such as the magnificent High Altar. This was carved out of Caen stone by Sir Thomas Earpe, sculptor of the large cross in the forecourt of Charing Cross Station. Suspended in front of the altar is an impressive array of sanctuary candles, suspended from the wooden roof.

Also in the church is a painted wooden statue of St Genesius, the patron saint of actors, with the symbols of his calling (the twin masks of comedy and tragedy) at his feet. The presence of St Genesius is important; Corpus Christi is associated with the Catholic Stage Guild, which holds a Mass here every other Friday (and an annual Mass which all the members attend). A small memorial in the church commemorates those members of the Guild who were killed in the Second World War. Occasionally, theatrical performances take place within the church itself.

Many famous people have been associated with the church. G K Chesterton, Hilaire Belloc and the poet Francis Thompson all worshipped here. At one time, the church had a great musical tradition; Dame Maggie Teyte, the opera singer, was discovered here in 1903 while singing at a parish concert. The tradition continues in the 5.45pm service on Monday evening, when the old style Latin (Tridentine) Mass is sung and celebrated. Attendance on Sunday numbers around 300 for the four Masses. Local people attend, but there are many tourists, especially Americans; cards are left in the foyers of nearby hotels, giving details of service times. Weekday Masses attract 60 to 70 people, largely office workers, with around 20 at the evening services. Since the local population is small, and the church has few facilities, there is little in the way of community activity.

Mass: Sunday (Sat 7pm), 9.30am, 11am (Sung Latin), 12noon, 5.50pm; Weekdays 1.05pm, 5.40pm (old style Tridentine Mass Monday evenings); Saturday 1.05pm □ Confession: daily 12.30–1pm; Saturday 12.30–1pm, 5.30–6.30pm □ Facilities: amplification (not always used) □ Wheelchair: difficult—steep stone steps □ Visiting: usually open 8am–7.30pm

Church of the English Martyrs

Prescot Street, E1 □ Bus: 15, 25 □ Tube/BR: Aldgate, Aldgate East, Tower Hill, Fenchurch Street □ Parking: difficult □ Priest-in-Charge: Rev Frank Flynn □ Address: 30 Prescot Street, E1 □ Telephone: 488 4654 □ Available: most times □ Other clergy: Rev Liam Dowling

This church stands where the City finishes and the East End begins; on one side there is a run-down terraced street, while on the other an ultra-modern office block looms above even the twin towers of the church. It was built in 1876 to serve the large Irish population. In those days congregations reached 5000, although now perhaps 200 attend on a Sunday. Few residents remain but worshippers travel back to the church and area with which, say Fr Flynn, they feel very special ties. While preserving this dispersed parish, Fr Flynn also promotes the church amongst the office workers as a place to pray or to celebrate Mass in the lunch hour.

The church is of an inevitably Gothic design by Pugin & Pugin who were accustomed to having rather more space to work with. The small size of the site resulted in an unusually short nave, and hence, in order to seat the huge original congregations, a large gallery was installed which extends halfway down each side of the nave. The impressive stained-glass window behind the altar depicts the 32 English Martyrs to whom the church is dedicated, grouped around the central figure of Christ. Installed in 1930, the window is the work of William Early of Dublin.

The crypt is used by an active youth club, and Fr Flynn hopes to extend the number of facilities available to parishioners by building a new community centre behind the church. There is a long tradition here of involvement with the community, and Fr Flynn is keen that it will continue.

Mass: Sunday (Sat 6pm), 8.30am, 11am (Sung); Holy Days 8am, 12noon, 1pm, 8pm; Weekdays 1pm; Saturday 9.30am □ Confession: Saturday 12noon and 7pm □ Wheelchair: several steps—difficult access □ Visiting: open 10.30am–1.30pm daily

Farm Street (Church of the Immaculate Conception)

114 Mount Street, W1 □ Bus: any along Oxford Street, Park Lane, Piccadilly □ Tube: Green Park, Bond Street, Marble Arch □ Parking: NCP Park Lane □ Superior: Rev Anthony Nye SJ □ Address: as church □ Telephone: 493 7811 □ Telephone: 493 7811 □ Other clergy: many other priests in residence □ Available: always duty priest

The Church of the Immaculate Conception is known everywhere simply as Farm Street. More than a parish church, it is the headquarters of the Jesuit movement

Farm Street Church, W1

in England and has a permanent community of thirty priests involved in a wide range of activities. Although Farm Street is famous for providing guidance on matters of great theological and philosophical complexity, the duty priest is available to all who need him, whatever their problems.

The Jesuits arrived to build their church in the 1840s, but of course they had been in England long before that. At first, in the reign of Elizabeth I, they came in disguise, but gradually Mass was celebrated more openly until, with the Catholic Emancipation Act of 1829, it was possible to build a church. However the scale and boldness of this venture was remarkable. The Superior, Fr Randal Lythgoe, decided to build a huge church, capable of seating a thousand people. The church, designed by J J Scoles in the Gothic revival style with strong French influences, was opened in 1849.

The interior was furnished by Pugin, to great acclaim at the time. The effect is one of attractive formality, a balance of warmth and order. Among the chapels housed in both aisles are ones to Jesuit saints, including St Francis Xavier whose death is depicted here in a painting by Charles Goldie. The largest chapel is to St Ignatius, at the north end of the church. It has been sound-proofed for use by the parents with babies during services; they can see the celebration of the Mass from there and a loudspeaker enables them to hear.

Given the non-residential nature of the area, it is not surprising that some three quarters of the congregation come from well outside the parish. About 1300 attend one of the seven Masses held on Sunday, and the daily attendance during the week is around 200. A great effort is made to introduce variety into services with due emphasis being given both to silence and to popular hymns. Farm Street is famous for the standard of its music, and the best attended service of the week is at 11am on Sunday when the professional choir sings a Latin Mass (the prayers and readings are in English).

Of the thirty priests in the community, only five work full-time in the church. The others may be involved in charity work for example: the community helps support various hospices and centres for the homeless, including 'The Passage' and places run by the Salvation Army. Ultimately though, the concern at Farm Street is to be available to anyone needing help and guidance.

Mass: Sunday (Sat 6pm), 7.30am, 8.30am, 10am, 10.35am (Czech), 11am, 12.15pm, 4.15pm, 6.15pm; Holy Days 7.30am, 8.30am, 11am, 12.05pm, 1.05pm, 5.35pm, 6.15pm; Weekdays 7.30am, 8.30am, 12.05pm, 1.05pm, 6pm; Saturday 7.30am, 8.30am, 11am □ Confession: Sunday & Holy Days—before all Masses; Weekdays 8–8.30am, 12–1.30pm, 5.30–6pm; Saturday 11.30am–12.30pm, 3.30–6.30pm □ Facilities: amplification □ Children: creche, chapel with sound relay for parents with babies □ Wheelchair: 1 small step at garden entrance □ Other details: bookshop □ Visiting: open 7am–7pm daily; written guides available

The Church of the Holy Apostles

Winchester Street, SW1 □ Bus: 11, 24 □ Tube/BR: Victoria, Pimlico □ Parking: on street; NCP nearby □ Parish Priest: Rev Alistair Russell □ Address: The Presbytery, 47 Cumberland Street, SW1 □ Telephone: 834 6965 □ Other staff: Rev Colin Davies

The arrival of Father Alistair Russell in 1983 ensured that this active parish church with its wonderful facilities would continue to flourish. The congregation has grown; now over 1000 people attend Mass here each Sunday. The priests are assisted in their pastoral duties by two lay sisters of Notre Dame. There is much home visiting, including the giving of Holy Communion to the housebound.

The social activities held at the church are legion, so much so that there is a full time youth worker who helps run the youth club and organise free holidays for children. There are regular tea parties and dances, discos and jumble sales, and a number of groups and societies meet here.

The church began in Claverton Street as a Chapel of Ease to Westminster Cathedral, but the present church owes much to Fr Hadfield, parish priest from 1938 to 1982. After the old church was bombed, he obtained the present site, which had been conveniently cleared by a doodlebug, and enlisted the help of his architect father. The church complex, together with presbytery and church hall was completed in 1957.

To enter the church, and most particularly the church hall below, is to experience a classic piece of 1950s design. The buildings are practical and uncluttered, and the church is particularly light and spacious. In the Lady Chapel are two modern stained glass windows, of Our Lady and of the Sacred Heart. The interior is ordered and simple, with photos of church committee members and children awaiting confirmation adding a homely touch.

Mass: Sunday (Sat 6pm), 9am, 10.15am (Family), 11.30am, 12.30pm (Spanish), 5pm; Holy Days 7am, 10am, 7pm; Weekdays 12noon, 6pm; Saturday 9am □ *Confession: Saturday 12–12.30pm, 5.30–6pm* □ *Facilities: amplification* □ *Wheelchair: ramp* □ *Other details: hall available for hire* □ *Visiting: open from 6.30am daily*

Holy Trinity, Dockhead

Dockhead, SE1 □ *Bus: 47, 47a, 70, 188* □ *Tube/BR: London Bridge, Tower Hill* □ *Parking: small car park* □ *Parish Priest: V Rev George Telford* □ *Address: Priest's House, Dockhead, SE1* □ *Telephone: 237 1641* □ *Available: all times* □ *Other clergy: Revv John O'Toole, Michael Bateman*

The life of this parish revolved around the Bermondsey Docks until their demise in the 1960s, causing another of the great social upheavals that have struck the area over the last 150 years. The people are used to hardship, and even the church has experienced tragedy—in 1945 the parish priest, Fr O'Riordan, and his two assistants were killed when a rocket hit the presbytery.

The more persistent hardships have been bad housing and sheer poverty, and Holy Trinity, with its succession of priests of considerable stature, has not shirked its social responsibilities. Fr Peter Butler, for example, who was responsible for the building of the second church (opened 1835), was a man prepared to put his faith into practice. During the cholera epidemic of 1832 he would lay out the bodies that the undertakers would not touch, sometimes even making their coffins himself. He also established a convent of Sisters of Mercy for the benefit, both practical and spiritual, of parishioners. The convent still thrives in the parish, and has a new building, completed in 1957.

In the same year, a new presbytery and church were also built. The church, described as 'stripped Romanesque', has an attractive interior dominated by the rounded white arches. These provide a sense of spaciousness and height, and an environment well suited to the fine organ, which is often used for a variety of recitals.

The docks' closure greatly reduced the congregation, though alternative local jobs were more easily obtained then than they are at present. Now, the warehouses are being converted into offices, and the new housing comprises luxury flats and terraces which, like their owners, do not blend in with the old Bermondsey. The church still attracts around 500 people for Mass on Sunday, however. Every two weeks there is a Folk Mass which contrasts with a traditional Latin Mass, held monthly, while most services have modern settings. Holy Trinity also runs a primary and secondary school, and has a looser connection with Downside Boys' Club, one of the best of its type, which was founded by Old Boys of the famous school who felt a 'Catholic concern' for the local boys on the street. Fr George Telford and his assistants are also involved with home visiting, especially amongst the elderly. Much of the parish life is centred at the Felton, the church's own social club.

Mass: Sunday (Sat 6.30pm), 7.30am, 10am, 6.30pm; Holy Days 7am, 9.30am, 8pm □ Confession: Saturday 9.30–10.30am, 6–6.30pm □ Facilities: amplification □ Wheelchair: 1 step into side door □ Other details: social club □ Visiting: open (porch only) 9.30am–6pm

Notre Dame de France

Leicester Place, WC2 □ Bus: to Leicester Square or Piccadilly Circus □ Tube: Leicester Square □ Parking: difficult □ Priest: Rev Raymond Jovenez □ Address: 5 Leicester Place, WC2 □ Telephone: 437 9363 □ Available: phone to enquire

This interesting round church in Leicester Place was originally a Victorian 'Panorama' where one could see views of Waterloo and Jerusalem. By the 1850s, however, the growing French population in Soho were in need of their own place of worship and the Panorama was converted into the Church of Notre Dame de France. Founded in 1865 by the Marist Fathers, the church has undergone one major rebuilding since then, when in 1955 the bombed site was restored to its present state, and a foundation stone was brought from Chartres. The church now stands an impressive round structure with Romanesque arches, supported by a circle of plain columns, and a huge round window in the centre of the roof providing a smooth, gentle light—the only source of natural light.

Colonel Rémy, a famous member of the French Resistance, had a great affection for this church. He would visit it often and grew especially fond of an old statue of Notre Dame de Victoires. In 1940, however, the church was severely bombed and the statue badly damaged. Concerned by this, Rémy asked if he could take the old head of the statue with him to France, saying he would return with the whole statue renewed. He was given permission and the new statue now stands above the baptistry in the gallery, presiding over the delightful interior which has several notable features. Above the altar is a modern Aubusson tapestry of Our Lady, designed by Dom Robert of Buckfast. In La Chapelle de la Vierge (now used to house the tabernacle) three walls have been painted with a striking fresco by Jean Cocteau (1960)—Cocteau himself is pictured to the left of this altarpiece.

Although the church is under the jurisdiction of Cardinal Hume and weekday Masses are celebrated in English, every effort is made to preserve a French atmosphere. Few French people now live locally, but the church keeps close links with the community and especially with the Lycée in South Kensington. Regular meetings are held with the French Protestant Church in Soho Square and there are joint Bible study groups. Notre Dame is a popular place to worship—one can find over 600 people at a Sunday morning Mass—and a most rewarding church to visit.

Mass: Holy Days 8am (English), 6.05pm (English); Sunday (Sat 6pm), 10am, 11.30am; Weekdays 12.15pm (English), 6.05pm (English). In July and August: Sunday (Sat 6pm), 11am; Weekdays 12.15pm (English) (All services in French unless specified) □ Confession: before Mass □ Facilities: amplification □ Children: catechism classes □ Wheelchair: very difficult access □ Other details: hall available for hire □ Visiting: open 8am–1pm and 2.30pm until last Mass of day

Church of Our Lady

Lisson Grove, NW8 □ Bus: 2, 8, 13, 16, 26, 49, 59, 74, 113, 159, 616 □ Tube: St Johns Wood □ Parking: car park for 40 cars □ Parish Priest: Rev Charles McGowan □ Address: 54 Lodge Road, NW8 □ Telephone: 286 3214 □ Available: when in □ Other staff: secretary during office hours

The Church of Our Lady, offering a Sunday Mass to suit every taste, is a listed building, built in 1833 and renovated in 1971. Sir John Betjeman, visiting to advise on the restoration, dubbed it 'Regency Classic'. Two Italian spinsters, daughters of Court ballet teacher Giovanni Gallini, not only financed the building of the church, but also lived in it. They made their home in the south transept (now the organ chapel), while the north transept, presently the Martyrs' chapel, housed the clergy. It was not until 1937 that these domestic quarters were opened to the church. One of the first four churches to be built after Catholic Emancipation, Our Lady was intended for Jesuit use, but in spite of an appeal to the Pope it was handed over to the seculars.

By 1971 the building was grimy and dilapidated, yet the incumbent Fr Michael O'Dwyer fell in love with it and initiated an ambitious and costly renovation project. He enjoyed inviting eminent people to look over the church and discuss its transformation. One of these, Sir John Betjeman, after sitting alone for a while in the church, said to Fr O'Dwyer 'You must do something splendid with that panel' (meaning the one behind the sanctuary). Eventually the interior was stripped of many of its accumulated furnishings and returned to the airy, well-lit starkness of John Scoles' 1830 design. The panel in question was filled with a 12 foot high bronze coloured statue of Christ in Glory, especially commissioned from Michael Clark, the sculptor also responsible for many other statues and features of the church. The painting in the organ chapel showing Christ's Baptism is by a famous Polish painter Merek Zulaski.

The congregation of Our Lady is made up of both rich and poor, old and young, and includes a high percentage of one parent familes. The church tries to serve them all. The Sunday Family Mass at 9.30am appears to be run almost by local school children. They read the lessons and part of the litany, and announce hymn numbers, all in a very confident manner. At 10.45 on Sunday mornings, a Renaissance choir sing the Latin Sung Mass and on the first Saturday in each month sing Vespers. On special Holy Days and high days an orchestra also play in the church. The 6pm Folk Mass, with guitar accompaniement to modern hymns and songs, is popular among the younger parishioners.

A small shop, situated at the back of the church, is open after each Mass for the sale of books and devotional objects. The Church of Our Lady also aims to encourage 'a social spirit within the church'. The many activities includes an over 60's club, scouts, ballet and Bingo. A bar in the adjoining hall is open during Bingo sessions on Friday nights, and also on Saturday if there is a dance or reception.

Mass: Sunday 8am, 9.30am (Family), 10.45am (Sung Latin), 12noon, 6pm (Folk); Holy Days 7.30am, 10am, 6pm, 8pm; Weekdays 10am, 6pm □ Confession: Saturday 10.30–11.30am, 5–6pm, 6.30–7.30pm, at call □ Facilities: amplification, deaf loop □ Children: special Mass 9.30am Sunday □ Wheelchair: ramp and help available □ Other details: hall available for hire □ Visiting: open 8.30am until last Mass of day (term-time); shop open after each Sunday Mass

Our Lady of the Assumption and St Gregory

Warwick Street, W1 □ Bus: 3, 6, 9, 9a, 12, 13, 14, 15, 19, 22, 38, 39, 53, 59, 84, 88, 91, 94, 95, 97, 98, 159, 502, 506 □ Tube: Piccadilly Circus, Oxford Street □ Parking: on street □ Parish Priest: Rev Francis Davis □ Address: 24 Golden Square, W1 □ Telephone: 437 1525 □ Available: when in

The Church of Our Lady of the Assumption and St Gregory is situated in the centre of one of London's most famous shopping areas and provides an ideal place to sit quietly for a while away from the bustle of Regent Street and Piccadilly Circus.

The history of the church reveals the importance of foreign embassies in keeping Catholicism alive when public worship was prohibited. The Portuguese first built a chapel on the site, and when they left in 1747 the Bavarian Embassy took over use of the chapel. In 1780 the chapel was badly damaged during the Gordon Riots but not totally destroyed, and services were soon able to be resumed. The present larger building was opened on 12th March 1790 on the feast of St Gregory the Great, to whom the church was dedicated, though it was still popularly known as the Bavarian Chapel. Following the Catholic Relief Act of 1791 the church became fashionable among the growing and more visible Catholic population. The second dedication to Our Lady of the Assumption seems to have come about after the acquisition in 1853 of a bas-relief of the Assumption by the Irish sculptor John Edward Carew.

The building is not architecturally notable, the facade of red brick in Warwick Street was built to escape notice as much as possible, and remains unassuming. A gallery of considerable elegance gives the interior its distinctive appearance and the apse, built in 1874 and designed by John Francis Bentley, contains a beautiful mosaic of the Virgin's Coronation, also designed by Bentley.

The church has two quite separate congregations during the week: office and shop workers attend lunchtime and early evening Masses, while local residents and tourist attend at the weekend. Of particular interest, is the Latin Mass (11am Sunday) when a professional choir sing from the gallery. Details of the music can be found in the Saturday *Times*.

Mass: Sunday (Sat 6pm), 8am, 10am, 11am (Latin), 12noon, 4pm, 6pm; Holy Days 8am, 12noon, 12.30pm, 1pm, 4pm, 5.45pm; Weekdays 8am, 12.45pm, 5.45pm (except Sat) □ Confession: Mon–Fri 12.15–12.45pm, 1.10–1.30pm; Saturday 12.15–12.35pm, 1.10–1.30pm, 5.15–5.45pm □ Facilities: deaf loop, amplification □ Wheelchair: 3 steps, no ramp □ Other details: 'Grotto Club' in basement of presbytery, evenings □ Visiting: open 7 days a week 7am–7pm for private prayer

Our Lady of Czestochowa and St Casimir (Polish)

Devonia Road, N1 □ Bus: 4, 19, 30, 38, 43, 73, 153, 171, 196, 214, 263a, 277, 279, 279a □ Tube/BR: Angel, Essex Road □ Parking: on street □ Priest-in-Charge: Rt Rev Mgr K Zielinski □ Address: 2 Devonia Road, N1 □ Telephone: 226 3439 □ Available: at service times or by appointment □ Other clergy: Revv Canon T Kurczewski, J Tworek, E Trojnar

The town of Czestochowa is considered an important centre of Catholicism in Poland, and it is a symbol of faith, hope and patriotism for the Polish people. To a much lesser extent the Church of Our Lady of Czestochowa and St Casimir is a centre for Poles in England, as a place of worship and as a means of contacting the community. It is both a mission and a parish church.

The Polish population of London has been growing steadily since the late 19th century and the mission developed alongside, so it was ready to cope with the influx of refugees during the Socond World War. At this time London became the seat of the Polish Government in exile and this was the only Polish church in Free Europe.

The Perpendicular style building was acquired from the Swedenborgians and was consecrated for Catholic worship on 12th October 1930 by Cardinal Hlond, the Primate of Poland. The church has a west front with a central doorway and six windows flanked by large buttresses and stairway pinnacles. Inside one is struck by the dramatic stained glass windows designed and made by a Polish soldier, Adam Bunsch, during the Blitz. They depict some devastating scenes, such as St Andrew Bobola looking down through clouds littered with bombers onto a battlefield where soldiers are stabbing a naked body and tanks roll relentlessly by. The windows are a harrowing reminder of Poland's troubled history.

All services are held in Polish, and there is no lay assistance with the Communion. Polish hymns are sung either by a choir or the youth group, who also give performances of Polish songs and dances throughout England.

Mass: Sunday 8am (Latin), 9.30am, 11am, 12noon; Holy Days 7.30am, 8am, 9am, 11am, 8pm; Weekdays 7.30am 8am, 8.30am, 9am □ Facilities: amplification □ Wheelchair: 1 step, easy access □ Other details: hall □ Visiting: open for services only or by arrangement

Our Lady of Dolours

226 Fulham road, SW10 □ Bus: 11, 14, 22, 31 □ Tube: South Kensington, Earls Court □ Parking: on street □ Prior & Parish Priest: Rev Nicholas Martin □ Address: St Mary's Priory, 264 Fulham Road, SW10 □ Telephone: 351 1037, 352 6965 □ Available: most times □ Other clergy: 5 other priests in residence

The Victorian Gothic Church of Our Lady of Dolours is deemed to be of some architectural importance. It has an impressive tower, but its most unusual feature is the long colonnade, or pillared arcade, through which the church is entered. This is unique in London, perhaps in England. The interior has much stained glass, and above the altar of Caen stone inlaid with marble, is a large sculpture of the Host and Chalice, with the legend 'I am the living bread'. Also of note are the two side chapels, both the gifts of benefactors.

The church was built in 1875 by priests of the Servite order, and the history of this church is also the history of the Servites in England. The church is alongside St Mary's Priory, and is still staffed and run by the Servite order. The parish priest and Prior, Fr Nicholas Martin, lives in the Priory, along with five other priests. A primary school nearby is run by the church, attended by the children of parishioners.

The church's congregation is very active in the life of the parish, and also very cosmopolitan; some 25 nationalities live in the area. Members take an active part in the running of the church and help with the services, both with the readings and by assisting with the Eucharist. There is no choir as such, but a music group leads the singing on Sundays. There are several groups attached to the church, including FIRE (Faith, Intercession, Repentance, Evangelism), a teaching group, and the Legion of Mary. A youth group meets after services on Sundays.

The parish is very involved in caring for people. Those in need call at the Priory for assistance, and genuine cases may receive financial help out of parish funds. There is great involvement with charitable and missionary work, and a peace and justice group has ties with Amnesty International, helping to free people imprisoned for their political beliefs.

Mass: Sunday (Sat 6.30pm), 8.30am, 10am (Sung), 11.15am (Spanish), 12noon (Latin), 4pm, 7pm (Folk); Holy Days 7.30am, 10am, 12noon, 7.30pm; Weekdays 7.30am, 10am, 6.30pm □ Confession: daily 6.15–6.30pm and at call (Italian, French and Spanish spoken) □ Facilities: amplification, deaf loop □ Wheelchair: level access; ramp to Priory □ Other details: hall, meeting rooms, etc □ Visiting: open 7am–12.30pm and 3.30–8pm daily; bookstall

Our Lady of Hal

Arlington Road, NW1 □ Bus: 3, 24, 31, 46, 53, 74, 137 □ Tube: Camden Town □ Parking: on street, meters □ Parish Priest: Rev Patrick Nolan □ Address: 165 Arlington Road, NW1 □ Telephone: 485 2727 □ Available: at all times □ Other clergy: Rev William Skeehan

The church was founded, as Notre Dame de Hal, by the Scheut Fathers who came to England from Belgium after the First World War. The first church was opened in 1922, but it was not until 1932 that the foundation stone of the present building was laid. It was officially opened in March 1933, and was visited by the then Crown Prince Leopold and Princess Astrid of the Belgians in November of that year. The Fathers carried out the usual duties of missionaries: preaching, praying and offering support to the community.

The congregation here has always comprised several nationalities. Since the 1840s the area has been the destination of Irish people seeking work and a new life, and now the Portuguese and Chinese communities are represented at the church and the Portuguese hold their own service on Sundays at 5pm. Of the other Sunday services, there is a popular family Folk Mass at 10am, and a sung Parish Mass at 11am with a small choir.

In 1982 the Scheut Fathers handed over responsibility for the parish to the Westminster Diocese, and Father Patrick Nolan became the first diocesan parish priest. His work includes a great deal of counselling and visiting, and helping parishioners with problems such as unemployment, loneliness and alcoholism.

Mass: Sunday (Sat 7.30pm), 8.30am, 10am (Folk), 11am (Sung), 12.15pm, 5pm (Portuguese), 7.30pm; Holy Days 8am, 10.15am, 12noon, 7.30pm; Weekdays 8am, 12noon (Mon, Wed, Thu) 12noon, 7.30pm (Tue, Fri); Saturday 10am, 12noon, 7.30pm □ Confession: Saturday 10.30–11.30am, 5–6pm (Portuguese spoken) □ Facilities: amplification, deaf loop □ Wheelchair: several steps; help needed □ Other details: parish rooms, used by Portuguese & Chinese for social functions etc, hall for hire □ Visiting: open 7.30am to 8pm

Our Lady of La Salette and St Joseph

Melior Street, SE1 □ Bus: 47, 70, 70a □ Tube/BR: London Bridge □ Parking: on street □ Priest: Rev Michael Cooley □ Address: 14 Melior Street, SE1 □ Telephone: 407 1948 □ Available: most days at home

As one comes out of London Bridge station and crosses the footbridge over St Thomas Street, a large painted sign— 'Catholic Church'—can be seen to the left. This is the Church of Our Lady of La Salette. The present building is the successor of an earlier chapel erected by missionaries last century and later pulled down to make way for the station. At that time, the congregation numbered in excess of 800 people, but a general decline in population, due to the change from residential to warehouse development, has reduced numbers to around 200.

The church itself is made of brick, and, while not of architectural significance, it does contain some attractive interior features, such as the unusual curved altar. (This is rarely used, since it is some distance from the congregation; a smaller free-standing altar before the sanctuary rail is used instead). There is a shrine, to Our Lady of Salette near Grenoble, where two local children had a vision of the Blessed Virgin Mary in 1846.

The present incumbent, Fr Michael Cooley, has been with the church since 1983, and is also the Roman Catholic chaplain to Guy's Hospital, which is in the parish. He makes regular visits and takes a service there every Saturday night. Fr Cooley describes his congregation as being split into four groups: the local residents, including various ethnic groups and young families; the hospital staff from Guy's; homeless people, many of whom attend the Manna Day Centre nearby; and lastly, the local business people who attend the weekday services.

The most popular service of the week, especially amongst younger members, is on Sunday morning, when a folk group, occasionally African in style, accompanies the worship.

Plans to demolish the church and build a modern replacement have come to nought, but new houses are certainly being built and people are moving back into the area. Social evenings in the Parish Hall are well attended and Fr Cooley feels 'there is a new lease of life within the area and there are great prospects for the future'.

Mass: Sunday 11am, 7.15pm; Holy Days 9.15am, 12.35pm, 8pm; Saturday 9.30am, 6pm (at Guy's Hospital) □ Confession: Saturday 12–12.30pm, 6–7pm □ Wheelchair: 1 step; large doors opened on request □ Other details: hall used for concerts □ Visiting: porch open 7am–9pm daily; church open for services only

Our Lady of Lourdes and St Vincent de Paul

Harrow Road, W9 □ Bus: 18, 28, 31, 36 □ Tube: Westbourne Park □ Parking: at back of church □ Parish Priest: Rev Frank Leonard □ Address: 337 Harrow Road, W9 □ Telephone 286 2170 □ Available: by appointment

The history of this church begins with a children's home on the site called St Vincent's Home, which had a chapel open to the public as a mission chapel and dedicated to Our Lady of Lourdes—hence the double title of the present church. In 1912, the chapel became a parish church and the orphanage became the presbytery, but it was soon clear that the facilities were inadequate for a growing parish. With the cost of land so high, it was decided not to buy a new site but to sell some of the church's own land, and thus finance the building of the modern church complex we see today, which finally opened in 1975.

Although it looks rather austere from the Harrow Road, the building is a clever solution to the problem of a very restricted site. Church, hall and presbytery are amalgamated in the design, not only to save space but also 'to express in stone, as in man, the essential unity of the sacred and the secular' as Fr Gerard Strain, priest at the time of rebuilding, explained. The relative sizes of the church and the hall can be adjusted to suit any occasion by the use of sliding partitions.

On entering the church, you are welcomed by a statue of the Risen Christ by Michael Clark of the Royal Society of British Sculptors. Another example of his work is the Statue of the Virgin and Child in the north-west corner. The reredos, demonstrating the unity of the cross and the altar, is the work of Robyn Denny.

A number of different nationalities are represented in the congregation here and there is a Caribbean Catholic Association which organises both social and religious gatherings. Every church member is expected to become involved in the life of the church and to contribute something towards it. This may be through the Society of St Vincent de Paul, for example, who provide both emotional and material aid for the lonely and elderly, or the Legion of Mary, who undertake so much visiting work. There is a Third World Group, committed to helping development projects in the Third World and to raising awareness throughout the parish of the terrible plight of so many of the world's inhabitants.

Lay people also help represent the church at the North Paddington Ecumenical Council. The church is keen to contribute to the vision of a universal church and values highly the work of the Council in encouraging contact and interaction between member churches.

Of the services at the church, one of the most popular is the 10am Family Mass on Sunday, when children participate through acting or singing, and a guitar group may lead the worship. The following Mass at 12noon is more formal, while the Saturday Mass again features guitars and popular hymns.

Mass: Sunday (Sat 6.30pm), 8am, 10am (Family), 12noon (Sung); Holy Days 10am, 8pm; Weekdays 10am □ Confession: Saturday 10.30am, 4pm, and by arrangement □ Facilities: amplification, deaf loop □ Children: Saturday 11am–12noon, preparatory classes for 1st Communion □ Wheelchair: ramp at side entrance □ Other details: 2 halls, available for hire □ Visiting: open 8am–11am weekdays, 8am–7pm Friday, 7am–1pm Sunday

Our Lady of Mount Carmel and St Simon Stock (Carmelite Church)

41 Kensington High Street, W8 □ Telephone: 937 9866 □ Bus: 27, 28, 31, 52, 52a □ Tube: High Street Kensington □ Parking: difficult □ Contact: Members of the Order □ Available: 7am–12noon and 3–7pm

The Carmelite monastery has been in this street for over a hundred years; the church is a post-war rebuilding by Sir Giles Gilbert Scott. Its design is modern, yet simple, unornamented as befits the church of this world-renouncing Order. The single exception is the giant reredos, with its central figure of the Virgin as Our Lady of Carmel, the Order's Patron.

Weekly attendances here top the 3000 mark. Every form of Mass is provided, from the solemn Sung Latin Mass to the modern approach of the Folk Mass. This range of styles goes some way to explaining the large numbers attending in an area with a small residential population. At the last count 40 nationalities were represented in the congregation.

Another factor is the excellence of the liturgical music here, which stands in the tradition of the founder of the church. Father Herman Cohen was a convert from Judaism, who became a Carmelite monk. Formerly he had been a concert pianist, and was a friend of the composer Liszt. The professional choir here is consistently rated among the finest church choirs in England.

A steady stream of visitors just come for quiet prayer and contemplation. It has been said that the atmosphere here encourages prayer. There is also a social centre, which is used by over 300 people, and not just for the bar which is open every Saturday and Sunday night. Regular talks on devotional or theological topics are arranged, and usually delivered by one of the ten resident monks.

In its full name the church carries a dedication to St Simon Stock, the 12th century founder of the Carmelite Order in Britain. He takes his surname from the curious circumstance that from the age of 12 he lived as a hermit in the trunk, or stock, of a tree.

Mass: Sunday (Sat 6pm), 6.30am, 7am, 8am, 9am, 10am (Folk), 11am (Sung Latin), 12.15pm, 4.30pm, 6pm; Holy Days 6.30am, 7am, 8am, 9am, 10am, 11am, 12.15pm, 6pm, 7pm; Weekdays 6.30am, 7am, 8am, 9am, 12.15pm, 6pm □ Confession: Saturday 10.30–11.45am, 3.30–6pm, 8–9pm; Weekdays to call at 6.45pm □ Facilities: amplification, deaf loop □ Children: Sunday school and other classes □ Wheelchair: ramp □ Other details: social centre with TV room, reading room and bar □ Visiting: open 6am–7pm; bookshop

Our Lady of the Rosary

Old Marylebone Road, NW1 □ Bus: 6, 7, 8, 16, 27 □ Tube: Edgware Road □ Parking: space for 20 cars on forecourt □ Parish Priest: Rev John O'Neill □ Address: Rosary House, 211 Old Marylebone Road, NW1 □ Telephone: 723 5101 □ Other clergy: Revv John Turner, Tony O'Connor □ Available: most times

Soon after its completion in 1961, this large church with adjoining hall complex may have seemed an unwarranted venture, for the sizeable Catholic population for whom it was built was dramatically reduced around this time as the area was redeveloped to make way for the Westway flyover. Another instance of unfortunate timing was that a fixed High Altar had been installed at the rear of the sanctuary, just before Vatican II decreed that forward altars should be used.

Fortunately these setbacks have been overcome. A temporary forward altar is used, and the congregation has been increased by people from neighbouring parishes, students, and tourists either from the new hotels or 'coach loads' in town for the day. Around 1200 attend Mass here over a Sunday and the 700 capacity church is far from being the near empty extravagance it might well have become. The church, designed by Goodhart-Rendell, is in brick, with a large high window in the rather blank west front. All other windows are high and clear, to minimise traffic noise and let in most light. The nave has five thick-columned arches supporting high transverse vaults, and the style of the interior is solid and uncluttered. Though the arches are pointed and the windows rounded they acquire unity through exclusion of detail.

The Rosary Church has a professional organist and a small but expert choir. This accounts for the quality and variety of music to be heard here on Sundays: both modern and traditional settings are used, and Latin hymns are sung at the popular midday Mass, while the spoken parts are in English.

The halls do not lie empty either. Regular clubs and dances attract people from both within the parish boudaries and beyond. They are also used for discussion groups and Bible study classes, and for numerous diocesan and extra parochial purposes. Indeed Fr O'Neill recalled a description of the Rosary Church, prompted by its frequent use by people outside the parish, as providing a 'spiritual buffet'.

Mass: Sunday (Sat 6pm), 8am, 9am, 10am, 11am, 12noon (Latin), 7pm; Holy Days 7am, 8am 12.30pm, 6pm; Weekdays 8am, 12.30pm, 6pm □ Confession: Saturday 10.30–11am, 4–6pm □ Facilities: amplification □ Wheelchair: ramp □ Other details: hall on two floors (ground floor available for hire) □ Visiting: open daily 7am–8pm

Our Lady of Sorrows

17 Cirencester Street, W2 □ Bus: 18, 36 □ Tube/BR: Royal Oak □ Parking: on street □ Parish Priest: Rev Anthony Cooke □ Address: as church □ Telephone: 286 2672 □ Available: most times

This parish was founded by the Oblate Fathers in the wake of the Great Western Railway which brought upheaval to this part of Paddington. At the opening of the church in 1912, Fr Miller, the Superior of the Order, gave a graphic account of the area's decline from a pleasant residential area to the 'present squalor'. Another drastic change was caused by bomb damage during the war, and the area is now dominated by high-rise blocks.

The church itself has undergone considerable alteration. It was built adjoining a school and when the school wanted a hall it was simply built on top of the church. The hall is shared by church and school. Further, in 1967, some children accidently started a fire by dropping candles into the Christmas crib. As the interior was largely furnished in wood the effect was catastrophic. Nowadays the church is quite plain with white walls.

The congregation is largely middle-aged with a few elderly members who can remember the early years of the parish. Many parishioners are Irish, but Chinese, Polish and Spanish residents also regularly attend. The combined Sunday congregations come to about 400 worshippers.

Services are led by Fr Cooke with help from lay readers and ministers and even tape-recordings to bolster the singing. Fr Cooke has to run things very much as a one man operation, and spends a lot of time visiting the ill and housebound. Despite the problems, he feels there could be more outreach—the church 'looks into itself too much', he feels—and he is only too pleased to accept assistance in this work.

Mass: Sunday (Sat 6pm), 8.30am, 10.30am, 12noon; Holy Days 9am, 7.30pm; Weekdays 9am (except Wednesday 7.15am); Saturday 10am □ Confession: Saturday 10.30am, 5.30pm □ Facilities: amplification □ Wheelchair: ramp □ Other details: hall □ Visiting: open for services only

Our Lady of Victories

235a Kensington High Street, W8 □ Bus: 9, 27, 28, 31, 33, 49, 73 □ Tube: High Street Kensington □ Parking: on street □ Priest: Rev Adrian Arrowsmith □ Address: 16 Abingdon Road, W8 □ Telephone: 937 4778 □ Available: generally □ Other clergy: Revv Gladstone Liddle, Christopher Webb

In 1794 the first Catholic place of worship since the Reformation was opened. It consisted of a small chapel in Kensington House intended for school boys but open to the public. It was formed by refugees from the French Revolution and run by French priests. During the next few decades, however, the population of Kensington grew considerably and by the 1860s Henry Manning, the Archbishop of Westminster, had decided to build a big church in the High Street and dedicated it to Our Lady of Victories. Within a century, the church suffered extensive bombing (1940) and was burnt out. Catholics had to find other places of worship for several years and they found themselves using variously the local

Odeon cinema, a High Street furniture store, the nuns' chapel in Kensington Square, and a chapel rented from the Congregationalists in Allen Street. It was not until the late 1950s, in fact, that this church was built by Adrian Gilbert Scott in the style of the modern Gothic Revival.

The church is rather plain inside with very little decoration, but the present incumbent does plan on adding some colour and items of devotion in order to give the place a lift. The most interesting feature is an unusual set of stained glass windows around the building which depict the story of Our Lady and Christ and the road to salvation, made by Blakeman in the 1950s. Also, at present, in a room behind the north wall, is a pictorial history of Pope John Paul's visit to Britain in 1982, together with the throne on which he sat in Wembley stadium.

The church offers a range of services to suit all its potential worshippers. They have a Low Mass (said rather than sung) during the week, while on Sundays there is the more traditional Latin Mass sung by a parish choir. Also on Sundays is a Family Mass with congregational singing of modern hymns to instrumental accompaniment. About 100 people attend Mass each weekday and 1500 throughout a Sunday. The congregation is mixed and includes Kensington residents, visitors and tourists, members of the significant Filipino and Latin American communities, and people from bedsit land. The church has numerous groups, both religious and secular, for young and old.

Mass: Sunday (Sat 6.30pm), 8am, 9am, 10am (Family), 11am (Sung Latin), 12.30pm, 6.30pm, (3pm Chaldean Rite Mass in Syriac); Holy Days 7.30am, 10am, 12.30pm, 6pm, 8pm; Weekdays 10am, 12.30pm, 6pm □ Confession: Saturday 10.30am–12.30pm, 3–6pm □ Facilities: amplification □ Wheelchair: several steps □ Other details: hall □ Visiting: open from 7am to last Mass

Our Lady, Queen of Heaven

Queensway, W2 □ Bus: 12, 88 □ Tube: Bayswater, Queensway □ Parking: on street □ Priest: Rev Philip Carpenter □ Address: The Presbytery, 4a Inverness Place, W2 □ Telephone: 229 8153 □ Available: most times

The church was built about 1860 as a Methodist chapel and about the turn of the century was sold to the Ethical Society. In 1954 it was bought by a Roman Catholic religious society and in 1973 was transferred to the Diocese of Westminster.

It is notable for the fact that it is a semi-circular building with two galleries supported by elegant cast iron pillars and is a good example of mid-Victorian church architecture.

The parish itself is small, but there is a large intake of visitors due to the fact that it is the centre of many hotels, and the congregations are composed of people from most parts of the world.

Mass: Sunday (Sat 5.30pm), 8am, 10.30am, 11.30am, 4pm; Holy Days 7.45am, 10am, 6pm; Weekdays 6pm (Mon, Wed, Fri), 7.45am (Tue, Thur) □ Confession: 10.30–11am, after evening Mass □ Wheelchair: very difficult; many steps □ Visiting: lobby open all day; church open only for services

Our Most Holy Redeemer and St Thomas More

Cheyne Row, SW3 □ Bus: 11, 19, 22, 49 □ Tube: Sloane Square □ Parking: on street □ Bishop: Rt Rev Patrick Casey □ Address: 7 Cheyne Row, SW3 □ Telephone: 352 0777 □ Available: when in □ Other clergy: Rt Rev Mgr David Norris

The church stands on a quiet Chelsea street close to Crosby Hall, once the home of St Thomas More. Based on a Florentine design, it was built in 1895 by Edward Goldie who also designed St James Place, Piccadilly. The interior was repainted in the early 1980s in pleasant shades of green, and has a number of paintings hung in alcoves, including reproductions of Murillo's Virgin and Child, and St Francis of Assisi by Corregio. The forward altar, installed since Vatican II, is an attractively simple marble structure, visible from all parts of the nave. The rear of the church is sectioned off by a grille, enabling it to be open for private prayer seven days a week with no fear of vandalism.

Although the neighbourhood retains a 'village' atmosphere and the Church of Our Most Holy Redeemer is regarded as very much a local church, worshippers come from all over south-west London each Sunday. The 11am service is the most popular, when a choir sings the Mass which contains 'a happy mixture of English and Latin'.

The few social events that are organised at the church, such as meetings of the Society of St Vincent de Paul or AA, take place in the vestry or crypt. For larger events, such as the annual bazaar, a room in Chelsea Town Hall is hired.

Mass: Sunday (Sat 6.30pm), 10am, 11am (Latin), 12.15pm, 6.30pm; Holy Days 8am, 10am, 6.30pm; Weekdays 8am, 6.30pm; Saturday 10am □ Confession: Saturday 5.30–6.30pm; Sunday before Masses □ Facilities: amplification, deaf loop □ Children: Sunday school in church □ Wheelchair: 2 steps □ Visiting: access to 2 rows of pews at back of church 7.30am–7pm daily

Church of the Precious Blood

O'Meara Street, SE1 □ Bus: 10, 21, 35, 40, 133, P2, P3 □ Tube/BR: Borough, London Bridge □ Parking: on street □ Parish Priest: Rev Danny Burns □ Address: The Presbytery, 22 Redcross Way, SE1 □ Telephone: 407 3951 □ Available: any reasonable time □ Other clergy: Rev Michael Doherty

The Precious Blood is a small church tucked away in the side streets behind Borough Underground station. The exterior of the church, recently renovated, opens out onto O'Meara Street, and is marked by its two distinctive Italianate bell towers. Inside, the first thing which strikes the visitor is the altar and impressive baldacchino. On the arch above this are the words 'CHRISTUS DILEXIT NOS ET LAVIT NOS IN SANGUINE SUO' ('Jesus loves us and washes us in his blood'). Each individual letter in this inscription was donated by a parishioner to whom the letter had some association (such as the initial of a loved one). The donors' names are inscribed on the back of the letters.

Also of note are the Stations of the Cross, made of teracotta. They were sculpted in Belgium and, on their arrival in England, were carried up from the docks by the parishioners themselves.

When the church was built by Canon Murnane, as an offshot of the parish of Our Lady of La Salette, this was one of the most densely populated areas of

Church of the Precious Blood, SE1

London. Redevelopment has changed the situation drastically, and now the local residents are few in number. Nowadays, the total Sunday congregation numbers around 250, spread over four services. All ages are represented, although the congregation tends towards the elderly.

There are youth groups and numerous social events which are held in the church's social club. The weekly newsletter, the Borough Piper, is lively and entertaining. It is named after the once-famous bagpipe band which was associated with the church. Also taking place here include a monthly meeting of the North Southwark Clergy, and occasional ad hoc charity events. The church also has a library of religious books which are available on loan to members of the congregation.

Mass: Sunday (Sat 7pm), 8.30am, 11am, 6pm; Holy Days 12.05pm, 1pm, 8pm □ Confession: Saturday 12.30–1pm, 6.30–6.50pm □ Facilities: amplification □ Wheelchair: 1 step; easy access □ Other details: social club; small religious library □ Visiting: open for services and 12noon–1.30pm daily

St Aloysius

Phoenix Road, NW1 □ Bus: 24, 27, 29, 68, 134, 137, 214, 253 □ Tube/BR: Mornington Crescent, Euston □ Parking: at rear of church □ Parish Priest: Rev Joseph Boward □ Address: 20 Phoenix Road, NW1 □ Telephone: 387 1971 □ Available: most times □ Other clergy: Rev Martin Mayes

Although the Church of St Aloysius, to the east of Euston station is very modern, the Roman Catholic parish of Somers Town dates back to 1808. At that time the area was a small outer London village, populated largely by Roman Catholic immigrants who had fled the religious persecution of the French Revolution. Under the auspices of their leader, Abbé Carron, the original St Aloysius was built. The old church was demolished in the 1960s to make way for the present building.

Oval in shape, the church was designed by A J Newton with Liverpool Cathedral in mind; hence the similarities, particularly the attractive stained glass lantern. The interior is simple but practical. The wooden pews radiate in a semicircle from the altar. The ceiling is made of pieces of carved wood in a geometric pattern; in addition to being decorative, this also acts as a sound baffle.

On Sundays the congregation is large and very mixed, with people of all ages and many families, and people from many different ethnic backgrounds, including Irish, Filipino, West Indian and Maltese. There is a concious effort to involve as many people as possible in the entire breadth of church life, from washing vestments to assisting with Holy Communion. The church choir is made up of parishioners and is intended to lead the singing rather than being elite and separate. Overall, the intention is to break down barriers between clergy and people, and restore people's awareness of the mysteries in everyday life. The church maintains an ecumenical dialogue with other denominations and there are regular study groups with Anglican and United Reformed church members. There is also dialogue with members of the Jewish community.

Adjoining the church is the One World shop, manned entirely by volunteers, which raises funds for the Third World countries. There is also a social club used by a variety of groups which is available for hire.

Mass: Sunday (Sat 6pm), 8.30am, 10.30am, 12.15pm, 6pm; Holy Days 9.30am, 12.30pm, 6pm; Weekdays 12.30pm, 6pm □ Confession: Saturday 11.30am–12noon, 5–5.30pm □ Facilities: amplification, deaf loop; other deaf/blind facilities by arrangement □ Wheelchair: ramp □ Other details: hall (available for hire) □ Visiting: open 7.30am–7.30pm daily

St Anne, Laxton Place

Laxton Place, Longford Street, NW1 □ Bus: 3, 24, 27, 29, 53, 134 □ Tube/BR: Warren Street, Great Portland Street, Regents Park, Euston □ Parking: on street □ Parish Priest: Rev Jeremiah Ryan □ Address: Laxton Place, Longford Street, NW1 □ Available: when in □ Other clergy: Rev Philip Najim, Chaldean Chaplain (387 0671)

St Anne's, built in 1970 and of a modern circular design, is situated next door to the Anglican church of St Mary Magdalene, giving an interesting contrast of the old and new. The history of St Anne's goes back to 1855, when it stood in Little Albany Street (now no longer in existence). In 1937 a new church was built in Seaton Place, and only in the late 1960s when property developers bought this site was the church moved to Laxton Place.

When Fr Ryan arrived in 1973, he was immediately concerned by the starkness of the building: 'it was more like praying in a fish bowl than a church'. Since then, however, the church has been transformed. The original clear glass windows have been replaced by gold tinted glass which gives the interior a warm glow, and the lighting is softer. The Stations of the Cross, originally just numbered plaques, were replaced by the stations from La Sagresse Convent, Golders Green, when it closed in 1978, and a wooden crucifix shipped out from Italy now hangs over the altar.

The church was designed for a small parish, and has no facilities for large social events. The worshippers are mostly elderly people, who like the intimate nature of the building and the services. St Anne's is not a tourist attraction and is kept locked except for services.

Mass: Sunday (Sat 6.30pm), 9am, 11am, 5pm (Chaldean Rite); Holy Days 7.30am, 12.30pm, 8pm; Weekdays 12.30pm (except Thursday 9am) □ Confession: Saturday 11.30am–12noon, 6–6.20pm □ Facilities: amplification □ Wheelchair: 2 steps, no ramp □ Visiting: open for services only

St Anne, Underwood Road

Underwood Road, E1 □ Bus: 10, 25, 225, 253 □ Tube: Whitechapel, Aldgate East □ Parking: on street □ Parish Priest: Rev Christopher Whelan □ Address: as church □ Telephone: 247 7833 □ Available: by appointment □ Other clergy: Revv Kevin Duffy, Peter Moore, Leo McIver

St Anne's Church has a small parish in the heart of London's East End, and is near the famous Brick Lane Market. Its origins are closely linked with the Irish Catholics who came to work at the docks of a flourishing Port of London in the years after 1848, to escape the famine and hardship in Ireland.

By 1850, there were 9,000 Catholics in Spitalfields, and 500 or so people were squeezing into a local school for each of the seven Sunday Masses held there. At this time, seven French priests moved to the area to found a London Mission. They were members of the Society of Marists, founded in France in 1824 to provide care and education for the poor and needy. They saw that a church was badly needed, and managed to raise the £600 to buy the site by subscriptions from the local poor. The church was opened in 1855, though building work lasted until 1894, and St Anne's was finally consecrated in 1905. Marist priests are in residence to this day. St Anne's was designed by Blout, a disciple of Pugin, in a familiar Victorian Gothic style. The interior has stone portraits of the founding Marist priests and some Victorian glasswork, while the north chapel is brightened by children's pictures. There are no fewer than eight confessionals—an indication of the original demand for the church.

Most members of the congregation now are English or Irish, although there are some from France, Italy and Malta, and others from as far afield as St Lucia and Domenica. Sunday Mass is attended by around 250, while during the week, 15 to 20 attend services held in the chapel between the church and the priest's house. The church is a centre for various social activities. The Social Club holds an annual senior citizens' party and a parish dance, and there is a lively festival of Irish dancing. To raise money, there are regular Bingo sessions (8pm, Wednesdays), frequent jumble sales, and a small shop selling books and cards.

The local Irish population has all but disappeared now, but St Anne's is clearly still a lively and much-used church. Indeed, there are no fewer than five priests in residence, as well as younger Marists who are training to become priests. There are regular meetings with Anglican churches and those of other denominations in the area, and the need is recognised for mutual respect between the Christian Churches and other Faiths, such as Islam and Judaism.

Mass: Sunday 10am (Sung), 7pm (Sung); Holy Days 9.30am, 7.30pm; Weekdays 9.30am (except Thursday & Friday, 7.30pm) □ Confession: before Mass, and on request □ Facilities: amplification □ Wheelchair: very difficult; 5 steps □ Other details: library □ Visiting: open for services only

St Anselm and St Cecilia

Kingsway, WC2 □ Bus: 5, 7, 8, 19, 22, 38, 55, 68, 77, 77a, 153, 188, 196, 501 □ Tube: Holborn □ Parking: difficult, except Sundays □ Parish Priest: Rev H J McAleese □ Assistant Priests: Revv D Murphy, Canon F J Bartlett □ Address: 70 Lincoln's Inn Fields, WC2 □ Telephone: 405 0376 □ Available: any time

If one arrives early enough of a morning at St Anselm and St Cecilia's, one will see a long queue of people forming along Twyford Place at the side of the church. These are down-and-outs from Lincoln's Inn Fields, waiting to receive free Luncheon Vouchers from the church. This has become a regular feature and has its roots in charitable work first carried out in the 18th century.

The present day church, in fact, carries on the tradition of Catholicism in the area that has existed since 1645 when there were complaints of 'sundry Papists, Forrainers, (and) leud idle wicked persons' attending furtive Masses. The church's immediate roots lie with the chapel of the Sardinian Embassy, one of the Embassy chapels that escaped the ban on Catholic worship and enabled English Catholics to attend Mass. The chapel was severely damaged during the Gordon

Riots of 1780 but survived to become, at the Sardinians' departure, the parish church of St Anselm, in 1853. The second dedication of St Cecilia, a reference to the fine musical reputation the church had acquired, was added in 1861. This building was finally demolished due to redevelopment plans and was replaced in 1909 by the church we see today, standing squarely on the Kingsway.

Much of the Renaissance architectural style of the old chapel is echoed in the new church. Inside, there is a large west gallery, and three round arches separate the nave from the single (south) aisle. From the old chapel are the 18th century font, the Lady Altar and the splendid organ, while a modern feature is a mosaic of St Joseph on the south wall. The Royal Sardinian Coat of Arms sits above a side entrance—a reminder of the church's past and of the troubled history of Catholic worship in Britain.

Of today's worshippers, about a third are local residents while the rest are commuters who work in the area and who use the church during the week. There are three Masses daily, at which some 200 to 250 communicants attend, while around 800 come to one of the Sunday Masses which include a Children's and a Latin Mass. The Parish Room under the church is used after Sunday Masses, when tea and coffee are served. Several Catholic societies and organisations meet at the church, and the popular Camden Catholic Youth Club, behind Holborn Library, attracts young people of all denominations.

Mass: Sunday (Sat 6pm), 8.30am, 10am (Sung), 11am (Latin), 12noon, 4pm, 6.30pm; Holy Days 7am, 8am, 9am, 10am, 12noon, 12.30pm, 1pm, 4pm, 6pm, 8pm; Weekdays 7.45am, 12.30pm, 6pm; Saturday 12.30pm □ Confession: Mon–Fri 12.30pm and 5.30pm, and at call; Saturday 12noon–12.30pm, 5.30–6pm, (available in Italian and French) □ Facilities: amplification □ Children: Children's Mass, Sunday 10am □ Wheelchair: 2 steps, then 2 swing doors □ Other details: Parish room □ Visiting: open 7am–6.30pm daily

St Boniface (German)

Adler Street, E1 □ Tube: Aldgate East □ Bus: 10, 15, 15a, 23, 25, 40, 67, 225, 253 □ Parking: on street □ Priest: Rev Karl Schmickler □ Address: 47 Adler Street, E1 □ Telephone: 247 9529 □ Available: most times

The German Church of St Boniface stands amongst a network of warehouses in the East End. Its story begins with the formation of the German Catholic Mission in 1809, and in response to the population shifts of London's German community, the church has been based in a number of locations. In 1862, for example, a Methodist 'Zion Chapel' in Whitechapel was acquired, altered to suit Catholic worship, and fitted out with a chime of four bells from the famous Whitechapel Bellfoundry. This 19th century church did not survive the bombings of the Second World War, but it wasn't until 1960 that the German Catholics were able to open their new church.

This modern church, designed by the firm of Plaskett Marshall & Partners, is visually quite stunning. A tall camponile by the entrance houses the four bells, hung one on top of the other, that were retrieved from the ruins of the old church and installed by popular demand of the congregation. Inside the church, one's gaze is caught by the striking *Christos Pantokrator* above the altar. Executed in coloured plasterwork by Herbert Reul, it shows St Boniface and the faithful at the feet of Christ.

Other features include the Stations of the Cross from Oberammergau on the organ loft gallery, and the stained glass window over the porch which depicts the Blessed Virgin and the Apostles receiving the gift of the Holy Spirit. To the present incumbent, Fr Schmickler, this represents the message that 'everyone is an apostle'. Overall, the church is airy and bright and gives an impression of space.

Since 1972 there has been a German school in the Petersham area of Richmond, and a large percentage of the German community has moved out there. Consequently, the congregation at St Boniface's is rather small for the size of the church and there is little organised by way of parish groups or events. However, a mission church, dedicated to St Thomas Aquinas, has been set up in Ham and the Sunday morning Mass is celebrated there and at St Boniface's, alternately. The sense of community is still strong, and the church magazine *Die Nachricht aus der Oase* is sent to over 2,000 homes in and around London.

The 'oase' of the magazine's title means 'oasis' and this is how Fr Schmickler sees the church in what he describes as 'desert times' amidst the bleak, monotonous landscape of towerblocks and terraces. The church can provide that moment of shade and respite we need to cope with the demands of daily life.

An important aspect of the church's work is Wynfrid Haus which was built adjacent to the church in 1970. It serves as a hostel and as a conference centre for all kinds of visitors. There are some 50 bedrooms available at reasonable rents to German visitors to London.

Mass: Sunday (Sat 6.30pm), 11am (2nd & 4th Sunday only); Holy Days 12.30pm; Weekdays 7am □ Confession: before and after Mass (German only) □ Wheelchair: level access by side entrance □ Other details: Wynfrid House hall (available for hire) □ Visiting: open early morning till 10am, evening till 8pm

St Casimir (Lithuanian)

The Oval, Hackney Road, E2 □ Bus: 6, 35, 55, 106, 253 □ Tube/BR: Bethnal Green, Cambridge Heath □ Parking: on street □ Priest: Rev John Sakevicius □ Address: 21 The Oval, Hackney Road, E2 □ Telephone: 739 8375 □ Available: most times

The only Lithuanian Catholic church in England, St Casimir's was specially built for this purpose in 1911. It remains an important centre for the Lithuanian community of London and the south-east, and Fr Sakevicius points out that his parish is 'personal, not territorial'. Around 50 people attend the most popular Mass (Sunday 11am), and after services the priest and congregation often adjourn to the hall for an informal social gathering and refreshments. The church maintains close links with the Lithuanian Sports and Social Centre in nearby Victoria Park.

The church is built in an Italianate style. The interior features include Stations of the Cross carved and painted by members of the community, as well as murals of Lithuanian scenes, one incorporating a painful portrayal of Christ. The south chapel is used for meditative prayer beneath a statue of the Virgin sprinkled with tiny bulbs, lit at the press of a switch. Close to this is an interesting plaque to the memory of Joseph Montvila, a Lithuanian priest who died in the sinking of the Titanic. The most notable feature, however, is the altarpiece, a huge wooden carving of Tyrolese design depicting the Holy Trinity and the Coronation of Our Lady. It was first widely seen at the Great Exhibition of 1851, and was displayed in a commercial art gallery before reaching its present, more suitable home.

Mass: Sunday 9am (Latin, readings in English and Lithuanian), 11am (Lithuanian); Holy Days 11am (Lithuanian); Weekdays 8am (Latin or Lithuanian) □ Confession: before Mass (in Lithuanian or Italian) □ Wheelchair: level access □ Visiting: open for services only, or by arrangement

St Charles Borromeo

8 Ogle Street, W1 □ Bus: 3, 8, 14, 25, 27, 29, 30, 53, 73, 134, 253 □ Tube: Goodge Street, Great Portland Street, Oxford Circus □ Parking: nearby NCP □ Parish Priest: Rev Alan Fudge □ Address: 8 Ogle Street, W1 □ Telephone: 636 2883 □ Available: most times

The internal design of this otherwise unremarkable Victorian Gothic church is most unusual. Since 1982, the pews have been arranged in collegiate fashion while the centre of the nave contains an extraordinary baptismal font and a large square eucharistic table or altar, while the original High Altar and reredos by J F Bentley, no longer the focus, now provide a splendid backdrop to the scene.

The sunken font, normally covered when not in use, is cruciform in shape with mosaics of the four Evangelists in the corners. Although large enough for an adult to be baptised in it by total immersion, it is mostly used for baptising babies. It was installed in response to the spirit of liturgical renewal urged by Vatican II, but the reason this particular church took this unusual step lies with the Neo-catechumenal communities at the heart of the church's life. These are groups of around 20 worshippers, guided by lay catechists and the priest, who meet three times a week for services, and who spend one Sunday a month together in prayer and meditation. The purpose, a process that can take six or seven years, is to rediscover the reality of their own baptism, described by Pope John Paul II as 'the source of the new life, of the divine life' in each. Thus, baptism is recognised as not merely a ceremony undergone by unknowing infants, but as the beginning of a radical alteration to people's lives.

The font, designed and installed by Neo-catechumenates, provides clear symbols of the full implications of baptism. It is made of marble and sunk into the ground to remind us that baptism follows Christ through death and rebirth. The seven steps down indicate the conquering of the seven deadly sins, and the seven steps up represent the newly granted gifts of the Holy Spirit, and the baptised person emerges in front of the large altar, indicating how baptism leads to the Eucharist. Fr Fudge hopes to continue the work of the Neo-catechumenates, and to form more communities from the congregation.

This regular congregation is composed of local residents, students, some elderly people, and nurses and domestics from the two nearby hospitals, the Middlesex and the University College, to both of which Fr Fudge is chaplain.

Around 300 attend Sunday services, while some 60 people can be expected during the week. Morning Mass is celebrated in a small side chapel. There are no great musical resources, but to supplement the traditional hymns and organ music, guitars are used for Psalms, creating a certain informal style in the celebration of the Liturgy.

Mass: Sunday (Sat 6pm), 9am, 11am, 6pm; Holy Days 8am, 12.30pm, 1.15pm, 6pm; Weekdays 8am, 12.30pm, 6pm (Bank Holidays 10am); Saturday 10am □ Confession: Saturday 10.30–11am, 5.30–6pm; daily after 12.30am Mass □ Facilities: amplification, deaf loop □ Wheelchair: level access □ Other details: 3 parish rooms □ Visiting: open 7am–7pm daily; postcards

St Etheldreda

Ely Place, EC1 □ Bus: 8, 17, 18, 22, 25, 45, 46, 171, 171a, 221, 243, 259, 501 □ Tube/BR: Farringdon □ Parking: on street, difficult except weekend □ Rector: Rev Christopher Cunningham □ Address: The Presbytery, 14 Ely Place, EC1 □ Telephone: 405 1061 □ Available: most times □ Other clergy: Rev C Smith (chaplain at St Barts the Less), Rev J-M Charles-Roux

Nestling between the offices in the elegant cul-de-sac of Ely Place is the 13th century chapel of St Etheldreda's, a small but remarkable church. It is Britain's oldest surviving Roman Catholic church, built in 1251, and except for part of Westminster Abbey it is the only remaining work from the reign of Edward I in London. It was here that the Barons swore alegiance to the Crown in 1302. During the Great Fire, the church was saved by a fortuitous change of wind direction. After the Reformation it was used as the Spanish Embassy church, and later for Anglican worship, before being restored to the Catholic tradition in the 1850s.

The church itself is quite beautiful, and has been described as one of the finest examples of Gothic architecture in Europe. The main body of the church is reached through a short cloister and up some steps. Many of the interior features are modern. Edward Nuttgens made the east window in 1952. The west window was designed by Charles Blakeman, who also designed the frescoes at the rear of the crypt. Older features of note are visible; some of the wooden beams in the roof are 13th century originals, and the Royal Coat of Arms hanging above the door dates back to the time of Charles I. Recently, some original medieval tiles were found in the cloister. Beneath the church is a famous crypt, now used extensively for worship. The statues and Stations of the Cross in the crypt are made of polystyrene and were the work of May Blakeman.

Restoration is currently the order of the day at St Etheldreda's. A major appeal is underway to provide funds for this work which is expected to take some time.

The Sunday congregation numbers around 170, with a wide age range. The usual form of service is English or sung Latin. There is a great choral tradition at St Etheldreda's; at the Sunday 11am Mass the choir sings settings of the Mass by such distinguished composers as Palestrina, Byrd and Haydn. The BBC often uses the church for musical recordings. On weekdays there are two services per day, ministering mainly to local workers.

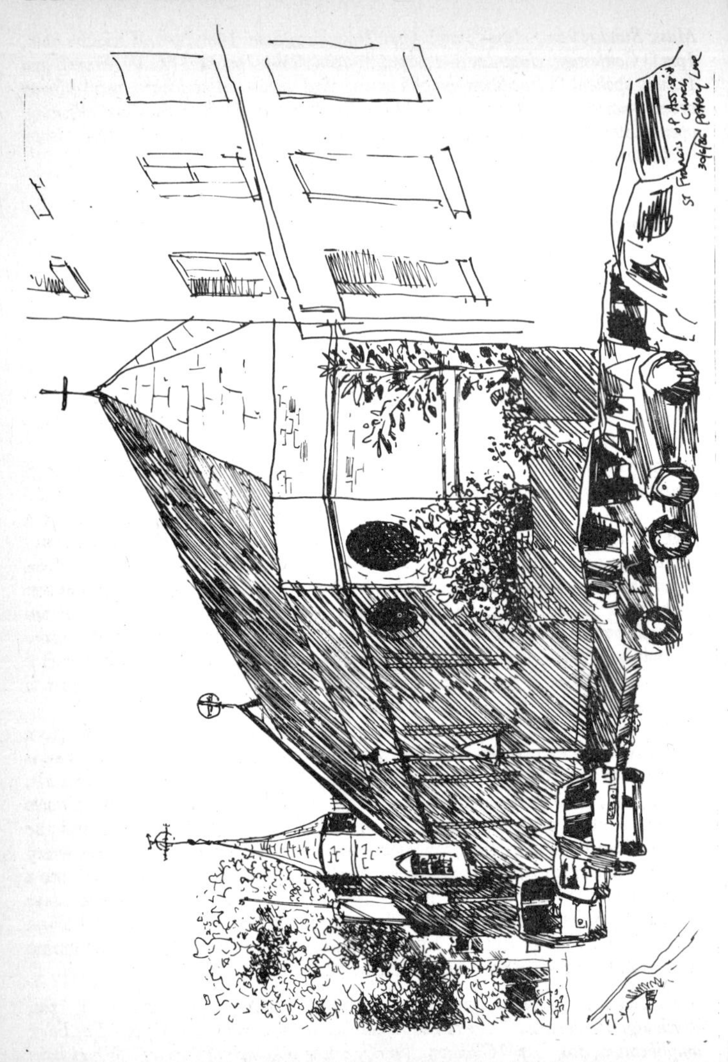

St Francis of Assisi, W11

Mass: Sunday 9am, 11am (Sung), 6pm; Holy Days 8am, 1pm, 6pm; Weekdays 8am, 1pm □ Confession: Saturday 1–1.30pm, 6–7pm; daily 1pm and at call (French and Italian spoken) □ Facilities: amplification, deaf loop □ Wheelchair: very difficult access—narrow passage and steps □ Other details: pantry (open most days) □ Visiting: open 7.30am–7.30pm daily; tours available through Clerkenwell Heritage Centre (Telephone: 250 1039)

St Francis of Assisi

Pottery Lane, W11 □ Bus: 12, 88 □ Tube: Holland Park, Ladbroke Grove □ Parking: on street □ Parish Priest: Rev Oliver McTernan □ Address: The Presbytery, Pottery Lane, W11 □ Telephone: 727 7968 □ Available: always □ Other clergy: Rev Gearoid Griffin

The Church of St Francis of Assisi, together with the presbytery and community centre, can be found at the northern end of Pottery Lane, at the junction with Hippodrome Place. Wrought iron gates, opening onto a central courtyard and locked only at night, give access to the church each day for private prayer.

The parish originated in 1859 when Henry Augustus Raw, a friend of Cardinal Manning and fellow Oblate, was asked to found a new church in the 'poor and populous district of Notting Dale'. Father Raw chose the site carefully, knowing that the rich could always come down the hill for Mass, but the poor wouldn't want to go up it. The church was designed by Henry Clutton and the work was supervised by his gifted assistant John Bentley, who later designed Westminster Cathedral. Smaller than most Catholic churches built at the time, St Francis' has great charm, and the atmosphere is warm and inviting. The Stations of the Cross are paintings on slate by the Victorian N H J Westlake. Just inside the entrance are portraits of St Francis and St Clare, painted in 1983 by Brother Bernard, a Franciscan monk.

The parish has changed greatly over the years and now contains people from over forty countries. To meet the needs of a multi-lingual community, the Mass is occasionally said in other languages than English, including French, Spanish, Portuguese, Ethiopian tongues and Gaelic. The church, presbytery and schools remained much the same until 1981, when the boys' school was sold and the Pottery Lane buildings were modified: the church was restored, the presbytery enlarged to house extra team members, and the girls' school was converted into a community centre, staffed and funded by the MSC. The centre, open seven days a week, has a long list of activities ranging from Bingo to AA meetings. The first floor is used by Pax Christi, information centres for Portuguese and Filipino immigrants, and a Catholic Education centre.

Mass: Sunday (Sat 6pm), 8am, 10am, 11.30am, 6.30pm; Holy Days 10am, 7pm; Weekdays as advertised □ Confession: Saturday 10–10.30am, 7–7.30pm □ Facilities: amplification, deaf loop □ Children: Sunday creche in community centre □ Wheelchair: level access □ Other details: community centre, coffee bar □ Visiting: open 7am–7pm daily

St George's Cathedral, Southwark

Lambeth Road, SE1 □ Telephone: 928 5256 □ Bus: 1, 12, 53, 63, 141 □ Tube: Lambeth North, Waterloo □ Parking: car park □ Administrator: Very Rev James Pannett □ Address: Clergy House, Westminster Bridge Road, SE1 □ Telephone: 928 3603 □ Available: most times □ Other clergy: Revv Peter Stodart, Michael Hayes

The often difficult history of St George's, a church regarded as a symbolic link between the days of persecution and the revival of British Catholicism, reached a marvellous peak in May 1982 when Pope John Paul II led a special Service for the Sick here. It is through events such as this and the Taize Meetings, when as many as 3,000 young people throng the cathedral and simply pray for hours, that St George's fulfills its role as a source of inspiration and encouragement to the faithful and the churches of the huge Diocese. The cathedral is similarly used for a special annual service of such groups as the Union of Catholic Mothers, who travel from all over south-east England to attend.

It was Father Thomas Doyle, a Southwark priest, who decided in 1829 to take advantage of the new freedom of worship and begin work for a great church to house the large Catholic population of the area. St George's was opened in 1848, just two years before the restoration of the Hierarchy when St George's was accorded cathedral status. It became the centre of Catholic life in the capital for half a century until the building of Westminster Cathedral.

In 1941 the cathedral was destroyed in an air raid and the painful process of rebuilding began. The new St George's, which opened in 1958, was designed to be more 'cathedral-like'—thus the nave is higher and better-lit, with tall French Gothic arches dictating the form, the sanctuary is large and impressive, and there are eight peaceful chapels. The stonework is light-coloured, an effect complemented by cream parquet tiles and polished oak pews. Perhaps the most striking feature is the nave ceiling, its decorated wood panels unfolding the story of man's redemption, bay by bay.

A recent feature is a stained glass window commemorating the Papal visit and depicting the Pope at the Service for the Sick. Such services are held twice a year and there are also regular Masses held at St Thomas's Hospital. Of the Sunday Masses celebrated at the cathedral, several are of particular interest: the 11am service is a traditional Sung Mass with an accomplished choir, the 12.15pm is sometimes a Folk Mass, and at the 10am Family Mass, the proceedings are often led by one of the families who worship here regularly. In all, around 900 people attend Mass here on a Sunday.

The worshippers at the cathedral are not expected to be passive; parents, for example, are encouraged to take more responsibility for their children's moral and religious education. To help them in this, many are members of an adult education group which organises lively discussions of all kinds of ethical issues. The cathedral employs a full-time Peace and Justice Worker to run events that promote awareness of these two concepts, and the cathedral has included a Peace Sunday in its calendar. Many activities are arranged through the local Council of Churches, of which St George's is a keen member.

Mass: Sunday (Sat 6pm), 8am, 10am (Children's), 11am (Sung), 12.15pm, 6pm; Holy Days 7am, 8am, 10am, 12.30pm, 6pm, 7.30pm (Sung); Weekdays 7.30am, 12.30pm, 6pm; Saturday 9.30am, 12.30pm □ Confession: daily 12.20–1.10pm, 5.30–5.50pm, after 6pm Mass; Saturday 11am–1.10pm, 5–5.50pm, after 6pm Mass □ Facilities: amplification, deaf loop □ Wheelchair: ramp available on request □ Other details: Amigo Church available for hire (seats 150–180) □ Visiting: open 7am–8pm daily

St James, Spanish Place

George Street, W1 □ Bus: 2, 13, 26, 30, 74, 159 □ Tube: Bond Street □ Parking: difficult except Sunday □ Parish Priest: Rev Mgr Canon F Miles □ Address: Spanish Place Rectory, 22 George Street, W1 □ Telephone: 226 3277 □ Other clergy: Revv J Davis, J Buckley

Despite the fact that it stands in George Street, St James' Church has acquired an alternative name from the nearby Spanish Place. This name gives an indication of the church's origins for it derives from a chapel built in 1791 with the help of the Spanish Embassy, which had long offered sanctuary to English Catholics during the years of repression. An unofficial connection with the Embassy continues today.

The present church is on a site immediately opposite the old chapel. It was opened in 1890 but not finally consecrated until 1949, by Bishop Craven. The building is Early English Gothic, with details taken from some of the best examples of this architectural style. The George Street entrance, for example, is a copy of the main entrance to Lichfield Cathedral. The nave is spacious, with a high groined roof, and the chancel is very decorative, more in the manner of the French cathedrals. The reredos, of black hammered iron is decorated with gilt scallop shell motifs (the symbol of the medieval pilgrim, of St James, and of the shrine of the Apostle, at Compostela in northern Spain). The Lady Chapel, which has been described as 'without a peer in the land' houses a delicately-carved altarpiece of the Immaculate Conception.

The congregation at St James' is quite large, including as it does many visitors to London. The church is centrally located, near Oxford Street and the big hotels of the area. Some fine singing, especially at Latin Mass (Sunday 10.30), infuses the church with a prayerful atmosphere.

Mass: Sunday (Sat 6pm), 8.30am, 10.30am (Latin, Solemn), 12noon, 4pm, 7pm; Holy Days 7.15am, 8.30am, 12.30pm, 1.15pm, 6pm, 8pm; Weekdays 7.15am, 12.30pm, 6pm; Saturday 8am, 10am □ Confession: Saturday 10.30–12noon, 5–6pm, 7–7.30pm & at call (French & Italian) □ Wheelchair: easy access □ Other details: hall □ Visiting: no details

St John the Evangelist

Duncan Terrace, N1 □ Bus: 4, 19, 30, 38, 43, 73, 277 □ Tube: Angel □ Parking: permit holders only □ Parish Priests: Rev George Haines SJ, Rev James Hayes SJ □ Address: 39 Duncan Terrace, N1 □ Telephone: 226 3277 □ Available: always

This imposing red-brick Romanesque church was described by Pugin as 'the most original combination of modern deformity that has been erected for some time'. This may be ascribed to pique however as, firstly, he was not invited to design it, and secondly, it is far removed from his beloved Gothic.

The building of such a large church in 1843 was something of an act of faith as there were few Catholics in the area to fill it or raise subscriptions. Indeed, it was not paid for and hence able to be consecrated until 1873. Designed by J J Scoles, the church was inserted snugly into the Georgian Islington terrace, which its twin towers utterly dominate. Its grandeur is nicely undermined by the fact that the south tower now houses bathrooms for the adjoining presbytery. The church, lit by the high clerestory, is a basilica with four side chapels and a rounded apse; it contains paintings and frescoes by E Armitage. The simple forward altar, in accordance with Vatican II, was consecrated in 1973 by Cardinal Heenan.

A notable early incumbent was Canon Oakeley, a Tractarian and friend of Newman who moved here following his conversion from Anglicanism. He became well-loved by the poor Irish community who are said to have renamed him 'O'Kelly'. Perhaps more famous is Monsignor Bruce Kent who resided here until recently. The parish priests, Frs Haines and Hayes are closely involved with St John the Evangelist RC Primary School, and the children help make the Family Mass (10.30am Sunday) the most popular. This is a Folk Mass and the children are encouraged to take part in the liturgy and the singing.

The priests are determined to make St John's a steady base for the community in the ever-changing area of Islington, and the church is indeed the centre of much activity. The crypt is in constant use as a Youth Centre and for other parish functions, and there are groups ranging from the single parents group to the Council-aided Sunday Club which offers voluntary aid for the homeless.

Mass: Sunday (Sat 6pm), 8am 9.15am, 10.30am (Family), 12noon, 6pm; Holy Days & Weekdays as announced □ Confession: Saturday 11am–12noon, 7–7.30pm □ Facilities: amplification, deaf loop □ Children: SW chapel is mothers' & toddlers' room, sound relay □ Wheelchair: 5 steps; help generally available □ Other details: crypt (not for hire) □ Visiting: always open during the week; postcards

St Joseph

Lamb's Buildings, Bunhill Row, EC1 □ Bus: 5, 43, 55, 76, 243 □ Tube/BR: Barbican, Moorgate, Old Street □ Parking: difficult □ Parish Priest: Rev Denis P Watters □ Address: St Joseph's Presbytery, Lamb's Passage, Bunhill Row, EC1 □ Telephone: 628 0326 □ Available: most times

The unusual underground Church of St Joseph, crouched beneath the offices of the Catholic Herald and its own church hall, is easily overlooked—though it is located off the busy Bunhill Row, just north of the Barbican. The carefree air of the hanging baskets and whitewashed walls as you descend the 14 steps to the door belies the church's recent problems. Faced with dry rot and a poor state of repair, it was threatened with closure, but parishioners, encouraged by the incumbent Fr Watters, rallied round with the money, materials and many of the skills needed to save the church.

St Joseph's, consecrated in 1901, now stands as a healthy example of an inter-city church. Fr Watters has fostered strong links with the small local community; the church organises outings and dances, and volunteers also help with projects for the handicapped. The church is well attended on Sundays by residents and students, and on weekdays it is used by City workers.

The simple interior is lit through stained glass depicting 'The Good Shepherd' and 'The Agony in the Garden' taken from the Catholic pro-cathedral St Mary Moorfields, as was the intricately carved water stoop. Other windows and the Stations of the Cross were donated by local families.

The hall, once the classrooms of St Joseph's RC School (closed in 1976), is put to good use, providing weekday office space for Islington's Mencap Project and room for meetings of local tenants' associations. A Sunday school for 6 to 8 year olds is held here, and it is used for rehearsals by the Barbican Players and for parish functions. Once a month Fr Watters holds a service at Moorfields Eye Hospital where he is a chaplain.

Mass: Sunday (Sat 6.30pm), 10.30am, 6.30pm (Folk); Holy Days 8.15am, 12.30pm, 8pm; Weekdays 12.30pm (Bank Holidays 10am; Saturday 12noon) □ Confession: Saturday 11.30am–12noon, and after 6.30pm Mass □ Children: Sunday school in hall (6 to 8 year olds) □ Wheelchair: very difficult—14 steps □ Other details: hall (not available for hire) □ Visiting: open daily 8am to 5pm

St Mary, Chelsea

Cadogan Street, SW3 □ Bus: 11, 19, 22, 137 □ Tube: Sloane Square □ Parking: NCP in Pavilion Road □ Parish Priest: V Rev Canon Michael Richards □ Address: The Rectory, Draycot Terrace, SW3 □ Telephone: 589 5487 □ Available: most times

The centre of an historic and flourishing Catholic parish, St Mary's has served the spiritual needs of Belgravia and Chelsea since 1798. It was then that the Abbé Voyaux de Fracous, a French priest exiled by the French Revolution of 1789, opened a chapel in a house in Lower George Street (now Sloane Gardens). The present site, tucked into an area framed by Sloane Street and the Kings' Road, was given by Joseph and Mary Knight in 1844, when the building of a school, almshouses and cemetery chapel began. The church itself, designed by J F Bentley in an English Gothic style, was opened for worship in 1879 and consecrated by Cardinal Manning in 1882. It incorporates chapels by Augustus and Edward Pugin and holds the remains of several well-known personalities, amongst them Madame Tussaud and the Abbé himself.

The social make-up of the parish is very varied—the formidable red-bricked houses of Belgravia rub shoulders with more modest blocks of flats, often literally next door. There are many Portuguese and Spanish residents, with a high concentration of embassy staff as well. The church provided a youth club for the families of the parish, but sadly it foundered through lack of response.

About a thousand people come on Sundays, with a hundred every week-day. Lay people play a prominent role—they administer communion to the sick as well

St Mary Moorfields, EC2

as at the normal services and participate in a Good Neighbours Group and a Senior Citizens' Committee.

Mass: Sunday (Sat 6.30pm), 8.30am, 10am (Family), 11am (Sung Latin), 12.15pm, 6.30pm; Holy Days & Weekdays 8am, 12.15pm, 6.30pm; Saturday 10am □ Confession: Saturday 10.30–11am, 5.30–6.15pm (French, Italian, Portuguese) □ Facilities: amplification, deaf loop □ Wheelchair: 3 steps, no ramp □ Other details: small church hall □ Visiting: entrance area only open 7.45am–7.15pm, allowing full view of church

St Mary Moorfields

4–5 Eldon Street, EC2 □ Bus: 9, 11, 21, 43, 76 □ Tube/BR: Moorgate, Liverpool St □ Parking: difficult □ Parish Priest: Rev Anton Cowan □ Address: as church □ Telephone: 247 8390 □ Available: telephone any reasonable time

The entrance to St Mary Moorfields is one of the most curious in London, squeezed as it is between two philatelist shops. Only the carved name of the church and a statue of the Virgin Mary give any indication that this is a place of worship. When one descends into the Romanesque interior, however, the church's beauty is revealed.

Foremost among several points of interest is the High Altar. This large white stone structure was originally intended to be the tomb of Cardinal Manning, but was never used as such. It sits in the soft light of the sanctuary before a curved wall panelled in pastel purple marble. On this wall is a small crucifix and a plaque with the words 'Be still and know that I am God' (Psalms 46.10). In the Blessed Sacrament chapel, lying parallel with the main body of the church, are two small icons of the Virgin Mary and a full-sized reproduction of the Turin Shroud. There is also a stained glass window depicting the Assumption, flanked by images of the Apostles. This, together with such items as the sanctuary rail and the pillars framing the altar, come from the original St Mary Moorfields, a large church (indeed a pro-cathedral) in Finsbury Circus, built in 1820 and later compulsorily sold for demolition when the underground railway was extended. Some of the money raised paid for the present smaller church, built in 1900, and some was put towards the cost of building Westminster Cathedral.

Under the motto 'Serving God and the Square Mile', the church's role is unlike that of most Catholic churches because so few people live locally. The Sunday congregation, consequently, is very small and most of the church's ministry takes place during the week, when there are well-attended Masses each day. These services are spoken, partly for the sake of brevity since most attending are there during their lunch hour. On Holy Days, nine Masses are celebrated and the congregation can swell to 2,000. Most of these will attend their own parish churches on Sunday.

The high-pressure life of the City can cause problems for many people, and Father Cowan, as part of his ministry, is available for counselling to anyone in need. Church activities are limited to occasional lunchtime talks by guest speakers and it is really worship that is the keynote at St Mary's Moorfields. The aim, as Father Cowan says, is 'to provide a place of worship, peace and quiet for anyone who wishes to visit the church'.

Mass: Sunday 10am (Sung); Holy Days 8am, 8.30am, 11.30am, 12noon, 12.30pm, 1pm, 1.30pm, 5pm, 5.30pm; Weekdays 1pm (Spoken) □ *Confession: Wed, Thu, Fri 1.30·2pm* □ *Wheelchair: several steps, difficult access* □ *Visiting: open 7am–5.30pm Mon–Fri and Sunday morning, leaflets available*

St Mary of the Angels

Moorhouse Road, W2 □ *Bus: 7, 15, 27, 28, 31* □ *Tube: Westbourne Park, Notting Hill Gate* □ *Parking: on street* □ *Parish Priest: Rev Michael Hollings* □ *Address: Church House, Moorhouse Road, W2* □ *Telephone: 229 0487* □ *Available: all times* □ *Other clergy: Revv John Buckley, Anthony Baxter*

The church was set up in 1857 by the prominent convert from Anglicanism, Dr Henry Manning, who later became the Archbishop of Westminster. He established a community of Oblates here, members of an order founded by St Charles Borromeo, and the community remained until 1974, when Cardinal Heenan handed over the Parish House to non-Oblate priests, and St Mary of the Angels, Bayswater, became an ordinary parish church.

Fr Hollings, the present incumbent, arrived in 1978 and put his plans for an 'open living system' into practice. All kinds of people, such as students, travellers and ex-convicts, live at the House with the priests and Marist Sisters of the parish team. Things are shared, chores are divided, and the community eat together in what was once a private chapel for the Oblates. People arrive and leave quite frequently, and there is usually a spare room.

This exceptionally welcoming attitude extends to the church. The Catholic Commission for Racial Justice is keenly aware tha Black Catholics can often have difficulty becoming accepted in British churches, but it commends the Bayswater parish for 'enormous efforts to be open to people of all races'. Positioned in the midst of the West Indian community of Notting Hill, St Mary's is indeed a genuinely multi-racial church—the worship reflects the ethnic backgrounds of parishioners, and the priest and team workers are closely involved with all issues affecting the community.

The church has a special role during the Notting Hill Festival, held each August. West Indian priests are invited to take the Saturday evening service, and the congregation crowd in for a Caribbean-style Mass. Other special services include a Portuguese Mass, and on the third Sunday each month, a service for the handicapped followed by a party for the congregation in the refectory. The refectory is also used to serve Sunday lunch to about 60 'men and women of the roads' each week, and for various parties and celebrations. The list of activities based at the church is as long and varied as might be expected for such a lively parish.

The church itself is a large Gothic-style building, originally designed by Mayer in 1857 but completed by John Bentley. The interior, although less pristine than many churches, is colourful with much stained glass, and has outstanding examples of ironwork in the choir. Most visitors, however, arrive not for the architecture, but to take up Fr Hollings' invitation: 'never be shy of coming to the parish house, . . . in order to talk with one of us and sort out your ideas with God'.

Mass: Sunday (Sat 6.30pm), 8am, 10am (Folk), 11am (Portuguese), 12noon (Sung), 6pm (Sung); Holy Days 8am, 10am, 12.30pm, 8pm; Weekdays 8am, 10am, 6.30pm □ Confession: Saturday 10.30–11am, 6–6.30pm, 7.15–8pm (available in French) □ Facilities: amplification, deaf loop □ Wheelchair: ramp □ Visiting: open 7am–7pm daily

St Patrick

Soho Square, W1 □ Bus: 2, 8, 24, 25, 29, 73, 134 □ Tube: Tottenham Court Road □ Parking: difficult except Sunday □ Parish Priest: Rev Austin Garvey □ Address: 21a Soho Square, W1 □ Available: generally □ Other clergy: Rev Louis Tchang, Rev Giuseppe Blanda

St Patrick's reflects the multi-ethnic nature of the area and, indeed, the universality of Catholicism. This is most evident on 17 March, when priests from all the foreign chaplaincies in London are invited to concelebrate Mass here, at possibly the only St Patrick's Day service where one can expect to hear hymns in English, Spanish and Cantonese. In 1986, Cardinal Hume led this very special Mass.

The parish has altered greatly since the war, because of the dramatic depopulation of the West End. Many who have moved out retain a family link with the church, but there are few local members and these are mostly elderly. Most of the hundred or so people who attend Mass here work in the area. On Sundays, 350 to 450 people come to Mass, a significant proportion being tourists, regular visitors, and those attending the foreign language services. Indeed, the only notable post-war influx of population has been from Hong Kong to Soho, and appropriately, St Patrick's is the only London church which celebrates Mass in Cantonese, while the crypt is used as an informal centre for the small local Chinese Catholic community. The services are friendly family occasions, when Fr Tchang has the willing assistance of several children, who lend the proceedings an exuberant air.

The site has been used for Catholic worship since 1792, when Fr Arthur O'Leary, friend to both the local Irish poor and English royalty, set up St Patrick's chapel here. The present church, built to an Italianate design by John Kelly, was opened in 1893. It is a red-brick basilica with a west tower of some 120 feet. The interior is light and pleasant in white and pale blue and is dominated by the dramatic painting of the Crucifixion over the High Altar. Despite its central location, St Patrick's enjoys the relative calm and seclusion of Soho Square, and at all times of day one can expect to find people having a quiet moment of prayer here away from the bustle of the West End.

Mass: Sunday (Sat 6pm), 8am, 9, 11, 2pm (Cantonese), 5 (Spanish), 6pm; Holy Days 8am, 9, 12.30pm, 1, 6pm; Weekdays 8am, 12.45, 6pm □ Confession: Mon to Thurs 12–12.40pm; Fri 12–12.40pm, 5.30–6pm; Saturday 11–12noon, 5–6pm □ Facilities: amplification, deaf loop, sign language by special arrangement □ Wheelchair: one step to church □ Visiting: open 7.30am–7.30pm for quiet prayer, meditation; please do not interrupt services

St Patrick, Waterloo

Cornwall Road, SE1 □ Bus: any bus to Waterloo □ Tube/BR: Waterloo □ Parking: on street □ Parish Priest: Rev D Ellis □ Address: 26 Cornwall Road, SE1 □ Telephone: 928 4818 □ Available: most times

The small Church of St Patrick is situated on the first floor of St Patrick's school and was built in 1820. The school was originally set up by the Benevolent Society of St Patrick, a charitable organisation founded in 1784, in order to educate, clothe and apprentice poor children born of Irish parents in or near London. It has since been an 'American' school and has recently been closed as a school altogether. The church functions as a parish church, although of a somewhat reduced parish since the area has become less and less residential.

To reach the church one must climb two flights of stairs. Because of the obvious difficulties this entails to the elderly and infirm, the present priest, Fr Dominic Ellis, would like to see the church built into a lower part of the building, but until this can be organised, services will continue to be held on the first floor. With seating for around 75 people the church is small enough to be maintained on a low budget. Some of the items in the church are gifts from members of the congregation.

Of the three Sunday Masses, the 11am Folk Mass is the most popular. A small choir leads the hymns which are accompanied by guitar. After the morning Masses on the first Sunday of each month, coffee and biscuits are served in the school hall.

Because of the size of the parish and congregation, people who wish to join certain Catholic organisations are referred to Southwark Cathedral. The church does, however, have use of the school hall for some social activities, such as musical events, and this includes concerts and musical evenings when parishioners join in for an evening's sing-a-long.

Mass: Sunday 9am, 11am (Folk), 5pm; Mon–Fri 8am, 12.30pm; Saturday 12.30pm □ Children: Sunday school (after 11am Mass) □ Wheelchair: no access, two flights of stairs □ Other details: school hall □ Visiting: open for services only

St Peter (Italian)

Clerkenwell Road, EC1 □ Bus: 19, 38, 55 □ Tube/BR: Farringdon □ Parking: difficult □ Superior: Rev Roberto Russo □ Address: 4 Back Hill, Clerkenwell Road, EC1 □ Telephone: 837 1528/9071 □ Available: most times □ Other clergy: Rev Carmelo di Giovanni

Opened in 1863, this was the first Italian church in the world to be built outside Italy. The facade, surrounded by offices and a school, gives no real indication of the size and splendour of the church within. The interior is decorated in a manner 'unique in Britain'. Two Italian masters, Arnaud and Gauthier, were brought over in 1885 to work on the church; they produced the Baroque sanctuary paintings and the magnificent frescoes, such as the one on the nave ceiling depicting St Peter. The fine painting of the Annunciation by Einler of Vienna is partially obscured by the High Altar with its ornate baldacchino on black and gold marble columns. In all, there is much to see in this fascinating church.

The design, by Sir John Miller Bryson, is based on the Roman basilica, with broad transepts and an apsed chancel. The north transept houses a statue of Our Lady of Mount Carmel, a major object of devotion for Italians in London. On the first Sunday after her Feast Day (16 July), there is a spectacular procession in her honour through Clerkenwell. There are floats, stalls and decorated streets; Italians gather from all over London.

Even apart from such special events, there is a strong sense of community at the church. Lay participation with services is strongly encouraged, even to the extent of assisting with the preparation of sermons, and there are many activities, both religious and secular, with which one can become involved. The Pallottine Fathers here are very active among the Italian community and are often the first point of contact for Italians new to Britain. An impressive church and community magazine called *Backhill* contains news of events from the parochial to the international—especially news from Italy.

The church choir continues a reputation for musical excellence gained last century when Italian artists working at Covent Garden would sing here. The choir still attracts leading singers to perform with them at concerts held in the church.

Mass: Sunday (Sat 7pm), 9am, 10 (English), 11 (Sung), 12.15pm, 7pm; Holy Days 10am, 12.15pm, 7, 8pm; Weekdays 10am, 7pm (All services in Italian unless stated) □ *Confession: Saturday 9am–7pm (Italian and English spoken)* □ *Facilities: amplification* □ *Wheelchair: difficult, 8 steps into church* □ *Other details: community hall* □ *Visiting: open most times*

SS Peter and Paul

Amwell Street, EC1 □ *Bus: 19, 30, 38, 73, 171, 172* □ *Tube/BR: Kings Cross, Angel, Farringdon* □ *Parking: on street* □ *Parish Priest: Rev Christopher Maher SCA* □ *Address: 5 Amwell Street, EC1* □ *Telephone: 837 2094* □ *Available: most times* □ *Other clergy: Revv Michael Kiely SCA, Timothy Hanley SCA*

This thriving church is the London base of the Pallottine Fathers, members of the Society of the Catholic Apostolate. Their founder, St Vincent Pallotti, emphasised the need for the whole Church, especially the laity, to become directly involved with the many aspects of the Church's work, whether pastoral, charitable, educational, missionary or liturgical. At SS Peter and Paul, this goal is clearly sought. For example, the Fathers are assisted at services by lay readers and by lay ministers for the distribution of the Communion; and a great deal of charity work is done, notably for the 'adopted' parish of Magugu in Tanzania, a Pallottine mission base. Another expression of Pallotti's concept of the 'lay apostolate' is the Legion of Mary, a lay group committed to spiritual care and pastoral work.

The Pallottine ideals of involvement and togetherness have found a suitable home in the 'village' atmosphere of Clerkenwell. The small church is full for family occasions such as the Confirmation ceremony, and at Easter and Midnight Mass. Throughout the year, there are 150 or so for Sunday Masses, when there is congregational singing to organ accompaniment, and once a month a popular sung Latin Mass. The church hall is reserved for parish activities, such as dances, a senior citizens' Bingo group, a youth club and an amateur dramatic group.

The elegant Georgian church was originally a Countess of Huntingdon's

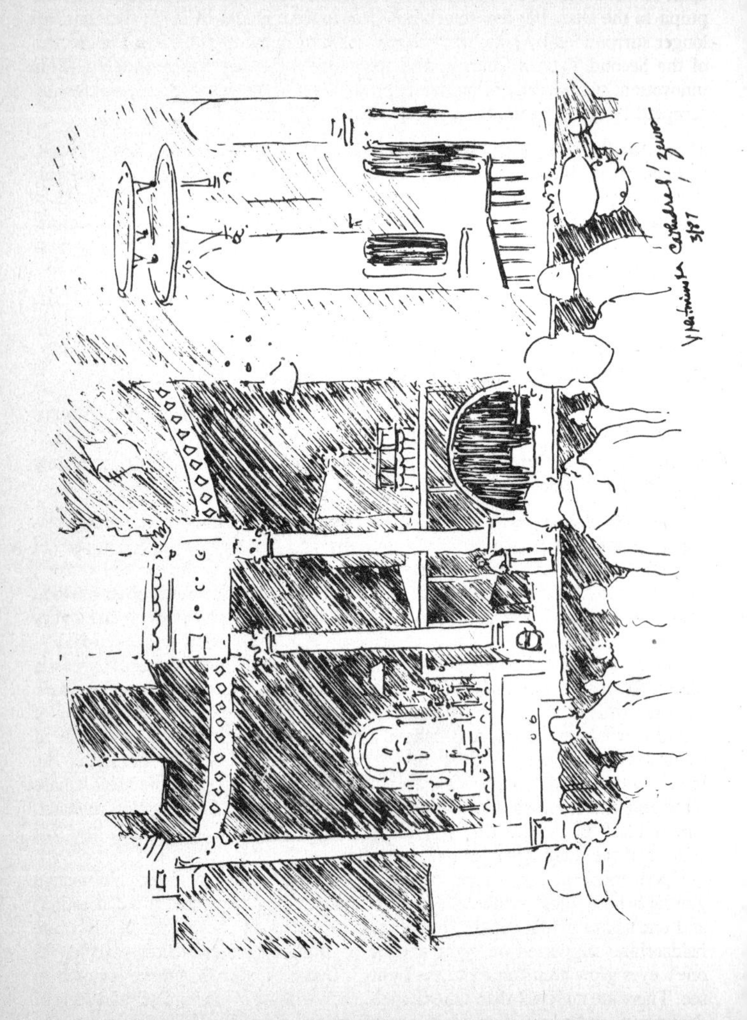

Interior, Westminster Cathedral, SW1

Connexion chapel built in true Methodist style, with internal galleries and no apse. It was acquired by the Catholic Church in 1847: the focus moved from the pulpit to the altar, but few structural changes were made. In 1985, the altar, no longer surrounded by rails, was brought forward in accordance with the dictates of the Second Vatican Council, and the whole sanctuary was re-ordered. This innovation, symbolically bringing the priest closer to the worshippers, was readily accepted by the parishioners and priests at SS Peter and Paul.

Mass: Sunday (Sat 8pm), 8am, 10, 12noon, 6.30pm; Holy Days 8am, 12noon, 6.30pm, 8pm; Weekdays 8.30am, 12noon (plus Wed, Fri 8pm) □ Confession: Saturday 11.30am, 7.30pm, and at call (Italian & Swahili spoken) □ Facilities: amplification □ Children: partitioned area and creche during services □ Wheelchair: ramp □ Other details: hall (not for hire) □ Visiting: open for services only; otherwise apply Presbytery

Westminster Cathedral (Metropolitan Cathedral of the Most Precious Blood)

Ashley Place, Victoria Street, SW1 □ Bus: any to Victoria □ Parking: difficult, meters □ Administrator: V Rev Canon Oliver Kelly □ Address: Clergy House, 42 Francis Street, SW1 □ Telephone: 834 7452 (828 4732 for service times) □ Other clergy: many other priests □ Available: at all times

Despite its obvious attractions for the tourists, Westminster Cathedral has managed not to become a national monument and remains very much a place of worship. At any time of day one will find people using it for private prayer, meditation and confession, and this imparts a certain sanctity and serenity which combines with the beauty and splendour of J F Bentley's interior to create a very special ambience.

The cathedral, completed in 1903 and standing in its own piazza off Victoria Street, is one of the most distinctive buildings in London. The Byzantine exterior, with its stripes of red brick and white limestone, rises in a cluster of rounded windows, turrets and domes, and culminates in the lofty campanile of some 284 feet. Even this does not prepare one for the austere beauty of the interior—due in part to the fact that it is unfinished. The tops of the great square piers and the resulting massive arches and domes have been left in unfaced, almost black brick, but this only adds to their grandeur and absorbs the soft colours of the many kinds of marble below.

Upon entering, one stands between two huge columns of red Norwegian granite (whose colour symbolises the Precious Blood of the cathedral's dedication) and one's gaze is first caught by the sanctuary straight ahead with its elaborate baldacchino supported on eight slender columns of golden yellow marble. As one's eyes grow accustomed to the light, it becomes clear that there is much to see. There are no fewer than nine chapels, each with its own character and style of decoration, and many other notable features including Eric Gill's Stations of the Cross, the tombs of Cardinals Hinsley and Heenan with their red hats suspended above, and Bentley's own elegant coronals of light hanging in the nave. There is also a crypt chapel which can hold around 80 people for Mass and which contains the tombs of Cardinals Wiseman, Manning, Griffin and Godfrey. Guided tours of the cathedral are available and, just to complete the visit, one can travel by lift up the campanile.

The informative guidebook available at the bookshop carries the statement by Pope Paul VI that 'the secret of a cathedral is an expression of the unity of believers', and indeed, in order to experience the cathedral at its best, one should attend Mass, when the building is being used for its supreme purpose. Mass is celebrated several times a day in various styles, ranging from a Solemn Sung Mass with a full choir to the more informal Folk Mass. Preachers from other Churches have been heard here and there have been many united acts of worship.

The cathedral runs a busy parish containing three hospitals and two schools. There is a recently opened centre for young people at risk called the Cardinal Hume Centre, and a day centre for the homeless called the Passage. There are conference facilities adjoining the cathedral where Bible study and discussion groups meet, and where a variety of lectures may be heard.

Mass: Sunday (Sat 6pm), 7am, 9, 10.30 (Solemn), 12noon, 5.30pm (Sung), 7pm; Holy Days 7am, 8, 8.30, 9, 10.30, 12.30pm, 1.05, 5.30 (Solemn), 7pm; Weekdays 7am, 8, 8.30, 9, 10.30, 12.30pm, 1.05, 5.30 (Solemn Sung); Saturday 7am, 8, 8.30, 9, 10.30 (Solemn), 6pm (Sung) □ Confession: Sunday 9am–1pm, 2.30–7.30pm; Weekdays 11am–6.30pm; Saturday 9am–7.30pm (French, German, Italian, Portuguese & Maltese spoken; also sign language) □ Facilities: amplification, deaf loop, sign language □ Wheelchair: separate entrance, easy access □ Other details: bookshop; conference hall (apply manager 834 4257) □ Visiting: open 7am–8pm; donation appreciated; please do not disturb services; gift shop; guided tours 11.15am–12.15pm and 2–4pm; there is a charge for the tower (closed Mondays & Tuesdays)

The Salvation Army

In 1865 when William Booth conducted the first service of what was then called 'The Christian Mission' his aim was not to create a new denomination, but to launch an organised campaign to save people from the spiritual and physical horrors of sin and deprivation. The adoption of the name Salvation Army in 1878 marked not only their independent status and military style structure, but the beginnings of a worldwide crusade which has now reached over seventy countries.

Working mainly with the elderly, the homeless, the young and single parents, the Army now has a network of citadels, halls and Goodwill Centres all of which provide practical help and organise groups and activities. Alongside the welfare work is the spreading of the Gospel and even the humblest Goodwill Centre will hold a service on Sunday. The Army's approach was succintly put by General Frederick Coutts during their centenary celebrations:

'If we ourselves, for want of a better way of speaking, refer to our evangelical work and also to our social work, it is not that these are two distinct entities which could operate the one without the other. They are but two activities of the one and the same salvation which is concerned with the total redemption of man.'

The Salvation Army is headed by the General and there are some 25,000 officers of rank around the world. There are also hundreds of thousands of other local officers and lay soldiers and all wear the same uniform, identical save for the indications of rank. Probably the most familiar image of the Salvation Army is the uniformed band playing hymns, and especially carols at Christmas, on street corners. This musical tradition dates right back to 1878 and since the 1960s the customary brass bands have been supplemented by 'rhythm groups' using guitars.

For further information, contact International Headquarters, 101 Queen Victoria Street, EC4 (Information service, Tel: 236 7020).

Chelsea Goodwill Centre

13 Blantyre Street, SW10 □ Bus: 11, 19, 22, 45, 49 □ Tube: Sloane Square □ Parking: on street □ Commanding Officers: Capt & Mrs Pearce □ Address: as Centre □ Telephone: 352 7557 □ Available: most times

This somewhat secluded Goodwill Centre, overshadowed by the tower blocks of the Worlds End Estate, is nonetheless well signposted from both Kings Road and the Embankment. It is one of six Goodwill Centres in London and is run by Captain and Mrs Pearce. Primarily, their work is to spread the Gospel whilst helping the destitute and the needy both materially and spiritually. The couple are engaged in social work and make regular hospital visits.

The centre is fully equipped with a reception room where refreshments are available, and an adjoining hall used extensively during the week. Most mornings are given over to a playgroup which arose because of the shortage of preschool facilities in the area. This is supervised by volunteers while Mrs Pearce is busy cooking a three-course meal for the 30 or so senior citizens who are members of the Luncheon Club. Thursday features a coffee morning and jumble sale, while the highspot of the busy week is, of course, the Fellowship Praise meeting and Sunday school. The centre relies on generous donations for the continuance of its work.

Services: Sunday 3pm Fellowship Praise meeting □ Children: Sunday school 3pm □ Wheelchair: level access □ Other details: reception room, etc □ Visiting: open most days

Falmouth Road Goodwill Centre

37 Ellington House, Falmouth Road, SE1 □ Bus: 1, 53, 63 □ Tube/BR: Elephant & Castle □ Parking: difficult □ Commanding Officer: Captain Christine Alan □ Address: next door to Centre □ Telephone: 407 4297 □ Available: most times at the Centre or at home □ Other staff: Captain Gael Huggins

Provision was made for this Centre when the council built a housing estate on Falmouth Road in the early 1940s. Using the allotted space of one ground floor flat, it consists of a hall and kitchen. The council also provides the next door flat, used by Captain Christine Alan, who runs the Centre with the assistance of Captain Gael Huggins.

As with all Goodwill Centres, this operates a full programme of weekday activities for all ages. Each day at 12 noon pensioners' lunches are served, mums and toddlers and a womens club meet on Monday and Thursday afternoons, and on Wednesdays there is a coffee morning open to anyone. The evening programmes are designed for young people. On Mondays there is a girls' club and

Salvation Army bandsman

on Wednesdays a meeting of SABAC (Salvation Army Boys Adventure Club). Both these clubs start at 6pm. At 5pm on Thursdays a Junior Club is provided for younger children.

The Sunday service is attended by a small number of mainly elderly people. The nature of the hall and the size of the attendance have led to an informal style of service based on singing and prayer. Sunday school is called Sunday Adventure and is attended by a multiracial group of children aged from 6 to 14, who live in the surrounding estates.

Jumble sales are held as a regular fundraising activity, every six to eight weeks. At Christmas, one of the most costly times for the Salvation Army, a larger Christmas Sale is held. Another fundraiser is the sale of *War Cry*, sold on Friday evenings when the two Captains tour the local pubs. They also make many hospital and relief visits, the latter for the donation of food and clothes to people in need.

Services: Sunday 3.30pm □ Children: Sunday Adventure; clubs □ Wheelchair: ramp at the rear □ Visiting: open only for meetings and activities

Hoxton Goodwill Centre

66 New North Road, N1 □ Telephone: 739 3313 □ Bus: 271 □ Tube: Old Street □ Parking: car park □ Minister: Captain David Bailey □ Address: as Centre □ Available: most times by appointment □ Other staff: officers and lay Salvationists

'Slum Posts' was the name given to the forerunners of the Goodwill Centres—Army establishments in deprived areas that placed more emphasis on community work than on formal worship. Built on the site of a Methodist chapel in 1939, Hoxton was the very first Goodwill Centre, part of a nationwide scheme to expand the work of the 'Slum Posts'.

The Centre is put to maximum use by the community. The basement is used for youth club meetings, while the first floor houses the worship room, kitchens, offices and lounge. The staff have their accommodation on the second floor, which is also used for a nursery, while the playgroup is held on the first floor. There are fees for both playgroup and nursery, which are run by professional staff. Other activities include a luncheon club and charity shop, and the Centre is used for meetings of the Hackney Victims Support Scheme and Hackney clinic. Even the flat roof is put to use—surrounded by high netting it makes an ideal football pitch for the youth club.

The Sunday service is attended by about 30 people. A number of them are elderly and for this reason the service commences at 6pm during the summer and 3pm in the winter. Services feature a good deal of singing, and the words of the hymns and songs are used again in the readings. Although there are only a few uniformed Salvationists present, the officers and soldiers take an active part in the service, gaining the leadership experience that they will need in later Army life. They also provide a Sunday school which is attended by children whose parents do not themselves come to the main service.

Upon entering the Centre, one's attention is immediately drawn to the large painting that covers the wall to the left of the chapel. Either side of a central depiction of St Christopher carrying Christ, it shows members of the Salvation

Army assisting a lame man, and also depicts Mrs Smith whose generosity financed the Centre. The text on the mural is a fair summary of the Centre's work: 'In as much as ye did it unto the least of these my brethren, ye did it unto me'.

Services: Sunday 3pm (winter) 6pm (summer) Gospel Service □ Facilities: amplification □ Children: Sunday school/Bible study, 1.45pm (3–16 year olds) □ Wheelchair: ramp at side entrance □ Other details: hall (may be available for hire), other rooms □ Visiting: open 8.30am–5.30pm daily, except Saturdays; literature and leaflets available

Notting Hill Goodwill Centre

Portobello Road, W11 □ Telephone: 727 5178 □ Bus: 7, 12, 15, 27, 28, 31, 36, 52, 88 □ Tube: Westbourne Park, Notting Hill Gate □ Parking: meters □ Commanding Officer: Captain P Charlesworth □ Address: 11 Exmoor Street, W10 □ Telephone: 969 2625 □ Available: every day □ Other staff: Captain N Richardson

The Salvation Army has altered the emphasis of its work at Notting Hill in direct response to the ever-changing character of the area. From 1924 to the late 70s it was a thriving Corps Centre—an evangelical headquarters with three open-air services every Sunday, a band, a 'Songsters' singing group, and all kinds of youth work which included guide and scout packs. It was a pleasant area to live, with many fine shops and elegant houses—and the Army enjoyed considerable support.

But the aftermath of the War brought decline to the district. Interest in the flavour of faith that the Salvationists were offering steadily waned. In the face of certain closure, a decision was made to turn the premises into a Goodwill Centre, a move that has proved to be highly successful. The building opens out straight onto Portobello Road with its famous market. Accommodation in the area can be summed up as 'bedsit-land', providing homes for many single-parent families, amongst others. The Army spends a lot of time counselling—typical problems may be debts or DHSS claims.

Elderly residents form another important part of the work. Lunches are served twice a week and an over-60's Club provides a mixture of quizzes, old-time songs, and an epilogue every Wednesday afternoon. More meals are provided twice a week for the many homeless men in the area—and beyond: one guest regularly walks eight miles to make sure of his share.

More hospitality can be found during the Notting Hill Carnival. The Hall is made into a First-Aid post, with refreshments made available to the police and members of the St John's Ambulance Brigade. Cheery music through loudspeakers heralds the service, together with a bookstall set up outside. More stalls can be found every Friday morning when a jumble sale is held from 10.30 to 11.30am. The Army finds just as much of a market for its listening ear as for home-made cakes: conversations during this brief period provide an outlet for much spiritual as well as practical help. In Notting Hill, the work has passed from forthright open-air meetings to quieter and more subtle ways of ministry, but the Army tradition of combining practical care and spiritual nourishment is still very much alive.

Services: Sunday 10.30am Morning Meeting, 3pm Bible study □ Facilities: large print Bibles and hymn books; sign language □ Children: Sunday school 12.30–1.30pm □ Wheelchair: 2 steps □ Visiting: open for services and activities only

Regent Hall

275 Oxford Street, W1 □ Telephone 629 5424 □ Bus: any along Oxford Street □ Tube: Oxford Circus □ Parking: difficult except Sunday □ Commanding Officer: Major Howard Heins □ Address: 9e Tedworth Square, SW3 □ Telephone: 352 8302 □ Available: most day at hall □ Other staff: Lieutenant Allan Hoffer

Situated on Oxford Street, just off the Circus and behind an unassuming entrance, is the main Salvation Army Hall in Central London. Built in 1830, it was designed as a roller skating rink, being taken over by the Salvation Army in 1875. This earlier use has led to the Hall being nicknamed 'the Rink'.

The building can be divided into three areas. The front section, that facing onto Oxford Street, is on three floors and contains canteens and meeting rooms. The middle section is the auditorium. This has a large stage, big enough for the choir, band and people leading the service to be seated comfortably, whilst the full balcony and stalls can seat over 600 people. The rear section has rooms at different levels used by young people for Sunday school and other meetings.

Sundays at Regent Hall are a hectic schedule of worship, street marches and open air services. The day starts with a quiet morning prayer meeting and then goes right through to 8pm, with two meals provided for those present. The first of six marches starts at 10am, returning to the Hall for the Christian Development Service. This is based on Biblical texts, aimed at furthering Christian knowledge. At 3pm there is a Praise Service, where Salvationists give witness and testimony to their faith and experience. The main open air service is at 5.30pm, held in Argyle Street, near Oxford Circus. Here the band accompanies the singing and there is again witness and testimony. When this is finished, the assembled group march the short distance back to the Hall, completing the day's activities with the Gospel Service. This has the largest number of the public present and is mainly a singing service.

During the week the hall is open from Tuesday to Friday, with activities for the public and Salvation Army members. On each weekday, except Monday, there is an Advice Centre open all day and to anyone. Other public activities are the Bible study class, the women's meeting and a senior citizens club, the last two providing an opportunity for people, who would otherwise be on their own, to meet, eat and socialise. On Tuesdays and Thursdays Army members go out on a soup run, giving it to the homeless and 'down and out' people, abundant in the area.

On an irregular basis there are Saturday evening music festivals and Songster weekends, when Salvation Army bands from all around the country come to participate. At Christmas, Salvationists from Regent Hall can always be heard around the busy shopping areas. In this period they raise enough money for the yearly costs of the Advice Centre and also to provide a Christmas Day meal and food parcel for 350 street people.

Services: Sunday 9.30am Prayer Meeting, 11am Christian Development Service, 3pm Praise Service, 6.30 Gospel Service □ Facilities: amplification, deaf loop □ Children: Sunday school in the afternoon, for ages 2–16 □ Wheelchair: level access to the stalls □ Other details: Advice Centre, halls and canteens □ Visiting: open 9.30am–5.30pm Tuesday to Friday, and for activities and meetings at other times

Sigsworth Hall Goodwill Centre

156 Globe Road, E2 □ Bus: 8, 8a, 106, 253 □ Tube/BR: Bethnal Green, Cambridge Heath □ Parking: on street □ Commanding Officer: Captain Randall □ Address: as Centre □ Telephone: 980 1912 □ Available: all times □ Other staff: Lieutenant Bardell

This Goodwill Centre carries on the work of the Salvation Army in the East End, where the movement began in 1865. On the nearby Whitechapel Road, a statue of William Booth marks the spot where he began his outdoor preaching.

Formerly a Wesleyan Chapel, and a mission attached to a local Children's Home, the hall was acquired in 1959 and renamed in honour of Major Alice Sigsworth, a tireless Army worker in Bethnal Green who received the Order of the Founder, the Army's highest honour. She paid special attention to the needs of the deaf and dumb—a ministry now revived by Captain Randall.

In addition to the 'lively' services—there is a children's choir and lay testimony is encouraged—the Salvanionist message is spread via the many activities and groups available for people of all ages. Liaising closely with Social Services, the Goodwill Centre is geared towards involvement within the community, responding to needs as they arise under the motto of 'helping people to be whole people'.

Services: Sunday 6pm plus occasional services at 2.30pm as announced □ Facilities: amplification □ Children: Sunday school 12–1.30pm □ Wheelchair: 2 low steps, help available; disabled picked up from home □ Visiting: open for services and activities only

Southwark Salvation Army Citadel

Princess Street, SE1 □ Bus: 1, 10, 12, 44, 45, 53, 63, 68, 70, 76 □ Tube/BR: Elephant & Castle □ Parking: on street □ Commanding Officer: Captain Judith Parker □ Address: as Citadel □ Telephone: 928 7136 □ Available: by appointment, but an 'open house' arrangement exists □ Other staff: Captin Jaqui Leswell

The area around the Elephant & Castle is one of the most deprived in London. Unemployment is high, and many young people with little sense of direction in their lives fall prey to drug and solvent abuse. One in four properties are occupied by squatters, while most people live in high-rise blocks which present their own problems of loneliness and isolation, especially for the elderly residents. The Salvation Army Citadel in Princess Street, built in 1967 and run by two officers, is an evangelical centre that tackles such problems head on, both by practical involvement and by spreading the 'Good News'. These two areas of work may take different forms but they are dependent on each other and are viewed as part of the same task.

Practical assistance is offered in various ways. The most visible, perhaps, is the home and hospital visiting, along with the luncheon club and the weekly food-run in conjunction with the Manna Centre for homeless men. The Army is also involved, however, with local bodies such as the South London Churches Initiative Unemployment Group.

An important medium for the Army's spiritual message is the Youth Fellowship. Amidst the music and games, the youngsters get to know the serious side of the Salvation Army while developing qualities of initiative and leadership. The young soldiers provide visual aids for the local open-air meetings, which feature the band to great effect. The band also provide the music at a monthly meeting at the Army's hostel in nearby Blackfriars Road. The more formal worship at the Citadel is based on the Wesleyan tradition of 'inner purity'. At the morning Holiness Meeting, whatever the content of the service, the focus is on the inner life of the believer. The evening service is geared more towards music—a choir together with the band aid singing of hymns from Mission Praise and the SA Songbook.

Services: Sunday 10.30am Holiness Meeting, 11.45–12.15pm Open-air Meeting (different venues), 6pm Prayer Meeting, 6.45pm Salvation Meeting; 1st Sunday of the month 5pm Meeting at the Blackfriars Road SA Hostel □ Facilities: amplification, large print Bibles □ Children: Sunday school □ Wheelchair: level access □ Other details: small hall, etc □ Visiting: 'open house' system; all welcome to services

Westminster Corps of the Salvation Army

Rochester Row, SW1 □ Telephone: 629 5424 (Regent Hall) □ Bus: 2, 10, 11, 16, 24, 25, 29, 36, 39, 52, 55, 70, 76, 77, 88 □ Tube/BR: Victoria □ Parking: on street, meters □ Officer: lieutenant Allan Hoffer □ Address: 57 Christchurch Hill, NW3 □ Telephone: 435 6935 □ Available: Tuesday 5pm–8.30pm, Wednesday 12noon–9pm

The Westminster centre is officially attached to Regent Hall and the lieutenant in charge, Allan Hoffer, finds his time divided between the two venues. He is, however, determined to keep the centre independent as he feels the largely elderly congregation of around 20–25 would not want to attend the much larger services in Oxford Street and would quickly disappear into isolation.

Today, one of the main concerns of the centre is for the young people arriving in London 'cold', running away or desperately seeking work. Victoria is a natural collecting point and so the Army runs a 150 bed hostel (which is always full) providing not only a place to sleep but a staff committed to helping guests bring some shape and purpose to their lives. There are many more in the area who have to live rough so a 'soup van' makes a twice weekly run, taking in Euston Station, Charing Cross, Lincolns Inn Fields and Blackfriars.

Services: Sunday 11am Holiness Meeting, 6.30pm Salvation Meeting □ Facilities: large print Bibles □ Children: Sunday school and 'kids club' Wednesday 6pm □ Wheelchair: level access □ Visiting: open at service times only

---

The Seventh Day Adventist Church

Adventism is common to a number of Christian groups who hold the Second Coming to be both literal and imminent. The American Baptist preacher, William

Miller, aroused much interest when he proclaimed that, according to his calculation of Biblical dates, the Second Coming should be expected in 1843. When the year passed uneventfully his following fragmented and one group formed the Seventh Day Adventist Church. Some members were former Seventh Day Baptists and that denomination's practice of worshipping on Saturday, the Old Testament Sabbath, was adopted.

Other features of the Seventh Day Adventists include their views on health, diet and fitness. They run stop-smoking courses, abstain from alcohol and stimulants, and their long-held advocacy of a high-fibre, largely vegetarian diet is now supported by most dieticians and doctors. Cookery classes and keep-fit groups are regularly found amongst church-based activities.

The Church is a fast-growing international organisation with over 3½ million members worldwide, and about 16,000 in Britain. At services one can expect to find people of many nationalities and backgrounds, and many family groups. One should find colourful pamphlets and editions of the magazine *Focus* which explains the Church's beliefs in simple terms, and the worshippers are usually friendly and enthusiastic in their welcome.

Further information can be obtained from the New Gallery, Regent Street.

Hampstead Seventh Day Adventist Church

66 Haverstock Hill, NW3 □ Telephone: 482 5022 □ Bus: C11, 24, 31 □ Tube/BR: Chalk Farm, Primrose Hill, Kentish Town West □ Parking: on street □ Pastor: Rev Murtagh □ Address: 26 Rudyard Grove, NW7 □ Telephone: 959 2170 □ Available: by appointment

Attending Divine Service here, one can be sure of a greeting from enthusiastic Adventists who are practised in the art of welcoming newcomers. As often as not, the 500-seat church is almost full with people from many walks of life and of all age groups and, though most are West Indian, many nationalities.

The service is led by Pastor Murtagh, helped by three or four elders. The pastor's sermon is strong on scriptural allusion and newcomers may find it helpful to take their own Bible along for reference. The hymns are led by either the adult or the youth choir. After the service, most people move next door to the hall for a meal, each family having brought their own packed lunches. A small bookshop is open at this time, selling religious titles and magazines on family life and health.

Adventists teaching on matters of health are widely accepted nowadays, and are even fashionable. They have long campaigned for people to stop smoking and change to a healthier diet, and Pastor Murtagh is encouraged to see these items vindicated and accepted. Health and fitness are topics regularly discussed in the youth meeting during the Sabbath afternoon, which despite its title is open to all. The Adventists run keep-fit and cookery classes as well as Bible study groups.

Their church, built in 1877 to designs by Thomas Arnold, originally housed a Presbyterian congregation. It was bought by the Adventists in the late 1960s and opened for worship after extensive renovation in 1972. The Gothic-style building is the sister church to New Gallery, Regent Street and the congregation today includes both members who made the move from Regent Street and local people who have joined since.

Hampstead Seventh Day Adventist Church, NW3

Services: Sabbath Day 11.15am Divine Service, 3pm Youth Meeting; Wednesday 7.30pm Prayer Meeting □ Facilities: amplification □ Children: Sabbath school 10am, ages up to twelve years □ Other details: hall (hire possible), library, etc □ Visiting: open at service times only

New Gallery

123 Regent Street, W1 □ Telephone: 734 8888 □ Bus: 3, 6, 12, 13, 14, 53, 88, 159 □ Tube: Piccadilly Circus □ Parking: difficult □ Pastor: Rev David Cox □ Telephone: 092 678281 □ Available: telephone for appointment □ Other staff: Mr Baynes (Manager)

The New Gallery in Regent Street with its large auditorium, offices, rooms and hall provides extensive facilities for this large and active SDA group. Originally a cinema, the large auditorium was left largely untouched when the SDAs took over in 1952. It is now a perfect setting for the 600 or so enthusiastic worshippers that met here on the Sabbath. It is always a refreshingly cosmopolitan congregation particularly in summer when numbers are increased by the influx of tourists. On Saturday evenings the different cultural groups often hold a service in their own languages.

During the week, when attendance is lower, the services are held on the first floor on the Heddon Street side of the building. Here, there is a comfortable, modern chapel that can accommodate 150. An adjoining room is used for Bible studies by the younger members of the congregation.

With everything portable, even the font, the chapel is easily cleared to provide a comfortable hall for a wide range of activities, many of them concentrating on health. Regular meetings include a weight watchers club, healthy cooking classes and programmes to help people to give up smoking. There always seems to be something going on, a concert for the blind is a weekly event and the auditorium is often used for meetings, seminars, campaigns and organ recitals, both by the SDAs and other groups. There is also a department which receives contributions and household items which are then distributed to the needy.

Services: Sabbath Day 10–12.30pm □ Facilities: amplification □ Wheelchair: difficult, many steps □ Other details: auditorium for hire, apply at New Gallery □ Visiting: open most days

---

Spiritualists (including Christian Spiritualists)

Spiritualism is a system of belief centring on communication with the spirits of the dead. It can claim parallels in most religious traditions, of visions, communications with angels, spirit-possession and the like. The main objectives of modern Spiritualism are: to spread the truth of survival after death, to practise spiritual healing, and to demonstrate and teach the exercising of psychic gifts and powers.

Modern Spiritualism originated in 1848, in Hydesville, New York, when the Fox sisters challenged an entity making noisy disturbances. Later the sisters became mediums. Interest grew and the movement spread rapidly across the

USA. Spiritualism was introduced to England in 1852. In 1884, Spiritualism was organised as a religious community with Sunday services accompanied by clairvoyant demonstrations and trance utterances.

Although Spiritualism and Christian Spiritualism share the basic objectives, there is a fundamental difference. The Christian Spiritualist movement, formed in 1931 under the auspices of the Greater World Christian Spiritualist Association, sees Christ as their leader, and much of the doctrine is based on the teachings of the spirit guide Zodiac, thought to be a Temple scribe at the time of Christ. Spiritualism, on the other hand, although recognising the teachings of Christ, includes elements of traditional Eastern philosophy, such as reincarnation.

Greater World Christian Spiritualist Association

3 Lansdowne Road, W11 □ Telephone: 727 7264/9795 □ Bus: 12, 88 □ Tube: Holland Park □ Parking: small parking area □ President: Mrs Nora Moor □ General Secretary: Mrs Beattie Scott □ Available: at HQ, office hours

The GWCSA was founded in 1931 with the following stated aims: 'To spread in all directions the truth of survival after death, of spirit communion, of healing by the power of the Holy Spirit'. It was set up by Winifred Moyes who was inspired by her spirit guide Zodiac, thought to have been the unnamed scribe who asked Jesus what was the greatest commandment of all (Mark 12.28–34). It publishes around 100 pamphlets of Zodiac's messages.

There are now some 200 affiliated churches around the country, but the only one in central London is the small sanctuary chapel in the HQ near Holland Park. There are divine services and spiritual healing sessions throughout the week. The services are comparable with those of many Christian denominations with hymns, prayers and readings, but include an address given by a medium through inspiration and are followed by demonstrations of clairvoyance. Messages by trained mediums are of a spiritual and material nature. The congregation are encouraged to participate especially by attuning themselves to the spiritual conditions. Private clairvoyant readings are available at a cost of £10.

Healing is available to everyone, and is performed on a voluntary basis by healers who regard themselves as a link between the patients and the healing power of God. Rheumatism and depression are common complaints, and the work is understood to complement that of orthodox medicine. Names may be submitted for absent healing.

Conditions for membership include belief in the survival of the human soul after death, belief that all is evolving towards perfection, and belief in the justice of divine law. Jesus is regarded as the pure vessel in which the Christ spirit was made manifest. Members pay an annual donation and have opportunities for training in healing and self-development. Mediums are registered and undergo a diploma training course.

Services: Sunday 11am Address and intercession, followed by healing, 6pm Service and clairvoyance, 7pm Prayers and healing; Thursday 2.30pm Service and clairvoyance; Saturday 6pm Service and clairvoyance □ Facilities: amplification, booklet in Braille □ Wheelchair: easy access □ Other details: library, bookshop □ Visiting: HQ open 9am–5pm Monday to Friday; chapel open further for services

London Spiritual Mission, W2

London Spiritual Mission

13 Pembridge Place, W2 □ Telephone: 229 2024 □ Bus: 2, 7, 8, 12, 15, 23, 27, 31, 52, 88 □ Tube: Notting Hill Gate □ Parking: on street □ General Secretary: Rosalind Cattanach □ Available: via the church

The London Spiritual Mission is a Christian Spiritualist Church and Centre for 'worship, communion, healing and teaching'. It is one of the 12 in the London area that are independent of both the Greater World Christian Spiritualist Association and the Spiritualist National Union. It follows the seven principles of Spiritualism with liberty of interpretation, for they are not seen as commandments, as there is no fixed creed or dogma. It is seen as a way of life which is universal and embraces all creeds, class and colour.

The church was built in 1900 on the site of former stables. Purchase was advised through a trance-medium and the church was opened in 1903, dedicated from 1912. It is financed from freewill offerings, donations and legacies, and also from the letting of three flats converted from the stablehouse which adjoins the church and church house. The whole property is quite picturesque and has a rural ambience. Inside the church, which has seating for 150, there are honeysuckle coloured walls, a sky blue and white ceiling and windows of stained glass. Fresh flowers are all around.

Services follow very similar lines to normal Christian services, followed by an address on the philosophy of the movement and a demonstration of clairvoyance, given by a different medium each time. However, spirit friends come of their own accord and cannot be demanded, so readings can never be given to order. Through the gift of mediumship it is believed survival of death can be proved by communication with those who have passed from this sphere of life who still wish to be in touch with us on Earth. This offers much comfort to be bereaved and can remove the fear of death.

Another aspect of the Mission is healing, performed twice a week, and there are special demonstrations of mediumship taking place from time to time, proceeds of which are donated to different charities such as 'Save the Children' and 'Counsel & Care for the Elderly'. Once a year a special service is held for the animals, proceeds of which go to animal charities. The healing sanctuary is upstairs and usually between 20 and 30 people attend each session, all of whom are seen privately.

There are weekly lectures on spiritual and psychic subjects such as Buddhism, Tarot, Astrology etc, on Tuesday evenings at 7.30, under the auspices of the 'Pembridge Open Forum'. There is library open to the 200 or so members who pay an annual subscription.

Services: Wednesday 7.30pm Clairvoyance; Sunday 7.30pm Service, 6.30pm Clairvoyance (1st Sunday is devotional, no clairvoyance) □ Facilities: amplification □ Wheelchair: easy access □ Other details: library, healing area □ Visiting: check with Secretary for opening times

Rochester Square Spiritualist Temple

Rochester Square, NW1 □ Bus: 29, 253 □ Tube/BR: Camden Town, Camden Road □ Parking: on street □ President: Mrs Susan Smith □ Available: via the church □ Other staff: Hon Secretary Mrs M L Taylor

Rochester Square Temple, the first Spiritualist church to be built in north London, is easily identified. On the roof is a blue neon cross that glows during evening services; it can easily be seen from Camden Road. The Temple was founded in 1926, by Mr Richard Ellis, who had had a dream in 1922 of how he might spread the truths of Spiritualism. He hired halls and engaged the best speakers of the day. The lectures attracted large crowds, and soon it became necessary to find larger premises. Mr Ellis decided to built a permanent temple, and after some search found the plot of land in Rochester Square. With a group of friends, he set about raising funds to purchase the land and build the Temple. Difficulties and delays presented themselves in various forms, but 'with faith and in faith, the Temple was built'.

During the twice weekly services, a clairvoyant, together with the President, lead the service. The clairvoyant not only addresses the congregation with a short sermon derived spiritually, but gives a clairvoyant demonstration, lasting up to 40 minutes. The message of the sermon is based on love, and may include references to reincarnation

Although the regular congregation is about 20 to 30 people, the Temple is usually full during special services. For the Tuesday clairvoyant demonstration and healing services the garden entrance is used. This can be found around the other side of Rochester Square, at the back of the Temple and garden.

Services: Sunday 11am, 6pm Service and clairvoyant demonstration; Tuesday 2pm Clairvoyant demonstration, 6.30–8.30pm Healing; Wednesday 7–9pm Healing □ Facilities: amplification □ Wheelchair: 1 step only □ Other details: hall □ Visiting: open for services only

Spiritualist Association of Great Britain

33 Belgrave Square, SW1 □ Telephone: 235 3351 □ Bus: 2, 2b, 9, 14, 16, 19, 22, 25, 30, 36, 36b, 38, 52, 52a, 55, 73, 74, 137, 500 (all go to Hyde Park Corner) □ Tube: Hyde Park Corner, Knightsbridge □ Parking: on street, meters □ General Secretary: Tom Johansen □ Address: c/o centre □ Available: all day, by appointment □ President: R Elsom □ Librarian: Miss Eason

The SAGB, founded in 1872, is the largest and oldest Spiritualist organisation in the world. To admit to being a Spiritualist in those years was to face losing one's job and social status, so meetings were held irregularly and at various locations. By 1928, things had improved to such an extent that premises in Tavistock Square were acquired and over 500 people would attend a single demonstration of clairvoyance.

The present premises are in a large building in Belgrave Square and contain a library, cafe area, hall, rooms for private reading, a chapel and a healing sanctuary. This list is a good indication of the nature of events that take place here. One of the most important is healing. Some 90 volunteer healers ensure that healing, including absent healing, is available daily. The General Secretary, Tom

Johansen, first discovered he had healing powers over 30 years ago when he met a monk who urged him to develop this ability. He can recount many instances of successfully healing people who came to him.

There are 50 clairvoyants and clairaudients here, whose sole purpose is to give assurance of survival after death. They do not predict the future, as fortune-telling is strictly illegal. Other practices include psychometry, sensing the history of an object, and clairsentience, giving character-analysis through some item owned by the subject. Fees are charged for all readings.

The Sunday services, led by a chairperson, follow a standard pattern of hymns and readings, though the speaker will often deliver the 'sermon' in trance. In addition to this, the Association runs an extensive programme including lectures and two clairvoyance demonstrations daily, for which a fee is charged. A 12-week Psychic Development course is available at a fee. All activities underline the Association's notion that 'this life is but a classroom in the Kindergarten stage of our true life ahead on the higher planes'. The SAGB publishes *The Spiritualist Gazette* and regular bulletins of events.

Services: Sunday 3pm, 6pm □ Wheelchair: lift □ Other details: Healing Clinic, Monday–Friday 1.30–5pm, 6–8.30pm; Saturday 1–4.30pm; Sunday 3–6.30pm; Other details: library, cafe, halls, rooms □ Visiting: open all day

The White Eagle Lodge

9 St Mary Abbots Place, W8 □ Telephone: 603 7914 □ Bus: 9, 27, 28, 33, 49, 73 □ Tube: Kensington Olympia, High Street Kensington □ Parking: meters on street, car park Warwick Road □ Contact: Colum Hayward □ Address: at Lodge □ Available: office hours

This movement was founded in 1936 by Grace Cooke who died in 1979. A trance-medium, she was instructed by her guide White Eagle, a Red Indian Chief whose teachings, along with the Bible, form the basis of the groups's philosophy. Thus, while they would regard themselves as *New Age Christians*, viewing the cosmic Christ as the light that shines in each heart, members also adhere to certain other principles and beliefs, including reincarnation. However, existence is not seen as an endless cycle and the ultimate goal of mankind is so to strengthen the inner light that physical cells are transmuted into finer substances which can overcome mortality. This is known as the *Christing of Man* or the *Blooming of the Rose upon the Cross of Matter*.

Prayer, inner spiritual communion, healing, astrology, yoga and meditation are all aspects of the movement's worship and activities. Members aim to follow a path of human unfoldment through meditation and providing a healing service to humanity. Mediums are not used.

Today there are around 5,000 members world-wide of whom over half are in Britain. The present Lodge was opened in 1941, a few years before the purchase of New Lands in Hampshire which serves as a country retreat centre. The Lodge is simply a converted artist's studio in Kensington, with a main chapel and three smaller ones. The main chapel, fronted by a sculpted white eagle and a Celtic cross, is used for the three weekly services. Two of these are devoted to contact healing; participants are asked to arrive early to discuss their individual needs. On

Sundays the service alternates between two forms. One is a conventional service with prayers and readings from the Bible and the teachings of White Eagle, while the other, complete with recorded music, is more like a guided meditation. Between 50 and 60 people attend on Sunday.

The two smaller chapels are used for absent healing. This is when many groups meet each week to give healing to people who, although not present in the chapel, do receive instructions in how to be receptive to the healing. The healers allow themselves to be used as channels through which the Christ spirit flows to the ill. Training is available to those who wish to unfold this healing capacity. There are membership fees, and charges for any courses given here, such as the Astrology class.

Services: Sunday 6pm; Mon, Tues 3.45pm Healing; Wed, Thur 6.45pm Healing □ *Facilities: amplification* □ *Children: monthly service, group with newsletter & projects* □ *Wheelchair: easy access* □ *Other details: reading room, bookstall, library* □ *Visiting: open 2.30–5.30pm Monday to Thursday*

Strict Baptist Churches

When in the late 18th century there was a strong movement towards softening the rigidly Calvinistic nature of the Baptist churches, a significant number protested against the change. It was from these ranks that the Strict Baptists formed; a group determined to remain true to the Calvinist tradition with only believers baptised in accordance with the church's teachings 'to be admitted into the communion of the church and to participate of all ordinances in it'.

Today, despite the rather forbidding name, Strict Baptist churches tend to be lively outgoing places of worship with strong outreach and social programmes. Services are increasingly informal and experimental and many young people are attracted to worship. All are welcome to attend these services though the Communion bar, of course, still operates.

Angel Baptist Chapel

Chadwell Street, EC1 □ *Bus: 19, 30, 38, 73, 171* □ *Tube: Angel* □ *Parking: meters* □ *Pastor: Rev Eric Holdstock* □ *Address: 16 Wynyatt Street, EC1* □ *Telephone: 837 9873* □ *Available: service times or by appointment*

Standing behind Sadlers Wells theatre, the Angel Chapel was consecrated as a Baptist church in 1851. Originally a Congregational church, it is now a listed building; the solid square frontage is largely unchanged and the interior retains its period feel.

The regular attendance at the Sunday service is around 35, and this is growing all the time as the chapel has been developed by the pastor to be very much part of the community. Many new businesses have opened in the area over the last few years and Rev Holdstock has been active in gaining support among them. A factory of the Royal National Institute For the Blind is close by, so the church now provides Braille hymn and prayer books. A regular feature is the lunchtime services for local workers, aptly named the 'Angel Oasis', every Thursday. Services tend to be informal with no rigid format. Modern moral issues, such as abortion, are discussed, and lay members are encouraged to take part in services through readings and the leading of prayers. The church has strong connections with the movement in USA and Americans visit regularly.

Missionary work is well supported through donations to the Grace Baptist Mission and the congregation is kept up to date with the news from around the world. 'Operation Mobilisation' is a group for young people around the world to become involved in voluntary Christian activities and the Angel Chapel has both received, and sent out, members of this movement.

Family atmosphere is encouraged through the unusual feature of a church family evening held every two weeks. This provides a recreational night for families; a games room is provided and the evening is concluded with a simple epilogue.

Services: Sunday 11.15am and 6.30pm; Thursday 'Oasis' Lunchtime service 1.05–1.35pm, Women's Fellowship 2.30pm □ Facilities: amplification, Braille books □ Children: creche, Sunday school □ Wheelchair: 1 step, help available □ Other details: hall □ Visiting: open at service times only

Bethesda Baptist Church

Kensington Place, W8 □ Telephone: 221 7039 □ Bus: 12, 27, 28, 37, 52, 88 □ Tube: Notting Hill Gate □ Parking: free car park □ Pastor: Rev D A Smith □ Address: c/o the church □ Available: at services and by arrangement □ Other staff: Simon Webb

The Bethesda Church is a small, unassuming building, tucked behind the elegant frontages of Kensington Church Street's modern offices and up-market antique shops. Until a few years ago the chapel had been almost forgotten, with only six people making up the congregation. Today 80 to 100 people worship here on Sunday and, in an area of such a transitory population, this is a testament to the energies of the present pastor and his assistants.

This has been achieved largely by the adoption of a much higher profile than in the past. Twice a week time is set aside for knocking on doors and promoting contact with the local residents. With thousands of leaflets sent out every year they, in their own words, 'blitz this part of London'. Written in a lively, modern style the leaflets target the many students who live in the area, or who work at the nearby Imperial and Kings College campuses, as a high priority. Many events are geared directly at this group. There is an active social club which organises trips to the swimming baths, excursions to museums and frequent 'socials' and functions. Concerts and lectures also feature regularly.

Worship is informal with lay readers and sermons that relate to modern life and modern problems. This is a popular, lively church with an energetic staff and, with students from all over the world attending, a young and very cosmopolitan congregation.

The church is unusual in that it practises tithing its members; this in accordance to Biblical teachings. Money from this and the many extra donations helps fund missionary projects all over the world through the Grace Baptist Mission.

When Pastor Smith moved here he also brought with him a fascinating collection of Bibles and manuscripts many of which are on show. Collected over many years, they now number over 450 and include first editions (one of the King James Authorised), as well as Pali scripts and 2000 year old cuneiform tablets.

The interior of the building is unremarkable except for the abiding darkness of the wood panelling that abounds. This, however, is one place of worship where it is the congregation, not the building, which sets the tone.

Services: Sunday 11am Morning Service, 6pm Evening Service; Wednesday 8pm □ Facilities: amplification; other deaf/blind facilities available if requested □ Children: Sunday school 10am □ Wheelchair: 2 steps, help available □ Visiting: open only for services

Ebenezer Chapel

Monnow Road, SE1 □ Bus: 1, 70, 199 □ Tube: Surrey Docks □ Parking: on street □ Deacon: Mr A J Jermyn □ Address: 101 Tissington Court, Luxford Street, SE16 □ Available: by arrangement, and after services □ Other staff: Secretary K J Taylor (660 9091)

There has been a Baptist presence in this part of Bermondsey since 1813 and it has always been an important part of the local community. The group moved to its present home in Monnow Road in 1951 after being bombed out of the original chapel during the war. It is very much a local church with the 20 strong congregation coming from the immediate area.

The regular services are simple and evangelical, based on the Authorised Version of the Bible. Like many Baptist services, however, the format is relaxed. Worshippers often take part through testimonies of faith, for example, and extempore prayer. There is also a regular Fellowship hour on Thursday afternoon.

At the moment there is little community or youth work carried out except at a personal level, although it is hoped that this will develop in the near future, and that use will be made of the chapel's facilities. The chapel itself is small and sparsely decorated, though the red brick of the walls and pulpit stage impart a warm, homely atmosphere. The baptistry lies covered in front of pulpit.

Services: Sunday 11am and 6pm; Thursday 2.15pm Fellowship hour □ Facilities: amplification □ Wheelchair: 1 small step; toilet for disabled □ Other details: large classroom □ Visiting: open only for services

Immanuel Community Church, Soho

Charles Norton Centre, Broadwick Street, W1 □ Bus: 3, 6, 9, 14, 19, 22 □ Tube: Piccadilly Circus, Oxford Circus □ Parking: only possible on Sundays □ Minister: Rev Michael Toogood □ Address: 26 St James Residences, 23 Brewer Street, W1 □ Telephone: 434 4056 □ Available: at all times □ Team members: Mary O'Neill (434 9537), Andrew Murray (434 0591)

Soho had been without a nonconformist church for more than 60 years until the formation of Immanuel Community Church in January 1987. Many of the problems of the area are well known—the sex industry, alcoholism, drug abuse and homelessness—but these are imported problems. It was out of the concern for the needs, particularly the spiritual needs, of the small resident community that the London In Reach Project was set up several years ago by a large group of churches. In 1982, the Project invited Rev Michael Toogood to move into Soho with the aim of establishing a local church.

He began with a Sunday morning meeting in a hired rom at the Charles Norton Centre in Broadwick Street, since no church building was available. From very small beginnings, a steady group of about 30 'regulars' has built up, though attendance varies each week, usually being around 20 people. Among those who attend are a few established Christians, and then a variety of mostly older local people, from a variety of religious backgrounds. Each one is glad to come, although only a handful are committed in membership to the new church.

The Sunday services endeavour to combine reverent worship with a friendly warmth, and simple clarity. Those who attend are encouraged to be involved, especially in choosing hymns and choruses, and bringing items of prayer. The Bible talks show how a clear Biblical message is relevant to the needs of ordinary men and women today. Coffee is available after services.

A Biblical message also reaches local people who do not attend the services, through regular leaflets delivered round the area. These deal with a range of material, from articles of local interest, through personal testimony and comment, to general subjects of debate. For the church, the community is of first concern and so a great deal of work is done beyond the one weekly service. Working in close contact with the welfare services, Michael Toogood and his energetic team are in the front line, contacting those in the are with problems, and offering help. One of the most important is the 24 hour helpline open to all. In the course of his work, which includes knocking on many doors a week, Rev Toogood is as likely to be helping someone sort out their DHSS claim as resolve a question of faith.

Services: Sunday 10.30am–11.30am □ Facilities: large print hymn books □ Wheelchair: 1 shallow step

St John's Wood Road Baptist Church

St John's Wood Road, NW8 □ Bus: 2b 13, 46, 113, 159 □ Tube: Warwick Avenue; St John's Wood □ Parking: difficult □ Pastor: Dr J K Davies □ Address: 9 Hamilton Gardens, NW8 □ Telephone: 286 3875 □ Available: by appointment

The original St John's Wood church was a large Victorian structure likened by the local paper to a Walt Disney fairy castle. Recently it became clear that the building was far too large (it could easily accommodate 700), and so was unsuitable for the 50 or 60 members of the local congregation. The radical solution was to demolish the old building and rebuild a modern, functional church of more suitable proportions, at the same time taking the opportunity to add other features to extend the work of the church.

One of the major developments will be a recording studio for the Grace Baptist Mission. Here radio programmes and sermons will be recorded for transmission all over the world. The church will also become the central office of the Grace Baptist Study Centre with a library and rooms set aside for courses, lectures and Bible study groups. A large hall will be available for public meetings (and

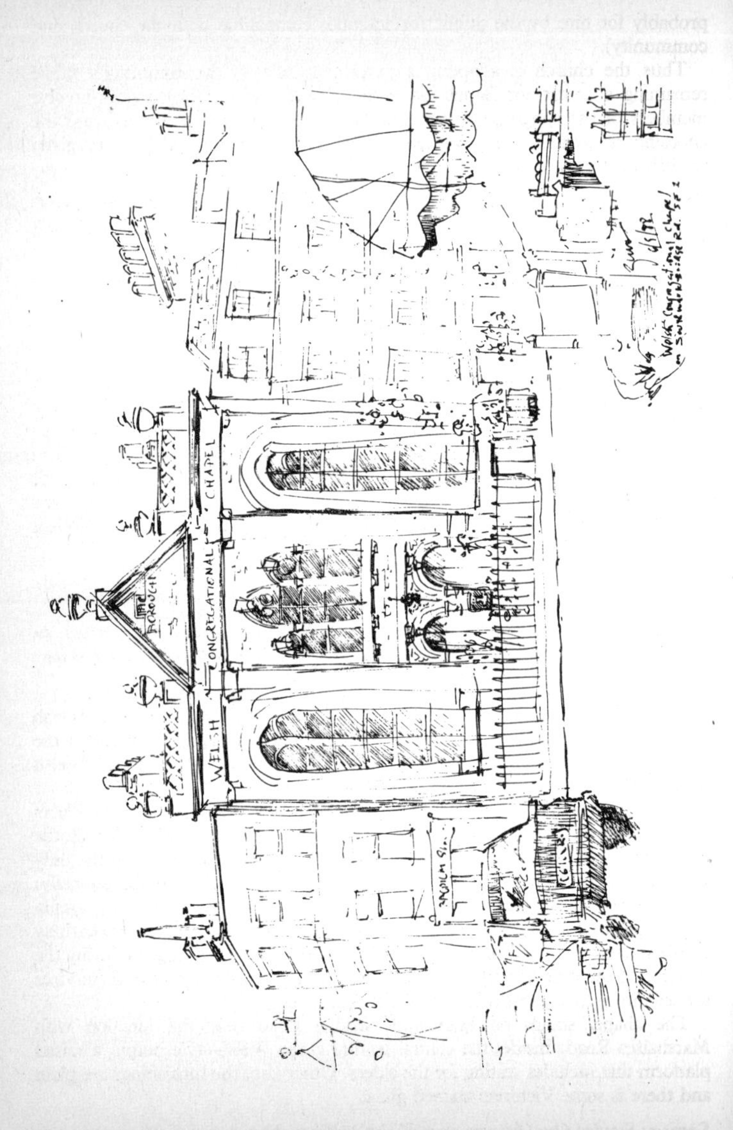

Borough Chapel, SE1

probably for hire by the public for activities compatible with the church and community).

Thus the church is adopting a prominent role in the community while remaining a centre for Baptist activities. Appropriately, the services involve members of the congregation with Bible readings, leading in prayer, and the choosing of hymns. The children at the morning family service are given worksheets for the sermons to aid them in understanding the service.

Services: Sunday 11am and 6.30pm □ Facilities: amplification, large print texts □ Children: Sunday school; Bible study □ Wheelchair: easy access □ Other details: hall, library □ Visiting: by arrangement, any reasonable time

---

The Union of Welsh Independents

There are some 60,000 members of Union churches but the vast majority live in Wales. Of the six churches remaining in London, the three most central are included here. Essentially, the Union is the inheritor of the traditions of Welsh Congregationalism, and as such is an association of autonomous churches. The churches are concerned with all things Welsh and come together regularly for Welsh festivals, the largest of which is the St David's Day festival, held at the Royal Albert Hall. Services and any leaflets or booklets are invariably in Welsh.

Borough Chapel

Southwark Bridge Road, SE1 □ Bus: 44, 95, 184 □ Tube: Borough □ Parking: on street □ Secretary: Byron Jones OBE □ Address: 66 Norbury Hill, SE16 □ Telephone: 764 5747 □ Available: most times at home

Ever since the chapel was founded in 1806 it has served the local Welsh community with nonconformist worship in the Welsh language. As part of the Union of Welsh Independents, its members have taken part in many Welsh festivals and cultural activities in London.

In 1872, when the present building was completed, there were many Welsh people living in the Southwark area. Nowadays however, the decline of the congregation has resulted in there being a single weekly service, and the only social activity based at the chapel is the Literary Society which meets occasionally. The tradition of singing is strongly upheld here and the congregation, usually numbering around 25, reaches a rousing volume. Hymns and prayers are entirely in Welsh, and there will be no more than a sentence or two of English during the service. At the time of writing, there is no incumbent minister here, so services are led either by a guest minister or a lay preacher.

The chapel stands on Southwark Bridge Road near the junction with Marshalsea Road. Inside, the central feature is the Welsh-style pulpit, a raised platform that includes seating for the elders. Otherwise, the furnishings are plain and there is some Victorian stained glass.

Services: Sunday 6pm (All services in Welsh) □ Wheelchair: very difficult, several steps □ Visiting: open at service times only

King's Cross Tabernacl

Pentonville Road, N1 □ Bus: 30, 73, 214 □ Tube/BR: Kings Cross □ Parking: difficult □ Minister: Rev Ieuan Davies □ Address: 98 Rhydytenau Road, Cardiff □ Telephone: (0222) 763 251 □ Available: at services

The Tabernacl was acquired from the English Congregationalists in 1889. Prior to this the congregation met at various venues around the City area of London. The Gothic church is set back from Pentonville Road and over the years has developed a black hue from all the fumes expelled by the passing traffic.

There are two services here on a Sunday. Both are held in Welsh and are based on nonconformist tradition. On the first Sunday of the month, the morning service is one for children. Sunday school is not specifically for children, as Christian learning is taught to all. The congregation is composed wholly of Welsh people and although largely elderly there are now a dozen or so young people who regularly attend. The evening service is attended by 60 people, double the figure present in the morning, which is no doubt due to the distance most must travel.

The hall underneath the church is let to the Community Service Volunteers whose main offices are further up Pentonville Road; this use provides an income for the church. On Sundays the hall is used for Sunday school and for drinks after the services. A Literary Society meets here fortnightly.

Services: Sunday 11am (Children's Service, 1st Sunday; Communion, 3rd Sunday), 6.30pm (Communion, 1st Sunday), (All services in Welsh) □ Facilities: amplification □ Children: Sunday school at 4pm (for adults also) □ Wheelchair: difficult, many steps into the church □ Other details: hall □ Visiting: open for services only

Welsh Congregational Church

Radnor Walk, SW3 □ Bus: 5, 15, 40 □ Tube: Sloane Square □ Parking: difficult □ Minister: Rev D Gwylfa Evans □ Address: 58 Bonnersfield Lane, Harrow □ Telephone: 427 7074 □ Available: by telephone during day

The discreet exterior of the Welsh Congregational church does not, at first, suggest a place of worship, since it has the appearance of an elegant Chelsea town house; bi-lingual signs are the only outward indication of its role. When one has climbed the steps and entered through the door of the porch, a small lobby leads to the church itself.

It is larger than the exterior would suggest, and simplicity is the keynote of the design; it can seat around 200 people on light wooden pews which face a large, carved wooden pulpit. At the rear of the church, a panelled partition leads to a committee room, where church meetings can take place. The large hall downstairs, adjacent to the vestry, is let on weekdays to a private medical clinic across the road in Radnor Walk.

Sunday services, led by Rev D Gwylfa Evans, are in the Congregationalist tradition and are entirely in Welsh. Chelsea once had many Welsh residents, but in recent times many of them have moved to more suburban areas; nowadays, most of the congregation travel some distance to attend. Welsh people, regardless of denomination, are especially welcome.

Between the months of September and April there is a Cultural Club, which meets once every three weeks, on Wednesday evening. Other activities include special celebrations on St David's Day, Eisteddfod events, and outings, including trips to the theatre. A quarterly newsletter keeps members and friends abreast of services and activities at this and other Welsh churches in the London area.

Services: Sunday 11am & 6pm (Holy Communion, 2nd Sunday; both services) (All services in Welsh) □ *Facilities: amplification* □ *Wheelchair: very difficult; several steps* □ *Visiting: open 30 mins before services*

Unitarian Churches

In some respects it is easier to say what Unitarianism is not, than what it is. Unitarians have no set creed, impose no test of belief on worshippers or ministers, and both except and encourage differences of opinion between members.

Although the denomination is firmly in the Christian tradition, there is no general acceptance of the doctrine of the Trinity (as the name suggests) or the concepts of Original Sin and eternal damnation. Jesus, who called himself the Son of Man and not the Son of God, is regarded as the messenger of divine love and a model of our potential worth.

The father of British Unitarianism is thought to be John Biddle (1615–62) who published tracts and addressed meetings in London in spite of the 1648 Ordinance decreeing death to those who denied the Trinity. The first congregation to adopt the name Unitarian (which was not legally recognised until 1813) was founded in 1774 by Rev Theophilus Lindsey (1723–1808) who had resigned his Anglican living the year before, unable to subscribe to the Thirty-Nine Articles.

The 19th century saw the development of the more rational, less Biblical Unitarianism of today, in which reason and conscience are held to be the sole criteria of belief. Religious revelation is understood in terms of an unfolding spiritual insight from within rather than as a written statement by God. The Church exists, not as repository of sacred truths, but to foster an environment for individual discovery and discussion, and to be a focus for a community based on principles of love and mutual respect.

Unitarians, who may style themselves Liberal Christians or even Religious Humanists, have strong traditions of social concern and works, and of educational innovation.

Brixton Unitarian Church

63 Effra Road, SW2 □ *Bus: 2, 37* □ *Tube: Brixton* □ *Parking: car park* □ *Minister: none at present* □ *Secretary: Mr P Tayler* □ *Address: 51 Anthony Road, SE25* □ *Available: evenings*

As with all Unitarian churches, the Brixton congregation welcomes people of any race, creed and denomination who seek truth and who respect the beliefs of others. A wide range of religious texts, not solely Christian, are used, and discussion is encouraged.

The Chalice Foundation, Mansford Street Church, E2

The long-serving minister, Rev Robert Tayler, retired in September 1986, and it is hoped that his replacement will bring new impetus to the outreach work designed to attract new worshippers to church. Present attendance is low, about 18 people from various backgrounds.

Meetings are held in a modern spacious church, built in 1962, very close to Brixton town centre. The original church was founded by eminent local families, such as the Martineaus and the Tates, in 1859. The founder members did much in the field of educational development, and this is one aspect of Unitarianism, amongst others, that the Brixton congregation hopes to revive as their church begins to thrive again.

Services: Sunday 11am, except first Sunday of month 6.30pm □ Wheelchair: 2 steps, help available at service times □ Other details: hall for hire □ Visiting: all welcome to services

The Chalice Foundation (Incorporating Mansford Street Church & Mission)

117 Mansford Street, E2 □ Bus: 6, 35, 55 □ Tube: Bethnal Green □ Parking: on street □ Minister: none at present □ Administrator: Mr Murray Bracey □ Address: c/o church □ Telephone: 729 7788 □ Available: most times

The Chalice Foundation was so named in 1985 to mark a renewed effort to revive the work of the Mission and to renovate and convert the Mansford Street Church to best suit the needs of the local community. An appeal for £175,000 was launched, and contributions are still welcome.

The Mansford Street Mission was the direct successor of the Spicer Street Mission set up in 1832 to bring comfort and help to the unemployed silkworkers of Spitalfields. This was one of the first religious initiatives in the East End, and with over 150 years of welfare work behind them, the present-day Foundation workers bear witness to the Unitarian tradition of social concern. The current plan is to create a church/community hall and office/workshop space in an area badly lacking such facilities.

Services to be based here include an OAP Social Club, job training for the young unemployed, and a Community Programme Welfare scheme offering advice and visiting the elderly and housebound. The Bangladeshi United Welfare Association plan to open an Islamic Cultural Centre in the basement. The hall will be available for sports, drama and concerts.

The building itself is one of very few of any character in the area. Built in 1871 to an Italianate design by W O Church, it has a monumental facade with double doors under a large leaded rose window. The whole is crowned by a neo-Classical pediment. The interior gains distinction from a fine tile mosaic, thought to be by Doultons of Lambeth.

For some years there has been no full-time ministry at Mansford Street, though the efforts of visiting and student ministers have resulted in some new faces at church. Attendance remains low—around 20 mainly elderly worshippers—and 'congregational development' is another priority of the Foundation. Especially welcome are young liberal Christians who would welcome non-dogmatic worship along with the chance of involvement with an exciting and worthwhile community scheme.

Services: 1st and 3rd Sunday 6.30pm □ Wheelchair: many steps to church □ Other details: hall (for hire to voluntary groups and charities) □ Visiting: open daily 9am to 5pm

Essex Church

112 Palace Gardens Terrace, W8 □ Bus: 27, 28, 31, 88 □ Tube: Notting Hill □ Parking: on street, difficult □ Minister: Rev Francis Simons □ Address: as church □ Telephone: 221 6514 □ Available: most times, telephone first

The church takes its name from the first established Unitarian congregation, set up in 1774, which met in Essex Street off the Srand. The present building, erected in 1977 on the site of a larger Victorian Gothic church, contains a library and a hall, as well as accommodation for the minister and warden. Designed by Thomas Atterton, it has a striking facade of white bays and has been praised for the dignified simplicity of the church interior. The hall is put to good use by various groups, including Amnesty and the World Congress of Faiths.

Sunday attendance is around 30 or 40, and there is a regular core of 12 lay members who can take services. The worshippers, mostly professional people, come from as far afield as Ilford and Wimbledon, and are supplemented by visitors here on business or to study. Catholics, Anglicans and Jews attend, for there are no credal tests and the value of all Faiths is recognised. Indeed, the church has connections with the Hindu Brahmo-Samaj, and joint services are held.

Rev Simons calls his services 'tradical': giving a radical message through a traditional form. Kensington Unitarians claim to attract 'the thinking person' and the atmosphere is discursive and inquiring; services often lead to lively debates, held over coffee, and may be dispensed with altogether if it was felt an event or topic needed to be discussed. There are weekly study groups and monthly 'Days of Re-Creation of Spirit, Mind and Body' when the service is followed by an outing to a place of interest.

Services: Sunday 11am □ Wheelchair: steep ramp 'not insuperable with help' □ Other details: hall, library □ Visiting: telephone minister

Rosslyn Hill Unitarian Chapel

Rosslyn Hill, NW3 □ Bus: 210, 268 □ Tube: Hampstead □ Parking: on street □ Minister: Rev David Usher □ Address: The Manse, Rosslyn Hall, Willoughby Road, NW3 □ Telephone: 435 3506 □ Available: most times

The Hampstead Unitarians trace their origins to a congregation founded in 1691, when John Biddle himself was preaching in London. Since 1862, services have been held in the Gothic chapel, built, as the Trust Deed declares, 'to be used, occupied and enjoyed as a place for public worship of Almighty God' free from 'any doctrine . . . or tenet'.

Members now number about 70 and take turns to act as hosts for the services. Most are under 40 years of age and are business and professional people. Not all would describe themselves as Christian, but there is a general consensus over basic values and principles. Rev Usher may take his text from the Bible or any source with something relevant to say, and his services are followed by coffee and discussion.

The congregation is noted amongst Unitarians for the excellent choir, and the acoustics of the chapel are very good. Concerts are regularly held here, and other activites include book fairs for charities such as Christian Aid, Help the Aged and Amnesty International.

There are many visitors to the chapel, usually friends of members, and anyone is welcome to the services. The church is best described by members of the congregation, twelve of whom met in July 1985 to produce a series of statements, including: 'this church exists to help its congregation achieve their full potential in both spiritual and social ways throughout their lives, in an open-hearted atmosphere'.

Services: Sunday 11am □ *Wheelchair: level access* □ *Other details: hall for hire* □ *Visiting: apply to minister*

The United Reformed Church

The United Reformed Church is a union of three nonconformist churches. Two of these, the Congregational Church in England and Wales and the Presbyterian Church in England, have a history that dates back almost to the Reformation and they joined together in 1972. The third member, the Reformed Association of Churches of Christ, a relatively new denomination founded in the 1830s, joined the URC in 1981. The Church upholds a Reformed tradition of Christian worship that embraces such figures as John Calvin, the Pilgrim Fathers, Oliver Cromwell and David Livingstone.

The Bible is recognised as the supreme authority for faith and conduct, and the URC recognises the Sacraments of Baptism (ie of both infants and adults), Communion (usually called the Lord's Supper), and the ordained ministry. The services of the three member churches were previously quite similar, and they have been further unified. They are Bible-based with hymns, prayers, readings and a focal sermon. Preaching is considered to be in the 'liberal' tradition. Communion or the Lord's Supper is held monthly or in some cases weekly. It can be described as 'low' in nature, using bread and wine and taken at the Communion table, and is open to all members of Christian Churches.

Indeed the URC is committed to ecumenical advance, which is not surprising as it origins lie in unification, and asserts there should be One Church. It is involved in inter-denominational activities from the local level to the World Council of Churches.

At present there are some 130,000 URC members in Britain attending 1,850 churches. As there are only 900 ministers—who may be men or women—many are responsible for more than one church, and there are also a number of part-time ministers who help carry the load. Lay preachers and elders are always on hand to help lead services and run each church.

For further information contact United Reformed Church Headquarters, 86 Tavistock Place, WC1 (Telephone: 837 7661)

Chelsea United Reformed Church

Edith Grove, SW10 □ Telephone: 352 2655 □ Bus: 11, 22, 14, 45 □ Parking: church car park □ Secretary: Mr David Mansfield □ Telephone: 351 1832

Edith Grove, on which the church stands, is a busy artery linking Kings Road and Fulham Road. The houses, tall and grand, are now mainly converted into flats. The church, built in 1959 to a functional and practical design, including a sloping floor to aid visibility from the back, lies on the east side.

The first church on the site was the West Brompton Congregational church, built in 1880. After bomb damage in 1942, the nine-strong congregation met at Fulham Baptist church, until the Congregational Union, responsible for use of War Damage Money, completed the church under the supervision of the Rev E M Hawkins. At the time of writing the church is without a minister, relying on guest speakers and ministers to take the services while the day-to-day business is handled by the church secretary and elders.

There is much congregational participation in the Sunday service, and the elders often try out new ways of worshipping: a visiting drama group from All Souls, Langham Place, was one innovation. Nowadays the church serves a mainly elderly congregation, but there are also well established Girls' and Boys' Brigades which hold a joint parade every second Sunday of the month.

Services: Sunday 11am Family Service (Communion once a month) □ Facilities: amplification and deaf loop □ Children: Junior Church during the 11am service □ Wheelchair: ramp; toilet for disabled □ Other details: hall and 3 rooms, all available for hire □ Visiting: open for services and activities only

City Temple

Holborn Viaduct, EC1 □ Telephone: 727 9704 □ Bus: 8, 18, 22, 25, 46, 501 □ Tube/BR: Holborn Viaduct, Farringdon □ Parking: difficult except Sunday □ Minister: Rev Eric Waugh □ Address: 124 Rotherfield Street, N1 □ Telephone: 359 7961 □ Available: most afternoons at church □ Other staff: Sue Arnold, Administrator

The classically styled Victorian facade of the City Temple that can be seen from Holborn Viaduct, a two storey portico with a small west tower, is most misleading. The building goes down at the back to the Farringdon Road level, and is therefore much larger than it appears. It is large enough, indeed, to contain office suites, conference rooms and a now disused theatre, as well as the substantial auditorium-style sanctuary.

The Temple was extensively refurbished following war damage, the sanctuary being refitted with square cut woodwork and large light blue panels on the walls. On the right of the entrance hall is a glass-walled chapel, open all day for quiet prayer, while to the left is the Weatherhead Room which contains pictures and plaques telling the story of the church and its congregation. Lunch is served here on Thursdays, and on Sunday it is used as a 'cry room' with a sound link to, and full view of, the sanctuary.

Unlike many City churches that close down for the weekend, City Temple has continued the practice of concentrating worship around the Sunday services. It is clearly succeeding in its stated aim of achieving 'maximum participation by the people and maximum outreach into the City', as each Sunday sees around 100

City Temple, EC1

worshippers, who travel from all over London, at both the morning and evening services; refreshments are served after each. On Thursdays, when the area is full of office workers, the church attracts around 60 people to the brief lunchtime service. At all services a spectrum of ages is to be found, but the Sunday morning service attracts the most family groups. This is the most traditional service, while the Sunday evening service is kept flexible and informal.

During the week, the Temple is open for a variety of activities, including Bible study and prayer groups and Women's League meetings. There are a number of housegroups who meet at various times at different locations. Organising all this is Eric Waugh and his staff of five—extra volunteers are always welcome.

Services: Sunday 11am (Communion 1st Sunday), 6.30pm (Communion 3rd Sunday); Thursday 1.15–1.45pm Lunchtime service □ Facilities: amplification, deaf loop □ Children: Junior Church 11am; creche and cry room □ Wheelchair: level access through side door □ Other details: conference rooms, Weatherhead Room, etc □ Visiting: chapel open 8am–5pm daily; rest of church open for services and activities only; Cross Talk magazine, cassettes of sermons, etc, available

Crossway United Reformed Church

100 New Kent Road, SE17 □ Bus: 1, 53, 63, 177, 188 □ Tube: Elephant & Castle □ Parking: on street □ Minister: Rev Patricia Wardle □ Address: Church House, Deacon Way, SE17 □ Telephone: 703 7803 □ Available: most times, at church or house

Camouflaged amongst the surrounding blocks of flats, Crossway was built as an integral part of the housing complex. Construction was on the site of the original Crossway, a large Victorian church, bought by the council under a compulsory purchase order so that the land could be used for the development, which was completed in 1975. The money received as compensation was sufficient to build a new church and the church house, and is still providing funds towards the running costs of the church.

The first church building on this site was founded as 'Murphy's Mission' in 1866, ten years after the first congregational gathering in this particular area. The building served as more than a place of worship, having many halls and rooms used for a day nursery and as workshops, and it also housed the community health centre. The new church is also designed to be of use to the community. Built on two levels, upstairs it has the sanctuary, sized to suit today's smaller congregations, whilst underneath is the hall and adjacent book room and kitchen. The church house is built at the rear, accessible through the warren of flats.

During the time when there was no building to house the congregation, the worshippers met in St Matthew's, an Anglican church on the other side of New Kent Road. When the United Reformed Church was completed, the links developed with St Matthew's continued. This has led to 'Elephant Churches', the name heading the joint publication of *Crossroads*, a community newspaper, and the weekly service sheet.

There are two services on Sunday at Crossway, the evening service being held with St Matthew's congregation. Crossway Praise at 11.30am is a flexible service for people of all ages, using music and drama as well as discussion and singing.

The evening worship is a quieter service with an emphasis on preaching. Crossway United Reformed Church is the only 'Free' church in north Southwark and serves people from a wide area.

On weekdays the church hall is used for a variety of activities. On Mondays there is a Bible study group, with further religious meetings on Thursday evenings in the church and on Wednesday evenings in people's homes. There is a Tuesday afternoon meeting for women. With the benefit of good leadership the Crossway Girls' Brigade has grown, now having four meetings for different age groups.

During the week Rev Patricia Wardle has a busy schedule, with pastoral visits and also an involvement in community organisations. With Rev Angus Galbraith and the curate from St Matthew's, she shares the responsibility of attending the meetings of local tenants associations, nursery associations and squatter groups, and there are links with local Social Services workers.

Services: Sunday 10am Parish Communion (at St Matthew's, SE1), 11.30am Crossway Praise, 6.30pm Evening Worship (Communion 3rd Sunday) □ Children: Sunday school 11.30am □ Wheelchair: ramps; toilets for disabled □ Other details: hall available □ Visiting: open for services and activities only

Harecourt United Reformed Church

Harecourt Road, N1 □ Bus: 30 □ Tube/BR: Highbury & Islington □ Parking: on street □ Minister: Rev Paul Whittle □ Address: 78 Aberdeen Park, N5 □ Telephone: 226 1300 □ Available: most times at home or Islington Claremount URC

This church originated in the City as Harecourt Congregational Church in 1648, the second Congregational church in London. It was moved out to Canonbury in the 1850s to a specially built Gothic church that housed congregations of up to 800 people. After escaping the Second World War undamaged, the church was later to fall victim to a simpler incendiary device. Following a candle-lit service in December 1982, local youths entered the church and, under suspicious circumstances, the building was gutted by fire.

Leaving the burnt-out shell of the original church as a rather striking ruin, the congregation now worship in the converted ground floor of a nearby house owned by the church. The conversion consisted of knocking out the walls on the ground floor and adding a Communion table, an electric organ and a portable pulpit. As the congregation now numbers around a dozen mainly elderly people, this provides a suitably intimate atmosphere for their weekly service.

The Sunday morning service is in a traditional nonconformist style with a leaning towards informality, incorporating discussion in the worship: at the same time however it is more 'formal' than the services at Islington Claremont URC, Rev Paul Whittle's other church. This co-pastorate leads to variation in the evening service: of the four Sundays in a given month, the first is used for a joint service held at each church alternately, though always led by Rev Whittle. The remaining services at Claremont are also taken by the minister, so services at Harecourt, held at the same time, are led by lay preachers.

Since the fire, various plans have been drawn up for the rebuilding of the church, but technical problems have so far prevented this work from starting. The hall was undamaged by the fire but the plans include its re-building. For this reason no maintainence work has been done so it is in a run-down state and is therefore virtually unused, save for an occasional jumble-sale. The only regular activity is the monthly study group attended by a dozen people—a small, but impressive number considering that the morning services attract the same total.

Services: Sunday 10.30am (Communion 4th Sunday), 6.30pm (Joint service with Islington Claremount URC, 1st Sunday) □ Wheelchair: 6 steps to worship room □ Other details: hall □ Visiting: open for services only

Islington Claremont United Reformed Church

White Lion Street, N1 □ Telephone: 837 3402 □ Bus: 4, 19, 30, 43, 73, 171a, 214, 279 □ Tube: Angel □ Parking: difficult □ Minister: Rev Paul Whittle □ Address: 78 Aberdeen Park, N5 □ Telephone: 226 1300 □ Available: most times at church □ Other staff: Hakan Pettersson, community worker

Islington Claremont, a small obscurely positioned church on White Lion Street, was once much larger. The front section facing onto Pentonville Road is now a factory, an arrangement that came about with it being let out in the 1960s.

In 1979 Islington Chapel, Upper Street, was closed down and joined with Claremont. The proceeds from the sale were used to refurbish the chapel at Claremont. It now has 50 free standing chairs in the small room which is simply decorated and has a wooden cross above the Communion table. There is an electric organ to accompany the singing.

The Sunday morning service is very similar to that at Harecourt URC but as the congregation is much larger and has people of all ages there is a monthly family service, where the children stay throughout the service. This is on the first Sunday and on the third there is a Communion service. The evening service arrangements are fully explained in the Harecourt entry.

Opened in 1819, Claremont Hall began as the Central Mission of the Congregational Union, serving the young, sick and elderly as well as having a 1000-seat auditorium. This mission work is still continued in the smaller premises, using the lounge, kitchen and dining room as a Day Centre for the Elderly which serves a daily lunch, followed by a variety of activities. The first floor is used for an under 5's playgroup. The other church organised activities are Women's Own, and Boys' and Girls' Brigades. There is a study group held at irregular intervals.

Services: Sunday 11.30am (Communion 3rd Sunday; Family Service 1st Sunday), 6.30pm (Joint service with Harecourt URC, 1st Sunday) □ Children: Sunday school 11.30am □ Wheelchair: easy access to church; steps to Day Centre; toilets for disabled □ Other details: Day Centre, etc □ Visiting: open 10am–5pm daily

Kensington United Reformed Church

Allen Street, W8 □ Bus: 9, 27, 28, 33, 49, 73 □ Tube: High Street Kensington □ Parking: difficult except Sunday □ Minister: Rev Kenneth Slack □ Address: The Manse, Allen Street, W8 □ Telephone: 937 8826 □ Available: most times at the Manse

This once Congregational church was built in 1854. With a portico facing on to Allen Street, inside it is wide and bright, providing a pleasant relaxed atmosphere for the Reformed worship now taking place. Although most churches of the time were Gothic in style, this church is Classical throughout with clear windows and an uncluttered interior; a recent redecoration has been carried out in period fashion. In the 1950s the church was reorganised with the pulpit being lowered and the organ moved to the rear of the church. One recent change has been the addition of stage raisers in the sanctuary area, so as to accommodate the performances of the Kensington Musica, which take place 8 or 9 times a year.

During the Second World War the hall at the rear of the church was destroyed and has now been rebuilt. It is a multi-storey building, including a large and small hall, and a flat for the minister. The halls are used by a local school and for the activities of the congregation.

The two Sunday services are in a typical Reformed style, occasional differences being in the use of music and visits from other ministers and preachers. Coffee and tea is served after both services, providing an opportunity for the congregation to meet and socialise.

The church has 100 Communicant members, by no means all of whom live in Kensington but who regularly attend. This number is slowly growing and becoming more multi-racial. Although the age of members varies widely, the predominant age groups are the young professionals and the elderly. There are not many families but a creche facility is provided and there is a Sunday school for the slightly older children.

Services: Sunday 11am (Communion 1st Sunday). 6.30pm (Communion 3rd Sunday) □ Facilities: deaf loop □ Children: creche and Sunday school, 11am □ Wheelchair: difficult access, several steps □ Other details: halls (available for hire in evenings and weekends) □ Visiting: open for services and activities only

Paddington Chapel

Worshipping at: St Mark's Christchurch, 255 Old Marylebone Road, NW1 □ Bus: 6, 8, 16, 16a, 18, 27, 36, 36b, 46, 176 □ Tube: Edgware Road (both stations) □ Parking: on street □ Minister: Rev Dr Daniel Jenkins □ Telephone: 628 5947 □ Available: telephone for appointment

Founded as a Congregational church in 1813, this once substantial and now greatly reduced URC congregation gave up its own large building in the late 1970s. They now worship in the nearby St Mark's Anglican church (qv).

The present congregation holds a single weekly service in typical URC form, although the close links between the two churches enable them to share the services of the same professional choir. As this is the nearest URC congregation to the West End, it is hoped to redevelop the activities to meet the need of the international residential community and the visitors to central London.

After his retirement from a career as a minister and a university teacher in both England and the USA, Dr Daniel Jenkins has returned to this country to take the post of acting part-time minister at the chapel. The future leadership is, at the time of writing, still to be decided.

Services: Sunday 11.15am (Communion 1st Sunday) □ Wheelchair: 1 small step

Regent Square United Reformed Church

Tavistock Place, WC1 □ Bus: 17, 18, 45, 46, 259 □ Tube/BR: Kings Cross, Russell Square □ Parking: car park behind church □ Minister: Rev John Miller □ Address: 3 Asmara Road, NW2 □ Telephone: 794 5045 □ Available: evenings

Built in 1966, the church stands as an example of modern Presbyterian architecture, retaining simplicity with little use of decoration on the exterior, and using internal concrete buttresses as a feature of the design. The pews and woodwork in the sanctuary are of pine, and the walls are bare and white.

The present building replaced one which was much larger and less typically Presbyterian in design. It was built to house the congregation of Edward Irving who, through his ministry in the neighbourhood, gathered so large a following that in 1827 the church at Regent Square was built to house it. However, by allowing the practice of 'Speaking with Tongues' in the service, Irving fell foul first of the Trustees and then of his Presbytery, and was dismissed from the ministry. He took with him the bulk of the congregation, wich subsequently founded the nearby church of Christ the King. Regent Square continued, first as a congregation of the Church of Scotland, then under the Presbyterian Church of England, until in 1972 it became part of the United Reformed Church.

In 1944 the building was so seriously damaged by a flying bomb that it had subsequently to be demolished, and the present church, together with a car park, was built on the site. The original four halls and ancillary rooms remained unchanged; they are in regular use by a number of community groups.

Present congregations number around 35 and are largely composed of members of the surrounding community and students from the various colleges nearby. The congregation also attracts a considerable number of visitors throughout the year. The URC Chaplain to the University is associated with the ministry at Regent Square, and there is a nearby hostel for URC students at Birkenhead Street.

Services: Sunday 11am, 6.30pm □ Facilities: amplification □ Children: Sunday school 11am, for ages 10–14 □ Wheelchair: 3 steps □ Other details: 4 halls □ Visiting: open only for services, URC bookshop next door in Wakefield Street

St John's Wood United Reformed Church

Worshipping at: St John's Wood Church Hall, St John's Wood, NW8 □ Telephone: 586 3864 □ Bus: 2b, 13, 74, 113 □ Tube: St John's Wood □ Parking: forecourt car park □ Minister: Rev John Miller □ Address: 3 Asmara Road, NW2 □ Telephone: 794 5045 □ Available: evenings

John Miller is also the minister of this church, a position he has held since 1973. It has a small congregation which meets in the hall of St John's Wood parish church, an arrangement that has taken place since the sale of the local United Reformed Church in 1980 when it was recognised as being far too large for the needs of the congregation which now numbers around a dozen people.

When the original church was built, for Presbyterian worship, it was reputed to be the strongest and wealthiest Scottish church in England. The decline of the congregation started when the surrounding residential area became more expensive to live in, causing many regular church-goers to move out. This has left a mainly elderly membership.

The service held is similar to that at Regent Square except that the musical accompaniment is provided on a piano. In the congregation's time at the Anglican church, the links between the two churches have been strong.

Services: 1st Sunday 11am Communion Service; Other Sundays 9.30am Morning Service ☐ Wheelchair: ramp

St Paul's Bayswater United Reformed Church

Newton Road, W2 ☐ Telephone: 727 9704 ☐ Bus: 7, 15, 27 ☐ Tube: Bayswater ☐ Parking: possible, better on Sunday ☐ Minister: Rev Harry Undy ☐ Address: 12 Urwin Gardens, NW10 ☐ Telephone: 459 4875 ☐ Available: Rev Undy's pastorate is part-time; not always available

The move in 1972 from the traditional church to the present multi-purpose building in Newton Road provided an opportunity to introduce a new more informal style of worship. This initiative sprang from the congregation and has been encouraged and developed by the ministers, including Rev Harry Undy, who has been here since 1982. Now one might find a traditional sermon with hymns and prayer, a parade, a special family service, or simply a discussion of matters relating to the church.

The congregation takes a good deal of responsibility for running the church. There are elected elders (of all ages), who are involved in all decisions. Membership and attendance at services is mixed not only in age, but in race, background and 'in nearly every way imaginable' as Rev Undy puts it. The church considers itself to be 'inner-city', and this presents particular concerns and responsibilities, and the need to look beyond its own community. Charitable work is carried out on a personal basis, and the Paddington Christian Council is well supported.

A special feature of St Paul's is that, due to the number of hotels in the area, there are often several tourists in the congregation. These are welcomed, and asked to sign the visitors book. Every autumn, this book is used as the inspiration for a special family service, with a map of the world used as a 'prop'.

The body of the church is a square hall with a stage added for use as a sanctuary. This is protected by sliding doors when the hall is used for other activities: the chairs can be stacked away to provide a large space. The church runs a Boys' Brigade who take part in the monthly parade service and brownies and guides also meet in the hall. The office suites in the building are leased to local charities recognised by the church as being of benefit to the community.

Services: Sunday 11am (Parade, Family Service once a month) ☐ Children: creche and Sunday school, 11am ☐ Wheelchair: difficult access, several steps ☐ Visiting: open for services and activities only

St Paul's Bayswater URC, W2

Trinity United Reformed Church

Buck Street, NW1 □ Bus: 29, 134, 253 □ Tube: Camden Town □ Parking: difficult □ Minister: Rev Istvan Kardos □ Address: 34 Willes Road, NW5 □ Telephone: 276 2280 □ Available: most times

Surrounded by derelict buildings, but near to Camden Market, which attracts thousands of people into the area every Sunday, Trinity URC has survived in this far-from-ideal location by involving local people in both services and activities.

Over the last 20 years, for example, there has been a large settlement of West Indians in the area and more recently an increase of the Ghanaian and Chinese communities. In this time members of both the West Indian and Ghanaian communities have joined the congregation, now making up a third of the total number of 60. The Chinese have also become involved by using the church building as the venue for some of the activities of the Camden Chinese Community Centre. This operates a weekly under 5's playgroup, a Vietnamese 'drop in club' and English lessons for all. In the four years that the centre has used the church, close links have been formed and the minister, Rev Istvan Kardos, is now director of the CCCC.

Other groups using the church include Mustard Seed, an evangelical group meeting twice weekly, and a country dance class on Tuesday evenings. The church also makes the hall available to one Narcotics Anonymous and two Alcoholic Anonymous groups.

The church was designed in 1905 as a multi-purpose building in order to cater for both community and congregational needs. The chairs can be removed to create an open space, which can be enlarged by opening the folding partitions to adjoining rooms. The most interesting feature is the organ, which requires the organist to sit in a cage formed by the pipes of the instrument.

Services at the church are mainly traditional, based on sermon, hymn and prayer. Variation to this is provided by frequent visits from other ministers and lay preachers to take services. Twice a year there is a Congregational Sunday when 40 to 50 people attend both morning and evening services and, in between, take part in activities like walks and discussion. Rev Istvan Kardos sees the church as 'being here to proclaim and demonstrate the supreme Lordship of God over every aspect of life'.

Services: Sunday 11am (Communion 1st Sunday), 6pm (5pm during winter); Wednesday 7.30pm □ Facilities: amplification □ Children: Sunday school 11am □ Wheelchair: level access via side entrance □ Visiting: open only for services and activities

---

Other Churches and Congregations

All Saints Liberal Catholic Church

205 Upper Richmond Road, SW15 □ Bus: 14, 22, 30, 37, 39, 80, 93, 264 □ Tube/BR: East Putney, Putney □ Parking: meters □ Regionary Bishop: The Most Rev Eric S Taylor □ Address: Drayton House, 30 Gordon Street, WC1 □ Telephone: 387 3260 □ Other staff: Rev R I Shepherd (who runs a church enquiry service-0784 55389)

The Liberal Catholic Church originated in a mission of the Old Catholics, prominent in the Netherlands, which came to London in 1908. Liberal Catholics have paid scrupulous attention to their *bona fides* (the preservation of the Apostolic succession, etc) but they are still viewed somewhat askance by many Roman Catholic and Anglican clergymen, largely because of their theosophical leanings. The Church's moral theology emphasises the concept of a loving God and thus their liturgy (an adaption of the traditional Western rite) excludes reference to the fear of God and eternal damnation.

The Liberal Catholic services are impressive and dignified without being distant. The liturgy is in English but incorporates elements from the Orthodox as well as the Western Catholic and Anglican tradition. The emphasis is on the beauty and solemnity of the ritual and, at High Mass, of the music (there is a fine organ). The singing is congregational. All who approach the Communion service in a spirit of reverence are welcomed.

The church seats about 50. Formerly it belonged to the Unitarians, who had it built in 1967. It stands adjacent to the little park formed recently from the old burial ground of Putney village. The Unitarians found their Richmond church to be sufficient for them in south-west London, and by happy chance the Liberal Catholics were looking for just such a small and modern building for their new London church, so in 1985 they purchased All Saints' and began to hold services there.

Although weekday attendances are low while the church is still getting established, more people come for the regular Sunday worship; some are long-time members (formerly there was a large church in north London), while others are perhaps attracted by the Tridentine flavour of the Mass. The Liberal Catholics acknowledge all seven of the Sacraments, and as well as Communion services the Church offers a healing ministry (part of the Sacrament of Unction) with a talk and benediction each Wednesday evening.

Services: Sunday 11am High Mass; Wednesday 7.30pm Healing & Solemn Benediction; Thursday 11am Low Mass; Friday 11am Low Mass □ *Wheelchair: level access* □ *Other details: church hall, office, refreshment room* □ *Visiting: open for services only*

The American Church in London

Tottenham Court Road, W1 □ *Telephone: 580 2791* □ *Bus: 14, 24, 29, 73, 134, 176* □ *Tube: Goodge Street* □ *Parking: very difficult* □ *Pastors: Rev Ron Allison, Rev Vernon Frazier* □ *Available: most times at the church, during office hours* □ *Other staff: Corporate Secretary, Bob Thompson; Minister of Christian education, Jerry Collins*

As its name suggests, this church provides a place of worship for the many Americans both living in and visiting London. It aims to hold services similar to those in America and is interdenominational. People of all nationalities are welcome.

The church is the third one to be built on the site, the first being built in 1756 and the second destroyed by a V2 rocket on Palm Sunday 1945. The present church was completed in 1957 for the United Reformed Church and then loaned to the American Church in London in 1969. The church is also used as a place of worship by Chinese Lutherans and Ghanaian Christians.

The body of the church is very modern in design, looking similar to a small hangar. It has a low altar and behind it the seating for the choir faces the congregation. Down the side walls there are large arched windows made up of squares of coloured glass, and above the porch there is a gallery. There is little decoration in the church, the main feature being a large cross on the east wall.

On Sundays, rooms below the church are used for a comprehensive Sunday school. The youngest go to the nursery, run by professional staff, then each age group, from 1st to 6th grades, have their own classes. There are also several adult classes including Bible studies and Koinonia.

Membership of the church is around 400, and the church runs programmes and groups that try to further members' involvement with the church and to encourage fellowship. To organise this work there are eleven committees made up from church members.

Due to the number of members and range of activities the church has two pastors, Rev Ron Allison and Rev Vernon Frazier, and a full time staff of five. The size of congregations vary between 175 and 300. This number is affected by members going on holidays and visits back to America during the summer months; congregations are therefore larger in the 'Fall'. During the summer there is an average of 15 visitors per service. To help these people find out about the church an advertisement is placed in *The Times* each week and, at services a 'visitors' form' is passed down each pew. Those leaving their name and telephone number may then be contacted later by members on behalf of the church.

Services: Sunday 11am Morning Worship (Holy Communion 1st Sunday) □ Facilities: amplification □ Children: nursery and full Sunday school during Morning Worship □ Wheelchair: ramp at rear then five steps to nave □ Other details: offices, library, hall, etc □ Visiting: open 8.30am–4pm weekdays

Arab Christians

Worshipping at: St Augustine of Canterbury. 117 Queen's Gate, SW7 □ Bus: 9, 52, 52a, 73 □ Tube: South Kensington, Gloucester Road □ Parking: on street □ Contact: Ven Rafiq Farah □ Address: 1 Finsen Road, SE5 □ Telephone: 274 3663 □ Available: at services and by telephone

This congregation started meeting at St Augustine's in late 1986, and hence its services are presently of an experimental nature. While using an Anglican framework, including ASB Rite A, Ven Rafiq Farah wishes the services to be as ecumenical as possible. This has resulted in a mixed congregation of many Christian denominations, and of many races, such as Palestinian, Lebanese and Jordanian. Although services are conducted in Arabic, hymns are sung in both Arabic and English, and as such anyone is welcome to attend services. Members come from all over the Greater London area, and are mainly professional people and their families. Visitors include students, business people and tourists from the Middle East. Normal services attract 40–50 people, while special services have been attended by up to 200 worshippers. Refreshments are available after the services. A group of women meets once a month, and confirmation classes have been set up recently.

Services: 2nd Sunday 4pm Holy Communion; Last Sunday 4pm Evensong □ *Wheelchair: shallow steps, wide door; wheelchair space inside*

British Christian Esperantists

Worshipping at: Hinde Street Methodist Church, Thayer Street, W1 □ *Bus: any along Oxford Street* □ *Tube: Bond Street* □ *Parking: on street, meters* □ *Chairperson: Miss Joan Dawson* □ *Address: 79 Bishop Ken Road, Harrow* □ *Telephone: 427 9596* □ *Available: by telephone*

Services in Esperanto, the international language, have been held in London since 1912, when the Esperanto New Testament, translated from the Greek, was first published. Early services were led by the late Montague Butler, compiler of the hymnbook *Himnaro Esperanta*. For the last few years, there have been monthly services at Hinde Street Methodist Church, held on the second Sunday of the month (excluding August).

These services last for about an hour, and have an adult congregation. They are entirely in Esperanto; worship is led either by a regular attender or by an invited speaker and, while the services are basically Christian and always include the Lord's Prayer, they are flexible and content is decided by whoever is in charge. Attendance is normally between ten and twenty, but on special services (such as anniversaries or at Christmas) this swells to between 60–100. People travel many miles to attend, from as far as Folkestone and Felixstowe, and it is not unusual for people to visit from abroad. This, of course, is where the advantage of Esperanto lies; foreign Esperantists, who may be unfamiliar with English, know that they can communicate through the international language.

After services, tea is served in a downstairs room. The wide dispersal of the congregation precludes activities outside services, but there is a magazine—*Kristana Alvoko*—which enables people to keep in touch.

All are welcome at the services, whether they can speak Esperanto or not, and can be sure of a warm greeting. People interested in the language can obtain information and advice from the members.

Services: 2nd Sunday 3.15pm (except August), other services as announced (All services in Esperanto) □ *Wheelchair: no facilities; assistance required.*

Central London Church of Christ

Worshipping at: New Gallery, 123 Regent Street, W1 □ *Bus: 3, 6, 12, 13, 14, 53, 88, 159* □ *Tube: Piccadilly Circus* □ *Parking: on street* □ *Contact: Mr Douglas Jacoby* □ *Address: 6 Gloucester Court, Swan Street, SE1* □ *Telephone: 403 7385/3078* □ *Available: most times*

Every Sunday a mass of enthusiastic and strikingly cheerful people flock to a service at the New Gallery in Regent Street. Most are young, many have come from far-flung parts of London, and they are members of the Central London Church of Christ.

This evangelical church strives to keep Christianity simple and upholds the Bible as its sole authority for beliefs and practice. Members are urged to apply their faith to their everyday lives, both in the home and the workplace. They are divided into some 50 groups who meet at a number of locations for Bible study classes during the week. Membership and classes are free, but a collection is taken on Sunday to pay for the hire of the New Gallery, and the ministers' salaries.

This Sunday service then brings together the various group members. Everyone is encouraged both to greet one another and to embrace during the singing of hymns. The lively service also features a talk given by one of the six regular speakers who take it turn to preach, or by a guest speaker.

The congregation regularly numbers around 500 people about half of whom are British. The other half are a good mixture of Asians, Africans, West Indians and Americans. Most are between 20 and 40 years old, but the oldest member is over 90 years of age! One thing is sure—anyone going along can be sure of a very warm welcome.

Services: Sunday 10.30am □ Facilities: amplification □ Children: Sunday school □ Wheelchair: help needed to reach auditorium

Chinese Church in London

81 Chiltern Street, W1 □ Telephone: 486 0592 □ Bus: 1, 2, 2b, 18, 27, 30, 74, 113, 176 □ Tube: Baker Street □ Parking: NCP and meters □ Pastor: Rev Tan □ Address: c/o church □ Available: telephone for appointment

Recognising the need for a place of worship that met both the cultural and spiritual needs of born-again Chinese Christians, Pastor Stephen Wang and friends founded the Chinese Church of London in 1950. From its small beginnings as a family church, it continues to expand as a spiritual home for Chinese Christians of many denominations.

The headquarters of the church are based across the road from the church in Chiltern Street, not far from Madame Tussaud's Wax Museum. The church itself is a former Welsh Methodist chapel. Services here now are conducted in Cantonese in the morning and English in the afternoon. The latter service is well-attended by British-born Chinese, young families and overseas students. The After Church Fellowship on Sunday evening includes group discussions, films, and perhaps even a delicious Chinese dinner prepared by members as a welcome to newcomers.

Chinese services in London are also held at Finsbury Park Methodist Church, Wilberforce Road, N4 (Cantonese, Sunday 2pm) and at the Seymour Leisure Centre, Bryanston Place, W1 (Mandarin, Sunday 10am). The Chinese Church Centre in Chiltern Street however is a focal point for worshippers from all these congregations, and organises a wide range of activities and social events, including groups for young people and students, and for families. District caring and Bible study groups meet on Friday evenings in various centres, and there is a Fellowship Group for those from catering and restaurant backgrounds which meets in Soho on Wednesdays.

Lastly, week-long conferences are held during Easter and summer at retreats outside London. Members and their friends participate in Biblical discussions, workshops and recreation. Further details of all the above activities are available from the Chinese Church Centre.

Services: Sunday 10am (in Cantonese), 3pm (in English) □ Facilities: amplification □ Children: Sunday school 10am (ages 5–14); creche; Bible study for older children after 10am service □ Wheelchair: 2 steps □ Other details: hall (available for hire) □ Visiting: by arrangement

Cole Abbey Presbyterian Church (Free Church of Scotland)

Queen Victoria Street, EC4 □ Bus: 6, 9, 11, 15, 15a, 17, 76, 95, 149, 184, 513 □ Tube: Mansion House □ Parking: not difficult on Sundays □ Minister: Rev J D Nicholls □ Address: church □ Telephone: (0689) 34302 □ Available: most days at church

A small denomination, the Free Church of Scotland owes its origins to the Disruption of 1843 when disagreements within the Church of Scotland resulted in nearly a third of the ministers leaving to form the Free Church. In 1900, many members of the Free Church united with the United Presbyterian Church (which later rejoined the established Church) but a minority remained independent. Presbyterian in nature, and committed to the Bible as God's Word, the Free Church believes and preaches the message proclaimed by preachers from Martin Luther and John Calvin through to John Newton.

The sole Free Church of Scotland congregation in England meets at the Cole Abbey church, situated in the shadow of St Paul's. To this former Anglican church comes a regular group of Scottish expatriates resident in London, as well as a number of visitors. The post-Great Fire church of St Nicholas Cole Abbey was built in 1677 by Sir Christopher Wren, but this was destroyed in the Second World War. There is a small section of an original wall built in to the present church completed in 1962 as a replica of the former design. The extensive use of woodwork in the interior also has pieces of original work saved from the fire, principally the pulpit and chancel rail.

There are three weekly services at Cole Abbey. These are plain Bible services having sermons and prayer, with some unaccompanied singing of hymns and metrical psalms. Since the Free Church of Scotland started using Cole Abbey in 1981 the congregations at each service have flourished, so that now on a Sunday morning there are 80 to 90 people present and at the other two services the figure is between 50 and 60. On Wednesdays the service is geared towards those working in the City and is followed by a light lunch.

The growth area has been with the young professionals, people in their 20s and 30s attracted to the church because of the fellowship that has developed through the worship and the social activities. There are many activities that bring people together, both religious, with weekly prayer meetings and study groups, and, more socially, house meetings, a monthly fellowship lunch and a married couples group. There is even a church football team.

The minister, Rev J D Nicholls, has been at Cole Abbey since 1981, seeing it grow to its present state. Apart form his pastoral work, he is also Chaplain to the Sheriff of London and has encouraged members of the congregation in their support of the Embankment Mission. Although the church is distant geographically from its Scottish origins, it clearly has a role to play in London providing, as the minister says, 'a definite Biblical and Reformed Witness coupled with warm fellowship'.

Services: Sunday 11am, 6.30pm; Wednesday 1.05pm, (The Lord's Supper is celebrated during the morning service three times a year; on the third Sundays of February, June and October) □ Children: children's class 11am □ Wheelchair: difficult access □ Visiting: open for services and activities only; bookstall; cassette library

The Dutch Church

Austin Friars, EC2 □ Telephone: 588 1684 □ Bus: 6, 8, 8a, 22, 35, 47, 48, 149 □ Tube: Bank □ Parking: difficult □ Minister: Ds H J J Waveren □ Address & Telephone: c/o church □ Available: telephone for appointment

The 'Liturgical Centre' is the name given to the end of a Protestant Dutch church dominated by the pulpit, and this church, in Austin Friars, is no exception. The pulpit is large and solid beneath a crown symbolising the Trinity, and—another feature of Presbyterian churches—there is no altar. Instead the congregation is invited to sit around a large Communion table which is extended to almost the entire width of the church.

If one looks under the Communion table one will find an altar stone inlaid in the floor which is one of the few remaining objects that survived the bombing of the old church during the night of 15th–16th October, 1940. It dates back to 1253 and comes from the original monastery church built on this site. The Friar Hermits of the Order of St Augustine of Hippo resided in the church from 1253 until 1538 when they were disestablished by Henry VIII, but to this day the surroundings of the church have been named after them 'Austin Friars'. The charter of 1550 granted freedom of worship to refugees from the continent, mostly Dutch, and the Friar's Church, renamed *Templum Domini Jesu* was given over to their use. Apart from a hasty exodus during the brief reign of Mary, the church has been used for worship by the Dutch community ever since.

The interior of the church is spacious and uncluttered. Stained glass windows throw a peaceful light on the interior. The large west memorial window is of particular interest as it shows a pictorial history of the Dutch church in London and was a gift from the Protestants in the Netherlands. Note also the tapestry depicting man, God and creation.

The services are ecumenical in character and attract members from various churches in Holland. They consist mainly of a sermon and singing, accompanied by the Dutch organ. The average attendance is around 40, but many find that they are only able to attend once per month as the church is too far away from their homes. The church is also used for events of special interest to the Dutch people and operates as a social focal point for the dispersed Dutch community.

Services: Sunday 11am □ Facilities: amplification □ Children: service every 3rd Sunday □ Wheelchair: 'stair-chairs' available; toilets for disabled □ Other details: hall, library □ Visiting: generally available for viewing—ring bell; postcards and leaflets; tours by arrangement

Fetter Lane Moravian Church, SW1

Fetter Lane Moravian Church

381 King's Road, SW1 □ Bus: 11, 19, 22, 45, 49 □ Tube: Sloane Square □ Parking: on street □ Priest-in-Charge: Rev G E Birtill □ Address: Moravian Church House, 5 Muswell Hill, N10 □ Telephone: 883 3409 □ Available: during office hours

The Moravian Church has its origins in 1457 in Bohemia (part of present-day Czechoslovakia) when a group of people, in protest against the moral corruption and political activity of the Roman Catholic Church, withdrew to a remote village called Kunwald and established a community based on the principle of the Sermon on the Mount. They called themselves 'The Unity of the Brethren' or, in Latin, *Unitas Fratrum*. This is still the official name of the Moravian Church, and this ecumenical doctrine of the unity of Christians, transcending all ecclesiastical divisions, is central to its teaching.

The Moravians' presence in London is largely due to Count Zinzendorf, the man behind the 'renewal' of the Church in 1727. In 1750, he aquired the stables and the garden of the Chelsea mansion that once belonged to Sir Thomas More, for conversion into a chapel and graveyard respectively. This chapel, a plain brick building, whitewashed inside with a simple wooden cross at the altar, is still used today. It is set behind the burial ground which contains around a thousand tombstones creating a peaceful, secluded spot, a world away from the noisy, hectic Kings Road.

The size and nature of Moravian congregations have fluctuated over the years: at present there are some 600 worshippers, many of them West Indian, in Greater London. In 1732 two Moravians had set sail on a mission to the West Indies and it is interesting to note that it was the eventual arrival of the descendants of those early converts that greatly revived the Church's fortunes in Britain—a rather long and roundabout route from Czechoslovakia!

Between 30 and 40 now regularly attend the simple services at Fetter Lane. Shared Holy Communion is taken on the first Sunday of the month, whilst on other Sundays there are services taken by the Moravian Women's Ancillary and the youth group. The Sacraments of Baptism and of the Lord's Supper are observed with the emphasis on the idea that those who take part do so not as individuals but as members of the fellowship or the congregation. In practice this means that the bread and wine are taken by all, including the priest, at the same time. There is plenty of lay involvement: some services are conducted without a priest present. Bible study groups meet on the first and third Wednesdays of the month.

Services: Sunday 3pm (1st, 3rd and 5th Sunday), 11am (2nd and 4th Sunday) □ Children: Sunday school during service □ Wheelchair: easy access □ Other details: hall (for hire for exhibitions etc) □ Visiting: open during daytime; tours by arrangement

French Protestant Church

8–9 Soho Square, W1 □ Telephone: 437 5311 □ Bus: 1, 7, 8, 14, 19, 22, 24, 25, 29, 38, 55, 73, 134, 153, 176 □ Tube: Tottenham Court Road □ Parking: difficult □ Pasteur: Rev Pierre Simon □ Address: c/o church □ Available: by telephone

L'Eglise Protestante de Londres in Soho Square is one of three French Protestant churches in Great Britain, the other two being in Brighton and Canterbury. It was founded in 1550 by Royal Charter of Edward VI, for Huguenots who had fled from the Continent to escape religious persecution; these events are commemorated in a stone tympanum in the church's porch. The congregation eventually split, since some spoke Dutch and others French. The French Huguenots set up their own church in Threadneedle Street, later moving on to St Martin's-le-Grand. The present church was erected in 1893, in the middle of what was then a large French community in Soho.

The architect was Sir Aston Webb, and the architecture is officially termed Franco-Flemish Gothic, with Romanesque influences. The exterior is attractive and imposing. As with all Reformed churches, the interior is unadorned; its attraction lies in the simplicity of the terracotta walls, the barrel-vaulted roof, and tripartate windows along each side of the nave and in the dome at the front of the church. Below the dome are semi-circular choir stalls and an organ. At the rear of the church, above the entrance, is an inscription, *Le Temple du Seigneur Jesus*, originally the official name of the church.

An open Bible on the Communion table is the focal point of services, rather than an altar. The importance of the sermon at services is reflected in the grandness of the pulpit. The congregation travels from all over London to attend, and is made up of French or French-speaking people of European, African and American origins, and of all ages and social groups.

The church is a registered charity, and undertakes a variety of charitable activities. Bursaries for schools, mainly in the UK, are made available. A youth officer is available to assist young French-speaking people living in London, and he also runs a *Groupe de Jeunes* which has a full programme of activities. The church is also associated with the Embankment Mission helping needy members of the French community. Appeals are made on behalf of French-speaking Protestant Churches overseas, such as in the Lebanon and Madagascar.

The church's other religious activities include an ecumenical Bible studies group in Kensington (an area with a large French-speaking population). Pasteur Simon is chaplain of the French Lycée School in London, and Bible study classes for the school are held at the church. There is an annual retreat, in conjunction with the French Roman Catholic Church, which is held in March at a convent in Crystal Palace. It may be an Anglican, Orthodox, Protestant or Roman Catholic clergyman who leads the retreat.

Services: Sunday 11am (Holy Communion 1st, 3rd and 5th Sundays); 1st Tuesday 12.30pm Bilingual Services (Services are in French unless stated) □ Facilities: amplification □ Children: Sunday school 11am, twice monthly □ Wheelchair: 1 small step □ Other details: hall (available for restricted hire), library, etc □ Visiting: open for services only

The Ghanaian Chaplaincy

The Whitefield Memorial Hall, Tottenham Court Road, W1 □ Bus: 14, 24, 29, 73, 134 □ Tube: Goodge Street □ Parking: very difficult, except Sundays □ Chaplain: Rev Tony Beeko □ Address: Ghanaian Chaplaincy Office, The Whitefield Memorial Hall, Tottenham Court Road, W1 □ Telephone: 580 6433 □ Available: during office hours

Founded in 1961 as a joint venture by the Presbyterian Churches of England and

Ghana to help Ghanaian students in London, the Chaplaincy has exceeded all expectations. Having recently celebrated its Silver Jubilee, the Chaplaincy now ministers to the Ghanaian community, not just students, all over Britain, and welcomes Ghanaians and other West African Christians of any denomination.

The Chaplaincy is a five-year post currently held by Rev Tony Beeko. He is based at the Whitefield Memorial Church (qv American Church), but spends a good deal of time travelling around the country visiting people and providing a link between individuals and the community.

It was only in 1985 that the regular London service was introduced: it takes place on the 3rd Sunday of each month. It is a part Free Church, part Pentecostal service, mostly in English with the lesson being read in Ghanaian languages. Anything between 50 and 200 people may attend. A prominent part is played by Nnwontofo Fekuw (Fellowship of Singers) who sing songs and hymns in the African idiom, accompanied by African drums, rattles and piano. This choir demonstrates the marvellous contribution made to Christianity by African music, and has given joyful performances at St Margaret's Church, Parliament Square and elsewhere. After the service refreshments are served and the worshippers make the most of the opportunity to meet friends and talk.

The aim is in no way to create a 'Ghanaian Church' but to bring members of a family together and to provide support and guidance to all Ghanaians in Britain.

Services: 3rd Sunday (except March); check times with church □ Wheelchair: ramp at rear, then five steps to the nave □ Visiting: open for services only

God's Kingdom Society

Worshipping at: Lambeth Methodist Mission, 1–5 Lambeth Road, SE1 □ Bus: 3, 10, 44, 59, 109, 159 □ Tube: Lambeth North □ Parking: small car park behind Mission □ Contact: Tony Agbanoma □ Address: 122 Thurleigh Road, SW12 □ Telephone: 675 4326 □ Available: by telephone

God's Kingdom Society was founded in Nigeria in 1934 by Gideon Meriodere Urhobo, a former postal clerk turned full-time evangelist. At first Brother Urhobo had links with the Jehovah's Witnesses but he rejected them as propounding doctrines inconsistent with Scripture. The GKS bases all its doctrines on Biblical authority and publishes tracts, strewn with scriptural references, to explain and justify their beliefs, especially those which differ from those of most Churches.

For example, rejecting Christmas Day as 'pagan', GKS members instead celebrate Freedom Day in October, a month calculated to be that of Christ's birth according to Biblical data. They also celebrate the Jewish Feast of the Tabernacles, both to obey God's commands (Leviticus 23:41) and to follow Christ's example (John 7). They share with Jehovah's Witnesses an Arian concept of Christ as less than God, and they condemn as blasphemous the veneration of Mary as the Mother of God. On a topical note, they oppose the ordination of women and quote St Paul exhaustively by way of argument (I Tim. 2:9–15, I Corinth. 14:34–36). Heaven is held to be reserved for 144,000 saints, all men, granted sainthood by the grace of God.

The Society has been represented in Britain since the 1950s, and members have been worshipping weekly at Lambeth's Methodist Mission since 1975. There are currently about 40 members, mostly in London, both students from Nigeria and Nigerians who have settled here. There is no minister, so the informal services are led by the chairman and members take turns to preach. The meetings provide a welcome source of community and welfare, especially for the students away from home.

Services: Sunday 2–4pm (in hall) □ Wheelchair: ramp

The Hungarian Reformed Church

17 St Dunstan's Road, W6 □ Bus: 11, 220, 283, 295 □ Parking: on street □ Pastor: Rev Alexander Varga □ Address: as church □ Telephone: 748 8858 □ Available: most times

The Reformed Church is part of the significant Protestant minority, largely Calvinist in theology, that has existed in Hungary since the 16th century. Presbyterian in structure, the Church is similar to, though not linked with, the Church of Scotland and the Swiss Church.

Branches have been established wherever Hungarians have settled, and it was set up in this country by Hungarian refugees from Germany and Austria who began to arrive in 1948. There are now almost 4,000 people in Britain who nominally belong to the Church. About 1,200 live in Greater London and the South East, the area served by the church in Hammersmith, and of these some 350 are active members. The building also serves as the denominational HQ and as the home of Pastor Alexander Varga.

Members travel from as far as Colchester and Brighton, and there are considerable transport difficulties, especially among the elderly. As a result, Pastor Varga does as much home-visiting as he can and Sunday attendance varies between 25 and 80. Services, apart from being in Hungarian, are similar to those of the URC; there is congregational singing accompanied by piano or harmonium. The worshippers are all either Hungarian or of Hungarian descent, except perhaps when the occasional guest speaker uses English. The congregation is mostly middle-aged, though some younger family groups attend.

As with all 'Churches Abroad', membership is an important element of cultural identity, and the church is used for popular Hungarian literary and musical evenings. The sense of community is strong, and there is a welcome opportunity to talk and drink tea after the services.

The building itself was designed in 1889 by C F A Voysey as a residence plus sculptor's studio. It was acquired in poor condition in 1958 and the studio was converted into a plain, wood-lined room for worship—once the dry rot was treated there was no money left to build on an apse. From the street, the central chimney, large low roof and pebbledash walls make the house at once unusual and familiar. Indeed, Voysey's modernist, utilitarian style became, in a debased form, the model for the ubiquitous suburban 'semi'; so while the church is scarcely a tourist attraction, Pastor Varga has, on occasion, been descended upon by 'coachloads' of architecture students.

Services: Sunday 5pm □ Wheelchair: some steps, help required □ Visiting: apply to Pastor

London Healing Mission

20 Dawson Place, W2 □ Telephone: 229 3641 □ Bus: 27, 28, 31, 52 □ Tube: Notting Hill □ Parking: on street □ Missioner: Rev Andy Arbuthnot □ Address: c/o Mission □ Available: ring for appointment □ Other contacts: Rev Thomas W Wood, Reg East

The London Healing Mission is the only organisation of its kind, having been involved in Christian Healing for nearly 50 years. It is run by Rev Andy Arbuthnot, who, prior to his involvement in the Mission for the last three years with his wife, Audrey, was Chairman of the only merchant bank to be run by a priest.

Counsellors see 50–60 people a week for one-and-a-half hours, on an individual basis, by appointment (which must be made a month in advance, due to demand). Problems range from depression, back trouble and migraine, to cancer. Healing of epilepsy and neuralgia has been claimed to be instantaneous, when people have opened themselves to 'the healing power of Jesus'. For others, it can take longer, though there is no set pattern.

There are four outside telephone lines through which people can request prayer, but it is stressed that there is 'no hot-line to God' here. The person can relate to the Lord directly through sessions taken with this awareness in mind.

There are two weekly services, on Thursday, attended by about 60 people. After the service, counsellors pray separately with people who require healing. There is not a regular congregation and everyone who comes is recommended by word of mouth. Those who attend are of all ages and social groups. A monthly newsletter gives numerous accounts and examples of those who have been healed. In the words of Rev Arbuthnot, 'The Lord moves in power every day at the Mission'.

Services: Thursday 11.15pm Communion (Anglican), 7.15pm Worship; Saturday occasional meetings □ Wheelchair: a few steps □ Other details: consultation and healing rooms □ Visiting: open 10am–8pm for visiting by appointment

London Mennonite Centre

14 Shepherds Hill, N6 □ Telephone: 340 8775 □ Bus: 271 □ Tube: Highgate □ Parking: on street □ Various elders can be contacted at the Centre □ Available: any time

The London Mennonite Centre, originally set up in 1953 as a hostel for foreign students, is now a teaching, administrative and resource centre for the movement and for Anabaptist theology. While members do worship here in a small chapel, the main place of worship is the Friends Meeting House at Muswell Hill.

The Mennonites recognise the basic Anabaptist concerns, those of Christian discipleship, peace-making and social justice. While being basically non-hierarchical, with no single leader, there are several elders (of both sexes) who have duties of pastoring, teaching and overseeing the life of the London Mennonite Fellowship. Emphasis is placed on the priesthood of the congregation, and on its responsibilities and rights; decision-making is by consensus.

Services at the Friends Meeting House are open to all and are informal, with singing, prayer, and scripture reading; occasionally drama and folk arts are performed. Services are led by a group, and participation by all is encouraged.

About 40 people attend, many in family groups, and most are from north London. Tea is available afterwards.

The Centre in Highgate contains a library of books, cassettes, magazines and journals. A teaching programme called Cross Currents encourages discipleship and holds four conferences a year.

Services: Sunday 2–4pm (at Muswell Hill FMH); Tuesday 8–10pm Shared Communion (at Centre, Members only) □ Children: Sunday school (at FMH) □ Wheelchair: easy access and toilets for disabled at FMH; no access to Centre □ Other details: library, bookstall, meeting rooms etc, at Centre □ Visiting: Centre open 9am–5pm Monday to Friday; FMH open for services only

Luther Tyndale Memorial Church (Evangelical Lutheran Church of England)

9 Leighton Crescent, NW5 □ Telephone: 267 3997 □ Bus: 27, 53, 134, 137 □ Tube/BR: Kentish Town □ Parking: car park at front □ Pastor: Rev Graham Jenks □ Address: 6 Dunollie Place, NW5 □ Telephone: 485 9638 □ Available: ring church for appointment

The Evangelical Lutheran Church of England has been growing at an impressive rate nationally for the past twenty years. The movement began over eighty years ago, and the story is told that it stems from the dissatisfaction of six young German-born Londoners with the scriptural accuracy of what they were hearing at the German churches. They extended a call to the Missouri Synod in USA for a pastor, and they formed a congregation in 1896, in the area around Regent's Park. The ELCE was a founder member of the Lutheran Council but withdrew in 1955. It maintains a less open, less ecumenical approach towards worship, and especially Communion, than do its Lutheran counterparts within the Council.

Luther Tyndale is the most central church of this same congregation, which has spread in the intervening years from central London to Wembley and beyond. The church is a brick-built 1930s structure, with a plain exterior softened by climbing ivy. The adjoining Montpelier Gardens provide an attractive setting. There are seven tall and narrow windows, and a little spire sits on the roof. An extension carried out in 1966 has provided the congregation with a large multi-purpose hall. Occasional choir concerts are given here and an American evangelist has preached to a large audience in the hall.

Pastor Graham Jenks sees his task as working to serve his own congregation before being able to do more neighbourhood work, but confirms 'the church is there to serve the needs of others, the neighbourhood as well as the congregation'. Visitors are made welcome. However, it should be noted that to take Communion one needs to have been confirmed in one of the churches with which the ELCE is in fellowship. The service follows that of the Missouri Lutheran's Hymnal. On the first Sunday of the month is Matins, on the second and fourth Holy Communion, while the third has a service more full than Matins but without Communion.

The main outreach of the church is through the recently formed youth club, which serves two age groups up to fourteen years. Younger and older children come together for a short period of worship and then are split up for play and craft activities.

Services: Sunday 10am (Communion 2nd and 4th Sundays); Wednesday 8pm Vespers □ Facilities: amplification, deaf loop, large print hymn books and liturgy □ Children: Sunday school, 11.30am □ Wheelchair: several steps, no ramp □ Other details: large multi-purpose hall, bookshop, etc □ Visiting: open for services only

The New Apostolic Church (London Central Congregation)

48 Warwick Gardens, W14 □ Bus: 9, 27, 28, 33, 49, 73 □ Tube/BR: Kensington (Olympia) □ Parking: on street □ Rector: Rev Cedric R Thomas □ Address: 59 East Road, West Drayton □ Telephone: (0895) 442261 □ Available: by telephone, evenings

With a world-wide membership of 2.5 million, most of whom live in America or India, the New Apostolic Church believes itself to be true to the principles of the early Church established by Christ and his Apostles. The Church dispenses three Sacraments, namely Baptism, Holy Sealing (ie laying on of hands) and Holy Communion. It is strongly millenarian in outlook and is concerned with preparing members for the Second Coming at the First Resurrection.

The small Gothic church in Warwick Gardens, originally Anglican, had been used for some years as a dancing school before it was acquired by the New Apostolic Church in 1959. Part of the building has been converted to flats and the room for worship is on the first floor; it is a plain auditorium whose only decoration is a cross set in front of waves and the sun's rays—the symbol of the New Apostolic Church—above the stage.

The congregation meets three times each week for worship. Services are not dissimilar from those of many nonconformist churches, but their own hymnbook is used. The officiating minister always has a text, but the sermon is spontaneous. A choir of a dozen members sings before, during and at the end of services independently of the congregation, although the congregation does sing at least once during each service.

During the year there are a number of special services and three times each year services are held for those who have departed this life, so that through prayer they can be invited to become recipients by proxy of the New Apostolic Church Sacraments. The Apostle for the New Apostolic Church in Great Britain lives in New York, USA, and he comes over twice each year to lay hands on prospective members, so that the gift of the Holy Spirit can be given (Holy Sealing). This provides full Church membership.

Church membership covers all ages and various social and ethnic backgrounds, and new members continue to join. Around a hundred regularly attend on Sunday mornings, while perhaps half this number come to the evening services. There is a cry room and disabled people are also provided for: although the auditorium is out of reach, services can be relayed to the easily-accessible entrance hall.

Rev Cedric R Thomas, the rector of the congregation since 1985, has been at the church since it opened. The ministry is unpaid and he has a full-time job. To

St Katherine's Danish Church NW1

help with the running of the church and to assist during the services, Rev Thomas has a group of twelve elected assistants. All ordinations are effected by the Apostle.

Services: Sunday 10.30am Communion, 5pm Communion; Wednesday 8pm □ Facilities: amplification, cry room □ Children: Sunday school during sermon of 10.30am service □ Wheelchair: difficult access, but sound relay to entrance to entrance hall which has a few steps only □ Visiting: open for services and activities only

Polish Reformed Congregation

Worshipping at: French Protestant Church, Soho Square, W1 □ Bus: 1, 7, 8, 14, 19, 22, 24, 25, 29, 38, 55 □ Tube: Tottenham Court Road □ Parking: difficult □ Contact: V Rev Bishop W Fierla □ Address: 2 Leighton Crescent, NW5 □ Telephone: 883 0396 □ Available: at all times □ Other staff: Deaconess Mrs Mazierska (693 3081)

About 50 Polish families, with members of all ages, meet for worship in the style of the Polish Reformed Church at the French Portestant Church in Soho Square. The services, which last for about one hour and feature a sermon usually by Bishop Fierla, are always followed by refreshments in the hall and a chance to talk. The services are usually conducted in Polish but, if non-Polish speakers are present (and all are welcome), some English will be used.

There are also prayer meetings in members' homes and many of the worshippers are involved in charity work.

Services: check times; services normally in Polish □ Wheelchair: 1 small step

St Katherine (Lutheran Church of Denmark)

St Katherine's Precinct, NW1 □ Bus: 2, 3, 53 □ Tube: Camden Town, Mornington Crescent □ Parking: on street □ Pastor: Rev Poul Erik Fabricius □ Address: c/o church □ Telephone: 935 1723 □ Available: any time

Recalling their great maritime past, the Danes have a tradition of hanging up a model sailing ship in the nave of their churches. The symbolism is apt, for nave (Latin: *navis*) means the ship, and the church is the vessel which sees one safely to the other shore, so to speak.

In its own precinct by the Outer Circle of Regents Park, St Katherine's was built at the time of George IV by Anthony Poynter (a pupil of Nash, the great architect of Regent Street and the stately terraces of the Park itself). It is said that the master was somewhat displeased by Poynter's church—certainly it could not be further removed stylistically from his own, for in 1827, with the new romantic spirit, Gothic was beginning a revival as a suitable style for places of worship. Thus St Katherine's has ornate twin steeples and a Perpendicular facade complete with gargoyles.

St Katherine's was originally a chapel to a hospice founded by Queen Mathilda, and was positioned near the Tower until that site was needed for the development of St Kathrine's dock. Hospice and chapel were transferred to Regents Park, and the hospice was closed in 1947, though its work is continued in the East End. The Danish Church was offered a lease on St Katherine's and has remained here ever since. There is regular Sunday worship in the Danish language and the Lutheran tradition; hymn-singing is a particular strength and is accompanied by a fine 18th century organ.

Among features of note is a great stained glass window, commemorating the Diamond Jubilee, and some fine brass candelabra from Denmark. At the beginning of the nave are four wood-carvings of saints by an 18th century Danish artist, which bring a surprising touch of rococo to the rather severe Gothic lines.

In the grounds of the church stands an old stone, (unfortunately rather garishly painted where the original would have more subdued tones) which is a copy of the famous stone of Jelling, erected in Jutland by Harald Bluetooth in 940. On one side are human figures, a battle scene, on the other a cross; the stone is sometimes called the baptismal certificate of Denmark.

Services: Sunday 11am (All services in Danish) □ Facilities: deaf loop □ Children: Saturday school for all ages □ Wheelchair: no ramp, several steps □ Visiting: by arrangement with verger

The Slavic Fellowship (Baptist)

Worshipping at: Kings Cross Methodist Mission, Crestfield Street, WC1 □ Bus: 14, 17, 18, 29, 30, 45, 46, 63, 73, 77a, 214, 221, 254, 355, C11 □ Tube/BR: Kings Cross, St Pancras □ Parking: difficult, meters □ Minister: Rev Antoni Kosciecha □ Address: 42 Woodwaye, Watford □ Telephone: (0923) 29453 □ Available: anytime when at home

The Slavic Fellowship is a group of Polish, Russian and Ukranian Baptists based mainly in Bedford and Luton. Here in London there is only a small group with a congregation of about a dozen, travelling to Kings Cross Methodist Church from all over the city. The evangelical service, conducted in the mother tongues of the worshippers, consists of Gospel messages, expository preaching and messages for Christians. The service lasts about one-and-a-half hours and the singing of hymns is accompanied by piano. Tea, cakes and sandwiches are served afterwards.

Services: usually on the first Sunday in the month at 3pm; (Languages: Polish, Russian, Ukranian) □ Wheelchair: several steps down

Spanish Evangelical Church

Worshipping at: Christchurch, Down Street, W1 □ Bus: 9, 14, 19, 22, 25, 38, 55 □ Tube: Green Park, Piccadilly □ Parking: on street, meters □ Elder: Mr Candido Giraldo □ Address: 55 St Mary's Flats, Doric Way, NW1 □ Telephone: 491 4996 □ Available: at services or at home most times

This is a small but active congregation, which has been worshipping here for twelve years. Members include students in London learning English, tourists passing through, workers from Spain or Latin America, and Spanish-speaking permanent residents of this country, many of whom have found employment in the catering and hotel industries. It is a very mobile group with a 20 percent regular attendance at any one time, and with an average age of 35 there is plenty of scope for young people, married or single.

Every week the group meets for 'socials' in members' homes. On Saturdays they go to the adjacent vicarage for Bible study. The Sunday school is also held here. Services are in Spanish of course, and take place on Sunday evening. People come from all parts of London to hear the sermon, join in the hymn singing, and perhaps give testimonies. There is often very good guitar music in the Spanish or South American style.

The area this group chooses for 'knocking on doors' is Portobello Road, where many Spanish-speaking people live. Purely social outings are also popular, and charitable collections have helped relief work after the natural disasters in Mexico and Colombia.

Services: Sunday 6pm, Holy Supper once a month □ Children: Sunday school, 7–8pm for ages 3–15 □ Wheelchair: good access

The Swiss Church In London (Swiss Reformed Church)

79 Endell Street, WC2 □ Telephone: 836 1418 □ Bus: 1, 14, 19, 22, 24, 29, 38, 55, 176 □ Tube: Tottenham Court Road, Covent Garden □ Parking: difficult except Sunday □ Pastor: Rev Philipp von Orelli □ Address: 1 Womersley Road, N8 □ Telephone: 340 9740 □ Available: most times □ Other staff: Ursy Muller, Youth & Community Worker (340 9740)

The Swiss Reformed Church is Calvinist in theology, and also Zwinglian, Zwingli having been the great reformer in Zurich. The two men were of similar views and little difference can now be detected between this and other Calvinist, Presbyterian Churches.

The church in London was founded in 1762 for the growing community of French-speaking Swiss merchants. It flourished right up to the Second World War when numbers began to decline. However, the nearby German speaking church was on the increase and a slow merging of the congregations began, officially recognised in the early 1980s. Services are now held on consecutive Sundays in German, French and English. These services are of a modern, informal nature often with guitar and piano accompaniment rather than the traditional organ. The singing of hymns is enhanced by the fine acoustics of the church.

Unfortunately, the building is in a poor state of repair due to a gradual deterioration. Its appearance was not improved by the decoration of some years ago when, for reasons best known to the decorator, the attractive gilt filigree of the barrel-vaulted roof was painted pink.

Services are now often held in the recently converted foyer, which is warm, comfortable and of more suitable dimensions for the 30 strong congregation than is the cold church. The foyer is also used for events and for the meetings of the active ladies' and mothers' groups, for example. Links are strong between members of the small Swiss community, and they come here from all over London both for worship and social contact. Due to the wide dispersal of the community, Pastor von Orelli presides over meetings in people's homes, best described as half worship, half discussion.

The church also runs a support and social group for Swiss au pair girls working in London. A regular programme of entertainment is arranged including trips to museums, theatres and restaurants, and, of course, the occasional fondue. In association with the welfare services the church can also provide counselling for problems they may face such as low pay and harassment.

Services: Sunday 11am, (1st Sun: German, 2nd: French, 3rd: English, 4th & 5th: no service) □ *Facilities: 1 Braille hymnbook* □ *Children: Sunday school for 5–12 year olds, monthly* □ *Wheelchair: 2 steps, help available* □ *Visiting: open only for services or by special arrangement*

Ukrainian Cathedral of the Holy Family in Exile (Ukrainian Uniat Catholic Church)

Duke Street, W1 □ *Bus: any along Oxford Street* □ *Tube: Bond Street* □ *Parking: meters* □ *Administrator: Rev Stephan Oracz* □ *Address: 21 Binney Street, W1* □ *Telephone: 629 1534, 992 1732* □ *Available: telephone for appointment* □ *Other clergy: Rev Roman Cholij*

The Ukraine, which borders Romania, Poland, Russia and the Black Sea, has its capital at Kiev, where the Slav nations accepted Christianity in the 10th century. After the state based on Kiev fell to the Mongol Tatars in 1237, the Ukraine became detached from Russia and was soon absorbed by the Kingdom of Poland and Lithuania under its Catholic monarch. Thus the area was to become a meeting place of the two traditions, Catholic and Orthodox. The Ukrainian Catholic Church still uses the Byzantine Rite in the Eastern tradition, but it is subject to the Pope: a Uniat Church. There is a separate Ukrainian Orthodox Church with its own hierarchy, the split between the two traditions being formalised in 1589.

Ukrainian Catholics in London had their first place of worship in Saffron Hill, Holborn, from 1946. The Exarchate (Bishopric in Exile) was established in 1957 to minister to refugees from the War and from the Communist regime in the Ukraine. This Cathedral church, as it became, was transferred in June 1968 to the former King's Weigh House Chapel, making it the only British Cathedral to have started up as a nonconformist church. The building is by Waterhouse, the distinguished designer of the National History Museum. Like the museum it is of hard brick and terracotta and is in a round-arched Italianate style.

In the old chapel certain changes had to be made. The Lady Altar and the high wooden pulpit were removed, and the organ was silenced in accordance with the Eastern tradition which forbids any instrumental music in church. The building is a masterpiece of compact planning. It has an oval auditorium and gallery which can seat 900. The sanctuary is flanked by two canopied towers of wood installed during the remodelling by Sir John Burnet in 1904. Above it are three stained-glass windows by Anning Bell. The Cathedral has no statues, as only icons are included in an Eastern church. Several of the icons are around the altar, one of which is of the Virgin, as Our Lady of Perpetual Succour. A stone carving of the Holy Family salvaged from the Saffron Hill church stands by the ambulatory wall, near the NE entrance to the church.

The parish priest, Fr Stephan Oracz, has a large congregation drawn from all over London and the surrounding area. He estimates that about 500 Ukrainians live in London and a further 700 close by. Some English people attend Mass, usually if they have family connections with Ukrainians here. Masses are typically Eastern and are chanted. They are held entirely in Ukrainian, and follow the old Julian calendar so Holy Days are usually celebrated about two weeks later than in the Roman and other Catholic Churches. Each Mass on Sunday is followed by lunch in the adjoining hall, where one can join together with Ukrainians and their families over a meal and a cup of tea.

In 1988 the Ukrainians throughout the world are celebrating the 1000th anniversary (Millenium) of the official introduction of Christianity into Rus-Ukraine.

Mass: Sunday 10.30am (High); Holy Days 6pm; Weekdays 7am □ Confession: before Mass and at call □ Facilities: amplification □ Wheelchair: difficult access; 8 steps □ Other details: hall, library □ Visiting: open around service times only

Zoar Chapel (Free Presbyterian Church of Scotland)

Varden Street, E1 □ Bus: 1, 5, 15a, 40 □ Tube: Whitechapel, Aldgate East □ Parking: on street □ Minister: Rev Alan McPherson □ Address: 5 Kempshott Road, SW16 □ Telephone: 764 5436 □ Available: at services

The Free Presbyterian Church of Scotland is a small denomination, but one which has congregations all over the world. It was formed in 1893 when it separated from the Free Church of Scotland, after objecting to the alterations made in the constitution. It believes itself to be in a direct line of spiritual descent from John Knox and the early Churches of the Scottish Reformation of 1560. The Church bases its doctrines and worship exclusively on the Word of God as revealed in the Bible, and stresses the importance of observing the Sabbath.

The Church has one London congregation which meets at the Zoar Chapel in Whitechapel, a small Victorian building acquired from the Strict Baptists in the early 1970s. The interior is simple and without decoration; several rows of dark wooden bench pews with a central aisle face a large pulpit, reached by steps from either side. This is in a commanding position, reflecting the importance of the preaching. Before the pulpit stands a table with an open Bible upon it.

The Sabbath services led by the minister, Rev Alan McPherson, have no set liturgy. There is much emphasis on prayer, praise and the reading of Scripture. The core of the service is the 55 minute sermon, based on Biblical texts. No hymns are sung. Instead, the congregation sings unaccompanied psalms directly from the Psalter.

The Lord's Supper is dispensed in May and October following the Church's usual practice of Communion Seasons. Services are held on the preceding Thursday (for the purpose of helping with confession and self-abasement), Friday (to promote self examination) and Saturday, in spiritual preparation for the Sacrament. The Communion service itself is held on the Sabbath morning following a sermon on the death of Christ. In the evening service, a Law and Gospel service is preached and the Communion Season concludes with a Thanksgiving service on the Monday.

The congregation is predominantly, but not exclusively, Scottish and none lives locally, some travelling from as far as Weybridge to attend. There are few activities outside services apart from a study group which meets at the vicar's home in Streatham.

Services: Sabbath 11am and 6.30pm; Wednesday 7pm Prayer Meeting □ Wheelchair: 2 steps □ Visiting: open for services only; women are required to cover heads during services

Other Churches and Congregations

Other churches we were unable to include for various reasons, but which may be of interest to some readers, are as follows:

Assyrian Church of the East: contact Rev Yonan Yowel Yonan, 579 7259;
Bible-Pattern Church: contact Pastor Albert Edsor, 228 7363;
Orthodox Church of the British Isles: contact Dr Judith Pinnington, 855 7892.

4 HINDUISM

Hinduism is a catch-all term first used by Westerners to cover the vast range of religious beliefs and practices they encountered in the Indian subcontinent. With 84,000 gods and goddesses in the Hindu pantheon and rituals varying from region to region, even village to village, it is difficult to isolate the central tenets of Hinduism.

There are, nonetheless, some very common beliefs, including reincarnation, the law of karma, the attainment of release *(moksha)* from the cycle of rebirth, the importance of gurus and the strong devotional element of worship. It is also widely held that, despite the many thousands of gods worshipped, they can all be seen as deriving from the One, Brahma. Brahma represents particularly the creative aspect of the Godhead, while the sustaining qualities are embodied by Vishnu, and the forces of destruction by Shiva. The best-known figures in Hindu mythology, such as Krishna, Murugan and Kali, are manifestations or aspects of these major deities.

It is estimated that there are some 130,000 practising Hindus in Britain today, but there are comparatively few Hindu temples. This is largely explained by the long tradition of family worship at home, the saying of prayers and the offering of food or candles before a domestic shrine. Another reason for the comparatively low profile of Hinduism in the West is its historical ability to adapt to and accommodate its surroundings. In India, for example, this meant that the rise of Buddhism in the 6th century BC presented no threat because the devotees were simply accepted as a cult within Hinduism, and the Buddha was regarded as an incarnation of Vishnu. In the modern West, an example of this flexibility has been the adoption of Sunday as a major worship day, something with no precedent in India. Similarly, dietary habits have been modified, and the need is not felt for the major festivals to be celebrated in the open air, as they are in India.

Attendance at temple worship by non-Hindus should present no problems, and one will normally be made most welcome. It is polite to telephone first, however, and to introduce oneself on arrival. Two points to remember are that shoes must be removed before entering a temple, and that dress should be respectful and modest.

Further information is available from the Hindu Centre, 39 Grafton Terrace, NW5 (Tel 485 8200, 267 6218).

Hindu Centre

39 Grafton Terrace, NW5 □ Telephone: 485 8200, 267 6218 □ Bus: 24, 46 □ Tube: Chalk Farm □ Parking: on street □ Secretary: Gopul Bhanot □ Address: at Centre □ Available: by arrangement □ Other staff: resident priest

The Hindu Centre in Grafton Terrace is a rather run-down looking building tucked away in the backstreets of Chalk Farm. It was set up in the 1950s as the headquarters of the Hindu faith in England. Its aim is to cater for the entire Hindu community in the UK, imparting information, representing the Hindu faith to official bodies, and providing religious guidance relating Hinduism to modern Western life.

The temple room is surprisingly small considering the status of the Centre. Hidden away in the basement, it is crowded with shrines and religious paintings all richly adorned with flowers, lights and tinsel. The largest shrine is to Lord Murugan though almost the whole pantheon of Hindu gods is represented. Every inch of wall space is covered by pictures of Krishna, Hanuman, Lord Mahavira, the Universal Form, episodes from Krishna's life, Kali, Shiva, Vishnu, Durga and many others. This is a truly multi-denominational temple where Hindus from any tradition can come and pray to their deity.

The main worship of the Centre is held on the first Sunday of every month. Lasting some four hours, it is a lively programme of mantra chanting, music, dance, scripture reading, prayers, and often talks from visiting speakers. Food is served afterwards. Up to 200 people crowd into the temple, meant for 150. It is hoped to add an extension soon.

Other planned developments include facilities for Yoga, and language classes, and a library of 3–4,000 books in both English and Hindi, covering the whole range of Eastern religion and philosophy. Books will be available for sale and for borrowing. Currently there is a reading area in the entrance hall, stocked with a variety of Indian newspapers and magazines provided by the Indian High Commission. A marriage bureau service is available and a resident priest is always at hand to give religious guidance and advice.

Major Services: 1st Sunday of every month, Evening ati □ Wheelchair: very difficult access; several stairs □ Other details: large hall □ Visiting: open most days; visitors welcome

Murugan Temple

200a Archway Road, N6 □ Telephone: 348 9856 □ Bus: 17, 43, 134, 263, 263a □ Tube: Archway, Highgate □ Parking: on street □ Chairman: Mr S Pillai □ Telephone: 540 3426 □ Available: most days □ Other staff: resident priests

Once a church, then a synagogue, 200a Archway Road has now been transformed into one of the largest and finest Dravidian temples in London. It was converted almost entirely through the hard work of volunteers and funded by donations from the Hindu community.

Against the walls are a variety of shrines to a wide range of deities, including Ganesh and Kali, and a lingam. The positions of all these have a particular significance for worship. In the centre is the main shrine, that of Murugan, second son of Shiva, it is a huge construction reaching almost to the ceiling and, like all the others here, built in the elaborate and busily ornate style of the Dravidian goporams of Southern India. Indian architects and craftsmen were used for the intricate work needed.

At regular *puja* times up to 300 people come to worship, even more on Friday and special occasions. Worship includes chanting, the singing of ancient Sanskrit hymns *(bajans)*, prostations, traditional music and offerings of food. The congregation is mostly from Sri Lanka, Malaysia, Mauritius and Tamil Nadu, though many other Hindus come to worship attracted by the splendour of the shrine room.

The temple, furthermore, is in the forefront of bringing a greater understand ing of the faith to others, so all are welcome to attend pujas or visit the temple. School groups regularly visit as part of their studies.

The temple acts as a centre for the local community and, between pujas, it attracts a steady stream of visitors and those coming to make personal offerings or prayers. Food is prepared and offered to Murugan each day by the temple staff.

It is a very new temple, only opened in 1986, and efforts have concentrated on the building of the shrine room. In the future however, it is hoped that there will be a variety of classes in the Tamil language, Indian dance, and traditional singing and music. It looks set to become an important cultural as well as religious centre open to all, irrespective of class or creed.

Services: Every day 8am, 10.30am, 6pm, 7.30pm, (All services in Tamil and Sanskrit); The main worship day is Friday □ *Facilities: taped music* □ *Children: classes planned* □ *Wheelchair: very difficult; several flights of stairs* □ *Visiting: Open 8am–1pm, 6pm–10pm; many visitors*

Radha Krishna Temple

9–10 Soho Street, W1 □ *Telephone: 437 3662* □ *Bus: any along Oxford Street* □ *Tube: Tottenham Court Road* □ *Parking: very difficult* □ *Contact: temple reception* □ *Available: throughout the day*

The Krishna movement arrived in the West in the late 1960s with the founding of the International Society for Krishna Consciousness (ISKCON) by His Divine Grace A C Bhaktivedanta Swami Praphupada. Today it is a worldwide organisation with around 40,000 members in this country alone. The faith is based on the teachings revealed by Lord Caitanya Mahaprabhu (a 16th century incarnation of Krishna) and the ancient Sanskrit scriptures, the Vedas. The central text, however, is the Bhagavad-gita in which was first outlined the movement's essential practice of *bhakti yoga*—the way of loving devotion. It is probably this text, as annotated by the Swami, that an orange-robed devotee has tried to thrust into your hand on street corners.

Although every action is devoted to Krishna and so life itself is a form of worship, by far the most important part of the day is the mantra meditation at the *ati* (prayer) sessions. This consists of the chanting of the now well-known mantra:

Hare Krishna, Hare Krishna, Krishna, Krishna, Hare, Hare,
Hare Rama, Hare Rama, Rama, Rama, Hare, Hare.

For the 30 devotees that live in the Radha Krishna Temple worship starts early with the first ati at 4.30am. Throughout the day there is a programme of ati, lectures and offerings concluded with the final ati at 9.30pm. All are welcome to attend, though the lunchtime meetings at 12.15pm are especially geared towards newcomers and so are recommended for first-time visitors. After the ati, all present are invited to a substantial vegetarian lunch (free for first attendance, £1 thereafter). One of the greatest acts a devotee can perform is to bring Krishna Consciousness to another, and if you do attend expect to hear not only the tenets of the faith but also criticisms of the sinful nature of your life.

The temple itself, a small room with ornate plasterwork abounding, is on the first floor of the building. There are two statues of Krishna in niches (which are covered in the late afternoon when the god is thought to sleep) which stand opposite a statue of a rather severe-looking Prabhupada.

Devotee, Radha Krishna Temple, W1

There is little organised community work beyond the efforts to proselytise, though, in recognition of the Hindu tradition that no-one should go hungry near a temple, the devotees have set up the 'Food for Life' programme, whereby volunteers take out regular meals each week for the homeless people of the area. Beneath the temple is the Govinda Restaurant, run by the movement, which provides wholefood vegetarian meals. The atmosphere is informal and any of the devotees present will gladly take the time to talk or answer questions.

Services: ati throughout the day; 12.15pm ati is recommended for visitors □ Children: welcome to ati □ Wheelchair: very difficult; many steps □ Other details: Govinda restaurant □ Visiting: open 4am–9pm daily; shop

---

5 ISLAM

Muhammad, prophet of Islam, was born in Mecca in c.570 but it was not until his middle life that he received revelation from God (Allah). His revelations continued from about 610 to his death in 632 and it is these that are collected together to form the Qur'an, regarded as the last of Divine Scripture.

Muhammad is seen as the last in a chain of prophets stretching back to Adam and encompassing Abraham, Ishmael, Isaac, Jacob, Moses and Jesus. As the last, Muhammad is venerated as the most important, and the Qur'an as the most original of Scripture. As such, it has to be read and learnt in the original Arabic; English editions of the Qur'an should always have the original Arabic on one side with an English explanation opposite.

The Islamic faith is based on the Five Pillars, all explained and expounded in the Qur'an. These are: the declaration of faith ('There is no God but Allah and Muhammad is his prophet'), compulsory prayers offered five times daily *(salah)*, the giving of alms *(zakat)*, fasting during Ramadan *(sawm)*, and a pilgrimage to Mecca at least once in one's lifetime *(hajj)*.

Since the Second World War people from all over the Islamic world,including Pakistan, Bangladesh, India, much of Africa and the Middle East, have made their homes in Britain. Islam, with around 1½ million adherents, is now firmly established as the second faith of Britain. There are now over 300 mosques throughout the country, in addition to which are many rooms in private houses devoted to congregational prayer. The large, modern, purpose-built mosques in London are exceptions to the general rule.

As well as being a place of worship, a mosque is also the focal point of the community and one will often find Muslims sitting in groups and talking, or reading and resting there at all times throughout the day. The mosque will usually run religious education classes for the children and larger ones may have libraries or even mortuary facilities. There is no priesthood in Islam, but each mosque will have at least one *imam* who leads the prayers. The imam is respected as a teacher and is a central figure in the community.

When visiting it should be remembered that each Friday, (the Muslim day of congregational prayer) the place will be packed out and if all you want to do is see the building this day is best avoided. Also, shoes must be removed when entering the prayer hall, women's heads should be covered and dress for both sexes should be modest.

For further information apply: Islamic Cultural Centre, 146 Park Road, London NW8.

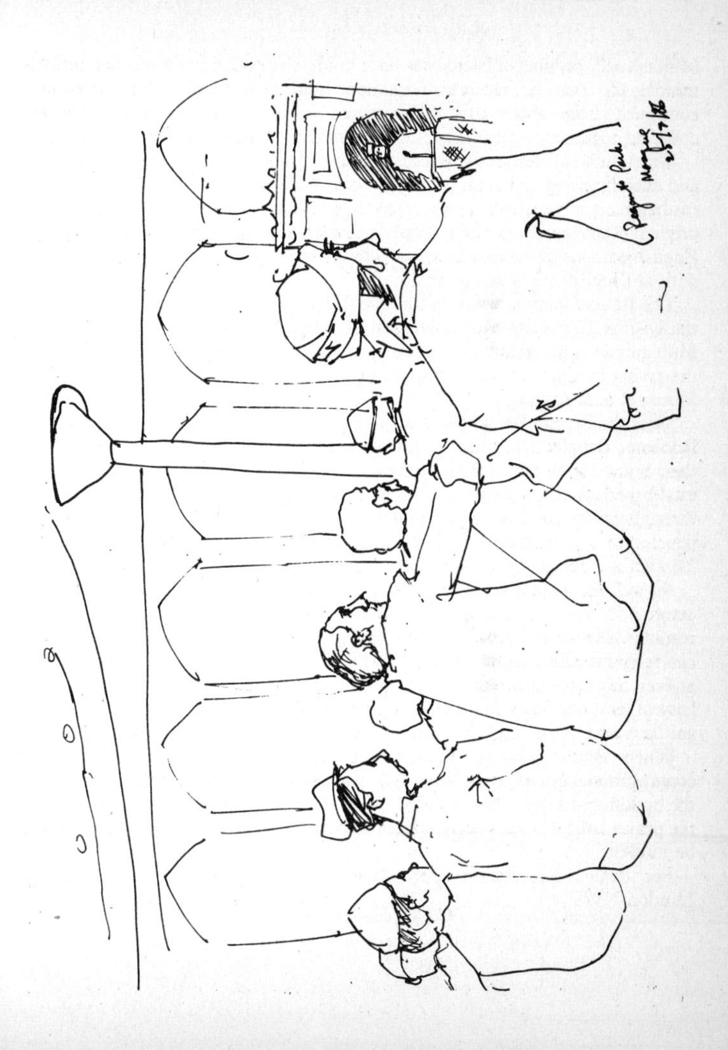

Worshippers, Central Mosque, NW1

Central Mosque

146 Park Road, NW8 □ *Telephone: 724 3363/7* □ *Bus: 2, 13, 74, 113* □ *Tube: Baker Street/ St John's Wood* □ *Parking car park (free)* □ *Lecturer: Abdullah* □ *Address: at mosque* □ *Available: at mosque most days; other staff also available*

The Central Mosque by Regents Park, with its golden dome and 141 ft minaret, has become one of the landmarks of London. On most Friday lunchtimes, not just those during festivals, the mosque is full to overflowing with worshippers assembling in the forecourt. At such times, judging by the variety of people and styles of dress, virtually the whole of the Islamic world is represented. People regularly come from all over London and beyond to worship here.

The first serious moves to establish a mosque in central London were made during the Second World War, partly because the Islamic world was fighting alongside the Allies, and partly in rcognition of the fact that the majority of the inhabitants of the then Empire were Muslims. The venture was taken up by the heads of Muslim governments and a trust was established, but various problems delayed the proceedings. It was not until 1969 that, following an international competition, the designs by Sir Frederick Gibberd, a distinguished British architect, were approved.

Gibberd's designs draw heavily on the tradition of Islamic architecture. From the courtyard one is met by a series of flattened arch windows reaching from the ground almost to the ceiling, and matching the flattened profile of the dome. These windows set the theme of order and simplicity that is carried throughout the building—their shape is repeated all around the inside of the congregational hall. There is little decoration save for the mosaic work around the inside of the dome and a splendid chandelier suspended from its centre. The main hall, together with the ladies' gallery, has room for some 1,400, but 4,000 regularly attend.

The building also incorporates ablution areas, offices, teaching rooms and a library of 10,000 volumes. Also on the site is a residential block and a discreet underground car park. As well as being a mosque this is the main Islamic cultural centre in the UK, to which nearly all enquiries are referred. It runs an intensive educational programme for children and classes in Arabic, Islamic civilisation and the study of the Qur'an, as well as producing an Islamic Quarterly. The centre will also act as intermediary between Muslims and the authorities in matters of education and welfare.

Non-Muslims are welcome to attend prayers, but an ideal time to visit is on a Sunday afternoon when a question-and-answer session is run by Western converts to Islam.

Services: 5 daily prayers according to Islamic calendar (Prayers in Arabic, sermon may be in English) □ *Facilities: amplification* □ *Wheelchair: no stairs except for ladies' gallery and ablution areas, which have lift for disabled* □ *Other details: classrooms, library, bookstall, mortuary* □ *Visiting: open most days and evenings*

East London Mosque

92 Whitechapel Road, E1 □ Telephone: 247 1357 □ Bus: 10, 25, 225, 253 □ Tube: Whitechapel, Aldgate East □ Parking: car park next door (fee) □ Imam: Abu Sayeed □ Address: at mosque □ Available: by arrangement □ Contact: MR M A R Khan (caretaker) for visiting appointments

With its Muslim population of over 40,000, it became clear in the early 1980s that the area needed a large purpose-built mosque. Since 1975, Muslims had been meeting in a prefabricated building provided by the GLC. The splendid mosque in Whitechapel Road, with its two-tone brickwork, gold-dome and twin minarets, was completed in 1984 and paid for almost entirely by voluntary donation.

Inside the mosque is plain and ordered, decorated only by calligraphic extracts from the Qur'an. There are two separate prayer halls, the lower one being used for the overflow during well-attended prayers. A sound system relays the prayers and the imam's sermon. Together the halls can take 2,500 people, but often up to 3,000 attend. The ladies' gallery is above the main upper hall. Sermons are delivered in three different languages—Bengali, Somali and Urdu—while the prayers are of course in Arabic.

There is also one meeting each month held in English to which non-Muslims would be especially welcome. This is part of the policy of breaking down barriers and promoting a wider understanding of Islam. Some 500 visitors a week, both individuals and groups, come to the mosque and school parties are particularly welcome. An indication of this meeting of two cultures is the venture to set up a scout pack of Muslim youngsters based at the mosque.

As well as the mosque, the complex also includes classrooms, function rooms, a library and a mortuary. In addition to the classes for children, there is a Tuesday class for converts or people wanting to learn more about Islam. Lectures and discussion groups are also regular features.

The three imams based here are available to offer guidance and advice and also undertake home visiting. There are eight teachers and other staff who carry out the educational and administrative work needed to run this busy mosque.

Services: 5 daily prayers according to Islamic calendar (Prayers in Arabic; sermon in Bengali, Somali and Urdu; monthly service in English) □ Facilities: amplification □ Children: classes in Arabic and the Qur'an □ Wheelchair: no access □ Other details: classrooms, library, mortuary, etc □ Visiting: by prior arrangement

Euston Square Mosque

Euston Square, NW1 □ Bus: 14, 24, 73 □ Tube/BR: Euston, Euston Square □ Parking: difficult □ Imam: Shah Abdul Matin □ Address: at mosque □ Available: at prayer times □ Other staff: available at prayers

Found in the basement of a ramshackle building tucked away near Euston station, the mosque is easily missed. Despite the outside of the building the small prayer room is, like all mosques, spotlessly clean. The available space is very limited however, and the mosque is able to accommodate a maximum of only 70 people. This area houses a high proportion of Muslims and so it is clear that the mosque is quite inadequate for the residents' needs. So small is it that the imam

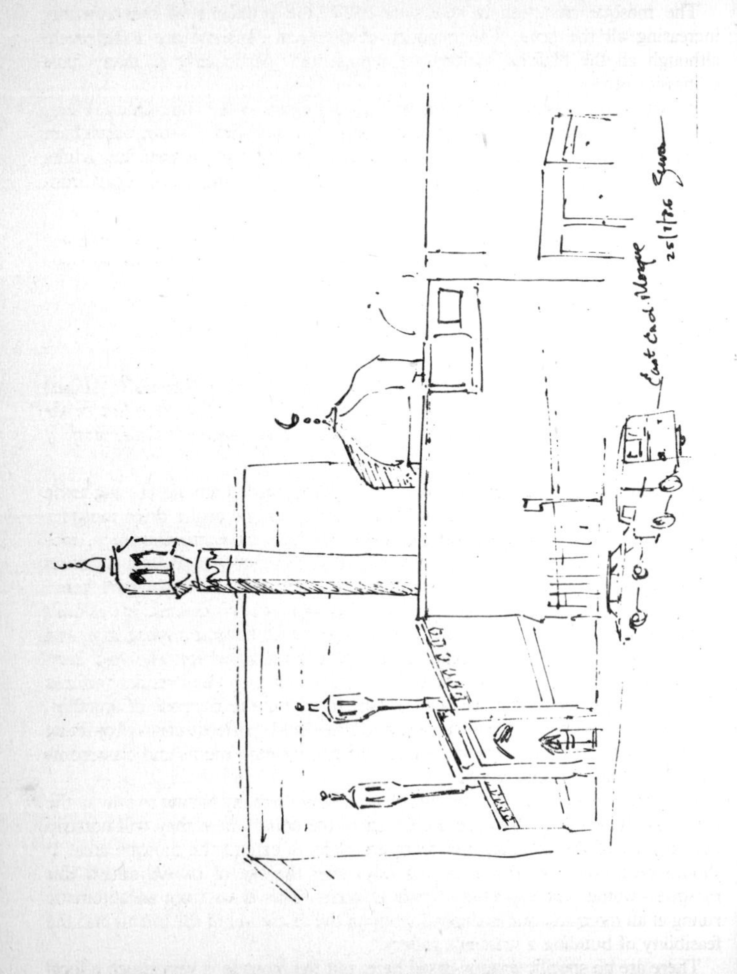

East London Mosque, E1

has had to take the unusual step of staging the Friday prayers in two separate 'sittings'. Many more of the residents have to travel to other mosques, most notably at Regents Park and the East End.

The mosque has been in use since 1967, the problems of overcrowding increasing all the time. The majority of the local Muslims are Bangledeshi although all the Muslim nations are represented, particularly as many have embassies nearby.

As with most mosques, the imam is a central figure in the community. Here, however, the imam sees himself as being concerned only with the spiritual welfare of his congregation. He holds the usual study groups for children and adults studying the Qur'an and Arabic which take place in the mosque, but apart from this there is little further outside work done.

Services: 5 daily prayers according to Islamic Calendar □ Children: study groups (boys only) □ Wheelchairl: no access □ Visiting: only during prayers; note this is for men only (no womens' gallery)

Jamme Masjid

45 Brick Lane, E1 □ Telephone: 247 3507 □ Bus: 25, 41, 88a □ Tube/BR: Aldgate Street, Liverpool Street □ Parking: very difficult □ Contact: The President or the Secretary, Mr Choudaury □ Available: at mosque, after prayers □ Other staff: 4 resident imams

This mosque is an unassuming red brick building nestled among the rag trade outlets and Tandoori restaurants of Brick Lane. It is one of the three mosques that serve the large Muslim population of the East End. The immediate area, once known for its Jewish community, now has around 20,000 Bangladeshi residents and it is these who make up the vast majority of the regular worshippers here.

The history of the building reflects the changing nature of the area. It was built as an Anglican church at the turn of the century; it then became a synagogue, and in 1976, in response to the needs of the Muslim community who had been meeting for prayers in private homes, it became a mosque. The President affirms he is pleased the building has always been used for the purpose of worship. Typically, the interior of the mosque is unadorned and spotlessly clean. Adjoining is a rambling collection of rooms used as offices, meeting rooms and classrooms where the imams teach the Qur'an.

Attendance on a Friday can be as high as 2,000 with many having to pray in the corridors. Indeed, numbers are increasing to the point where they will outstrip the capacity of the building and there are plans to extend the mosque area. It should be noted that only men and boys over the age of twelve attend this mosque—women are expected to pray at home. This is far from an automatic ruling at all mosques, and is dependent upon the discretion of the imams and the feasibility of building a women's gallery.

There are no specific groups based here, but the mosque is very much a focal point of the community. The Islamic religion is indivisible from its society, and so people will come here to talk over all kinds of matters with the elders and imams. Religious instruction and discussion are considered to be highly important, and it is not unusual for impromptu groups to form in one of the rooms or the mosque itself, quite apart from the regular classes.

Services: 5 daily prayers according to Islamic calendar (Sermons in Arabic, Bengali, Urdu and occasionally English) □ Facilities: amplification □ Children: Islamic instruction □ Wheelchair: several steps □ Other details: offices, classrooms, meeting rooms, etc □ Visiting: at prayer times; no women

---

Included in this chapter is the London Mosque of the Ahmadiyya movement, of particular interest as the first to be built in London. It should be made clear that the Ahmadis are not necessarily recognised by orthodox Muslims.

Also in London is the Ismaili Centre, open only to Ismailis (members of an exclusive group of Shi'ite origin headed by the Aga Khan). One may, however, be invited on one of the quarterly guided tours. Apply in writing to the Ismaili Centre, 1 Cromwell Gardens, SW7.

The London Mosque

16 Gressenhall Road, SW18 □ Bus: 16b, 37, 39, 77a □ Tube: East Putney, Southfields □ Parking: on street, small car park □ Imam: Ataul Mujeeb Rashed □ Address: at mosque □ Telephone: 870 8517 □ Available: at visitors convenience when possible; office hours 9am–6pm □ Other staff: Mr Bangvi, General Sec

In 1924, this attractive white-walled building became the first mosque to be built in London. The people who worship here are part of the Ahmadiyya movement founded in 1889 by Hasrat Mirza Ghulam Ahmad of Qadian, India, who claimed he was the expected reformer and promised Messiah, prophesied in both the Bible and the Qur'an. As such, Ahmadis are not recognised as true believers by other Muslims, and they have faced persecution in some countries.

The UK mission was established in 1913, the first in Europe. It was based in two wooden huts in Wimbledon until the present site was developed. Other branches exist in about thirty other British towns. Throughout the world there are about ten million members. The 'missionary' element of the mosque's activities is fundamental—about 100 converts are made a year, many from the Christian faith.

About forty volunteers work in the building during the day on such projects as the recording on audio and video cassette of every sermon preached in the mosque, particularly those by international leaders of the movement. Tapes are sold world-wide. Other work includes lectures in clubs, schools, colleges and churches, visiting the sick and imprisoned, and producing a wide variety of publications. The mosque has a comprehensive reference library containing books on Islam and other religions. The *Muslim Herald, Ahmadiyya Bulletin* and *Akhbar Ahmadiyya* are also available monthly.

Women play an important role: they have their own monthly meeting and help maintain good relations with the local people. The monthly youth group study circle may cover issues not discussed in many mosques, such as the study of comparative religion.

Services: 5 daily prayers according to Islamic calendar □ Facilities: braille Qur'an; amplification □ Children: study classes and groups □ Wheelchair: ramps provided □ Other details: women's prayer hall; offices; Mahmud hall; meeting room/dining hall □ Visiting: open at prayer times only

6 JUDAISM

Jews have a history in Britain far longer than any other major non-Christian religious group. Initially, in the early Middle Ages, the relationship with their Christian neighbours was good, the Jews providing important teaching and trading skills. However, by the 13th century, the Jews, regarded as 'Christ-killers' and blamed for the Black Death, were widely and openly persecuted before being expelled by Edward I in 1290.

Their slow, disparate return from different parts of Europe goes some way in explaining the diversity within Judaism in Britain today. First to return, at the time of Cromwell's Commonwealth, were the Jews of the Sephardi or Spanish and Portuguese tradition, from Amsterdam. They were granted freedom of worship and the Bevis Marks synagogue was built during this period of relative calm. Anglo-Jewry had become well established, chiefly under the United Synagogue, the mainstream central European group, when the Jews of the Ashkenazi (North European) rite began to arrive during the last century. Fleeing poverty and persecution, these people saw little in common with the wealthy British Jews and set up their own orthodox Federation synagogues in the East End.

Later arrivals from Poland and Russia with their 'enlightened' Judaism brought with them the seeds of the Reform and Liberal movements. These place emphasis on making worship contemporary and of the broadest appeal. Where the United synagogues had a prayer book with a running translation, these new synagogues worshipped in the vernacular, with hymns set to organ music. Along the way a number of independent synagogues, some orthodox, some radical, have also sprung up in response to a variety of circumstances. In London the widest range of Jewish traditions and styles of worship can be found.

There are certain features that are common to all strands of Judaism. Because of its unsettled past of oppression, Judaism is to a lesser or greater extent 'low key' in its worship, and centred as much on the family home as the synagogue. There is no established style of architecture and the synagogues are a reflection of Jewish circumstances at the time; thus some are unobtrusive, others rather grand, and by no means all were purpose built. A common factor will be the rather plain interior; the only embellishment being reserved for the Ark in which the Scrolls of the Law are kept. It must be remembered that a synagogue is quite different from a church, just as there are no sacraments in Judaism and a rabbi is not a priest.

Worship is entirely congregational, merely needing a quorum of ten males. Many psalms are used as well as medieval prayers that evoke a period of great suffering. This is not to suggest that worship is mournful or abject. There are many rousing hymns, and an element of rejoicing in God and his creation. It is interesting that Judaism has never shunned this world no matter how unbearable it became.

In London, the central and East End synagogues no longer serve the main centres of the Jewish population, and Judaism struggles in the face of falling attendences and internal debates about how the faith should be interpreted today. The Chief Rabbi has remarked to the effect that Judaism has distinguished itself by the ability to survive hardship; the challenge today is to be meaningful in a free and pluralistic society.

For those wishing to attend a synagogue for the first time there are some points to note about orthodox worship. Call the synagogue beforehand to check times and find out if there is anything special you should know—it may be a festival, for example. For men, head covering is obligatory; for women it is usual. Women will often be directed to a ladies' gallery, overlooking the main area where the men congregate. Drinks and light refreshments are often provided after the service on Saturday morning.

Further information is available from:

United Synagogue: Head Office, Woburn House, Upper Woburn Place, WC 1, Telephone: 387 4300

Federation of Synagogues: 9–11 Greatorex Street, E1, Telephone: 247 4471

Reform Synagogue: The Manor House Centre for Judaism, 80 East End Road, N3, Telephone: 349 4731

Liberal and Progressive Synagogue: 109 Whitfield Street, W1, Telephone: 580 1663

Sephardi: 1 Ashworth Road, W9, Telephone: 289 2573

Federation of Synagogues

Synagogue of the Congregation of Jacob

351–353 Commercial Road, E1 □ Bus: 5, 15, 15a, 40 □ Tube: Aldgate East, Whitechapel □ Parking: on street □ President: Mr Emmanuel Lixenberg □ Address: 316 Commercial Road, E1 □ Telephone: 790 3925 □ Available: ring for appointment □ Other staff: secretary

The Jewish community in the East End is not as thriving as it once was. Where the East London docks once saw an influx of 100,000 refugees from the Russian persecutions, today only 6,000 Jews remain. You will still find Jewish bakers, butchers and poulterers, restaurants, and even the occasional bookshop and Judaica specialist, but you have to know where to look among the now predominantly Bengali streets, and there is no longer a *mikvah* for the ritual bath which one takes before devotions of special occasions. Still, several synagogues remain, and the Congregation of Jacob in particular tries valiantly to stay viable in the face of the decline.

This is a small congregation, without rabbi or cantor, and sometimes it even has difficulty in meeting the quorum of ten adult males, meaning that formal worship cannot take place and is replaced by private prayer. The services are taken by the synagogue president, Mr Emmanuel Lixenberg. Members of the congregation are mainly middle-aged to elderly, with very few young people, and almost all who attend live locally.

The synagogue building dates from 1921, and stands on the Commercial Road in Stepney, opposite the vast, modern Watney Market. It is a small building, sandwiched snugly between shops, the name inscribed in large letters above the doorway. Inside, the design is low-key, with blue-painted walls and dark wooden seating which is numbered. There is an upstairs gallery for women.

There are very few activities here outside worship on Friday evening and Saturday. Needy members are sometimes put in touch with the Jewish old people's welfare centre, and members may belong to social groups like B'nai

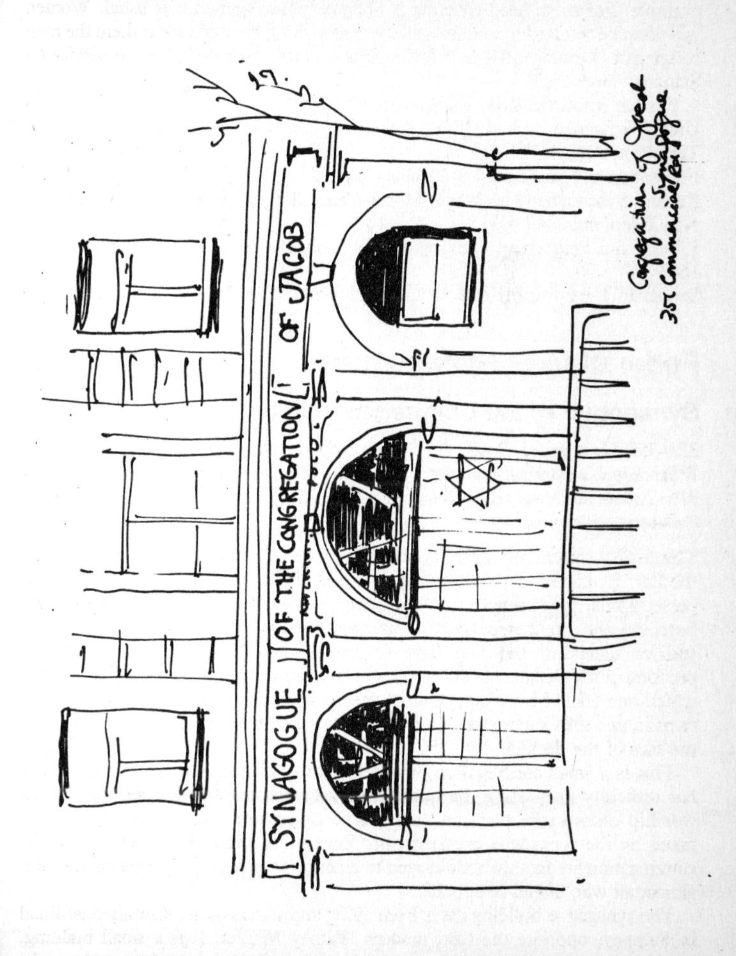

Synagogue of the Congregation of Jacob, E1

Brith, but generally the only time apart from the Sabbath the synagogue is open is on Sunday mornings, when members come to give contributions and talk with Mr Lixenberg.

Services: Friday Sunset; Saturday Sunrise and Sunset, (Services in Hebrew) □ Wheelchair: easy access □ Visiting: open for worship and on Sunday morning; men must cover heads

Fieldgate Street Great Synagogue

41 Fieldgate Street, E1 □ Telephone: 247 2644 □ Bus: 10, 25, 225, 253 □ Tube: Aldgate East □ Parking: on street □ Minister: Rev Louis Gayer □ Address: c/o synagogue □ Available: ring for appointment □ Other staff: two wardens

The title is perhaps a little misleading, for the synagogue building is no more than a three storey terraced house, with the prayer room at the top after a narrow flight of steps. It stands next to the much larger East London Mosque, with which it enjoys a good relationship. It was built at the end of the last century for the victims of the Russian pogroms of 1881, many of whom fled to Britain. The majority of the congregation even today are immigrants from before the Second World War, and the minister himself has worshipped here since 1933 when he arrived from Poland. He became the minister in 1952, and honorary life president in 1965.

The house was rebuilt in 1950, following wartime bombing. The local Jewish tradespeople—tailors, bootmakers, cabinet-makers, etc—all gave donations. There is a core of regular worshippers and far more who attend only rarely, but the minister encourages helping and supporting those who need to find more meaning in their lives. Local charities, and Israeli ones, are also supported, usually through collections.

Rev Gayer is at the synagogue every day from 12.30 to 2pm and from 4pm to 6.30pm, as well as prayer times. There is also a weekly meeting on Tuesday evenings. The minister's faith is that God helps and punishes us in ways we do not necessarily understand, but we must continue to praise Him come what may. Indeed, throughout its history Fieldgate Street Great Synagogue has sustained a loyal worshipping congregation, even managing to hold services during wartime.

Services: Sabbath 9am and Sunset; Monday–Friday 7.45am and 6.30pm (men only), (Services in Hebrew and English) □ Wheelchair: no access □ Other details: meeting room □ Visiting: open 12.30–2pm and 4–6.30pm; men must cover heads

---

Reform Synagogues

Settlement Synagogue

Beaumont Grove, W1 □ Telephone: 790 6262 □ Bus: 10, 25, 225 □ Tube/BR: Stepney Green □ Parking: on street □ Rabbi: Rev L Rigal □ Address: c/o synagogue office □ Available: 10am–2.30pm □ Other staff: secretary

At the moment the synagogue is in rented premises in a large Jewish community centre. The original Settlement Synagogue and social centre was founded soon after the First World War, and since then it has become the only synagogue in Britain that is affiliated to both the Reform and Liberal movements. In the community centre there are extensive facilities to provide for a variety of social and festival gatherings, as well as the actual place of worship, a large, rather plain, room. The congregation is elderly, in common with all Jewish communitites in the East End, but there are some signs of young Jewish families moving back into the area.

At the Sabbath services many of the prayers are in Hebrew, but some are recited in English. Families sit and worship together, and services are accompanied by a choir and organ. The atmosphere is pleasant and friendly. There is also an association with the Anglican Royal Foundation of St Katharine. This involves an organised series of weekends at which the congregation of the synagogue welcomes the Anglicans to take part in its services, and vice versa; and there are social gatherings as well. This contact is aimed at increasing understanding between the two groups. Rabbi Rigal hopes that the local Muslim community will also be joining in soon.

Services: Friday 8pm; Saturday 10.30am, (Services in Hebrew and English) □ *Children: Cheder (religious class) Sundays, 10am–12.30pm* □ *Wheelchair: lift* □ *Visiting: preferably by arrangement*

West London Synagogue of British Jews

33 Seymour Place, W1 □ *Telephone: 723 4404* □ *Bus: 6, 7, 8, 15, 15a, 36, 36b* □ *Tube: Marble Arch* □ *Parking: difficult* □ *Rabbis: Tabick and Gryn* □ *Address: c/o synagogue* □ *Available: ring for appointment*

This congregation stems from pressure for reform at Bevis Marks synagogue (qv) which resulted in some families leaving and setting up the first West London Synagogue, in Euston, where they could follow a revised form of the traditional service. It was very popular. More families joined, and in 1870 the present synagogue was built.

The first members were mainly Sephardim, but the new prayer book they introduced took what they considered to be the best sections from both the Sephardi and Ashkenazi rites, looking at the beauty of the services as well as their appropriateness for worship in the present day. They were interested in setting up a strong educational programme for their children, and 1986 in fact marked the one hundredth anniversary of the West London Synagogue Religion School. These days there is a great deal going on here for children—and adults—and most Sabbaths one will find a *Barmitzvah* or *Batmitzvah* taking place, to which one is more than welcome. The focus of the school itself is shifting from Bible studies to the development of an understanding of Jewish identity in the modern world; however, the Friday evenings of Torah study and Hebrew classes are an integral part of activities here.

The building is a fine example of Victorian architecture with a strong Moorish (Sephardi) influence. The *bimah* is now at the front of the building instead of its traditional central position. There is mixed seating, and an organ (the original one

West London Synagogue of British Jews, W1

from 1870) is used. The focal point of the synagogue is the *Aron Hakodesh*, the Holy Ark, which unusually has an open grille front, enabling one to see the *Sifre Torah* (scrolls of the Torah) throughout the service. The interior of the building is grand, but not overwhelming, and most congenial to worship. Here one can find both male and female rabbis leading services for a congregation of around 350.

Services: Friday 6pm; Sabbath 11am (followed by Kiddush*); Monday–Thursday 6.30pm Prayers (contact rabbi in advance)* □ *Facilities: amplification, deaf loop (Jewish Deaf Circle meets here, 1st Tuesday of month 7.30pm)* □ *Children: children's services, Sabbath 11am or 10am; Religion school, Sunday 10am–12.45pm; kindergarten; creche* □ *Wheelchair: easy access* □ *Other details: halls (available for hire)* □ *Visiting: by arrangement outside service times; men must cover heads; Judaica shop open Sunday mornings*

Sephardi Synagogues

Bevis Marks Synagogue

St Mary Axe, EC3 □ *Telephone: 289 2573* □ *Bus: 5, 15a, 22a, 25, 47, 78* □ *Tube: Aldgate* □ *Parking: very difficult* □ *Contact: Superintendent* □ *Telephone: 626 1274* □ *Other staff: rabbi, secretary, etc, at synagogue* □ *Available: by appointment*

The first Jewish house of worship after the resettlement of the Jews in England was opened in 1656 in the upper floor of a house in Creechurch Lane near Bevis Marks. An early visitor was Samuel Pepys. The famous diarist was less than impressed, perhaps because he visited the synagogue during a festival *(Simhat Torah)* when Jews tend to rejoice in a somewhat light-hearted manner.

By the turn of the century the congregation had outgrown the building in Creechurch Lane and in 1701 the present synagogue in Bevis Marks was constructed, which makes it the oldest one in Britain. The architect, Joseph Avis, is said to have been a Quaker, and to have returned his profit rather than take a financial gain for building a House of God. Another story is that Queen Anne, as Princess Anne the then heir apparent, presented an oak beam from one of the Royal Navy's ships to be incorporated in the roof of the building. Even if untrue, these stories attest to an interesting circumstance: that the small and often harassed Jewish community owed gratitude to two diametrically opposed groups of friends, the House of Stuart and the Puritans.

The ancient synagogue has remained virtually unchanged over the years. Features to note include the Ark whose design is classically inspired: the entablature of the Ark has as its central feature the Ten Commandments written in Hebrew (abbreviated) above which are inscribed in Hebrew the words 'Know before Whom thou standest'. In the centre of the synagogue are seven great hanging many-branched candelabra held to represent the seven days of the week, while the twelve columns supporting the gallery traditionally signify the Twelve Tribes of Israel.

The congregation at Bevis Marks comprises families of Spanish and Portuguese Jews, though for most of them English has long been the vernacular. Unfortunately, the shift of population away from the City for many years past has gravely thinned the ranks of worshippers, but Saturdays may see an attendance of around 50, and up to 18 men come for the Monday and Thursday morning services. The Chief Rabbi of the Spanish and Portuguese Congregation is titled the *Haham* (Wise Man). One of the most famous was Jacob Sasportas, who successfully combatted the doctrines of the false Messiah from Smyrna, Shabbetai Zvi, and stopped them gaining ground in England.

The congregation is proud of its traditions and can justly say that in its Welfare Board, which still operates, and provisions for free medical facilities, it anticipated the National Health Service by some two hundred and fifty years. After the Saturday morning service a *Kiddush* is held in the downstairs hall, with wine and other refreshments. This is an opportunity to meet the rabbi and members of the congregation.

Services: Saturday times vary; Monday & Thursday Sunset (men only), (Services are in Hebrew) □ Wheelchair: 1 step into synagogue though no access to women's gallery □ Other details: hall downstairs □ Visiting: by appointment; men should cover heads, women should dress modestly; postcards, leaflets, tapes available

The Spanish and Portuguese Synagogue

Lauderdale Road, Maida Vale, W9 □ Telephone: 289 2573 □ Bus: 8, 16, 16a, 46, 176 □ Tube: Maida Vale □ Parking: some spaces available □ Rabbi: Abraham Levy □ Address: 4 Biddulph Road, W9 □ Available: by appointment □ Other staff: Rev Israel Elia (assistant), Beadle

Located in Maida Vale on the corner of Lauderdale Road and Ashworth Road, is the large, domed Spanish and Portuguese Synagogue. It is a home of worship for the Sephardim, descendents of mainly Spanish and Portuguese Jews. Opening in 1896 to cater for the Sephardi community living in the area, the synagogue is an offshoot of Bevis Marks (qv) in the City, the oldest synagogue in London. Originally, the main Jewish community was around the City area, but in the 19th century people started to move westward, and the need for a new synagogue grew; hence the new building.

Today the congregation also contains those whose families are Iranian, Iraqi, Egyptian and Moroccan—all of them Sephardim. Many people attend here, up to 700; on some special festivals such as New Year, overflow services have to be held. The children have a 'little synagogue' once a fortnight—they organise the service themselves, under the supervision of the assistant minister.

The synagogue interior is very pleasing to the eye; most of the fittings being of rich varnished wood, including the excellently-carved readers desk. The Ark containing the Books of the Law is surmounted by a large, bronzed dome, reflecting the exterior of the building.

Adjoining the synagogue is the Communal Centre, with its own hall and classrooms, which is used for many of the synagogue's activities, including the youth club. The Friendship Club, founded in 1958, meets on Wednesday afternoons and there is a Women's Guild which organises many social events and fundraising activities.

Education has always been an important facet of the life of the synagogue, especially that of a religious nature. There are classes for children on Sunday mornings, and an adult Jewish Education Institute, both held in the Communal Centre. In addition to this, the synagogue has its own Jewish school, of which Rabbi Levy is the honorary principal. Opened four years ago, it caters at present for children up to nine years, although as the school builds up it will provide for schoolchildren up to fourteen.

Services: Friday 1 hour before Sunset (7.30pm at latest); Sabbath 8.30am–12 noon, afternoon & evening services— times vary; Monday–Thursday mornings Reading from the Books of Moses □ Children: Little Synagogue once a fortnight; Sunday morning religious classes for young people □ Wheelchair: ramp for access to synagogue and Communal Centre; no access to ladies' gallery □ Other details: Communal Centre with hall, classrooms, meeting rooms, etc; bookshop □ Visiting: open for worship only; men should cover heads

---

Union of Liberal and Progressive Synagogues

Belsize Square Synagogue

51 Belsize Square, NW3 □ Telephone: 794 3949, 435 2024/1148 □ Bus: 46, 268, C11 □ Tube: Swiss Cottage □ Parking: some space in grounds □ Rabbi: Rodney Mariner □ Address: c/o synagogue □ Available: ring for appointment □ Other staff: Rev Harry Fine, cantor; Mrs Benaiah, secretary

It is difficult to attempt to categorise Belsize Square, because although it belongs to the Liberal movement, services follow the (traditional) Singer's Prayerbook. Services are described as 'conservative' (rather than orthodox), 'faithfully preserving the 19th-century romantic tradition of synagogue music, with rabbi, cantor, choir and organist'. The congregation was founded in 1939 by refugees from the continent, and of the 1300 adult members, 65% are over 65.

Half the congregation lives locally, the rest travel in from as far as Radlett attracted by the special nature of this synagogue. From small beginnings in the house of its first minister, it grew to acquire the present premises in 1947. The house, which contains offices and classrooms, was originally the manse of nearby St Peter's church. The synagogue, an undistinguished post-war building, was added on—it has a seating capacity of 400, and about 60–80 attend regularly.

Men and women sit together, but additionally there are occasional special women's services. A children's service, taken entirely by the youngsters themselves, is held at monthly intervals. There are lots of clubs for young and old, and an active women's group, and many special interest groups. Members of St Peter's are regularly invited to the social and community events; Rabbi Mariner is Vice-Chair of the Hampstead Council of Christians and Jews.

Services: Friday 6.30pm; Saturday 11am, (Services in Hebrew) □ Facilities: amplification □ Children: Religion school, Sunday 10am–1pm; Youth service once a month □ Wheelchair: ramps; toilets for disabled □ Other details: hall (available for hire), classrooms, etc □ Visiting: open 9.30am–2.30pm

The Liberal Jewish Synagogue

28 St John's Wood Road, NW8 □ Telephone: 286 5181 □ Bus: 13, 74, 82, 113, 159, 707, 717, 734 □ Tube: St John's Wood □ Parking: in own grounds □ Rabbis: David J Goldberg, John D Rayner, Alexandra Wright □ Address: c/o synagogue office □ Secretary Raymond Benedyk □ Available: during office hours

This is the largest and oldest of the twenty-six Liberal Jewish congregations in Britain. The stately building, seating 1300 worshippers, was erected in 1925 but the synagogue was first established in 1912 by C G Montefiore, Israel Abraham,s the Hon Lily Montagu and other members of the Jewish Religious Union. Described as 'traditional Judaism bought up to date', the Liberal Jewish Synagogue, and Liberal Judaism generally, grew out of the Jewish Religious Union, founded in 1902. Members of the JRU were dissatisfied with the religious reforms made by the West London Synagogue, founded in 1840, particularly noting that women still sat apart from men at Reform synagogue services. Liberal Judaism, then, has always accorded equal status to men and women, regards upbringing and Jewish education as the decisive factors in determining the Jewish status of a child of a mixed marriage, and places more emphasis on ethics than on ritual.

About 55% of the services are conducted in English, with some readings and all of the singing in Hebrew. The prayer book is 'Service of the Heart', for Sabbaths and all festivals except *Rosh Hashanan* and *Yom Kippur*, when 'Gate of Repentance' is used. There is a professional choir, and an enthusiastic members' choir which is taking an increasing role in services. The synagogue has some 2,500 members. An average Sabbath morning attendance is around 250. The Sabbath Eve service, held in the attractive, more intimate New Synagogue, is followed by *Kiddush* and a discussion (*oneg shabbat*), finishing at approximately 10pm. The interior of the Main Synagogue is simply decorated to encourage a spiritual atmosphere and the attention of worshippers. The building's facade is dominated by the imposing portico with its six massive Ionic columns. The synagogue has a well-stocked Israel Abrahams library for the use of members, and runs a Religion school to teach children Hebrew and Jewish knowledge. There is an active women's group, and much emphasis is placed on courses, outings to conferences and weekend retreats in order to further knowledge of Judaism.

The London Society for Jews and Christians was founded here, and the synagogue has always been active in inter-faith and communal ventures. Regular interfaith Trialogues take place with St John's Wood Anglican Church and Regents Park Mosque, as an aid to understanding between members of the Jewish, Christian and Moslem faiths in the area.

Services: Saturday 11am (with sermon & choir; folowed by Kiddush*); Friday 8pm (followed by* Kiddush *& discussion), (Services mostly in English with some Hebrew readings and singing) □ Facilities: amplification, deaf loop, Braille texts □ Children: Religion school; creche on Festivals □ Wheelchair: 4 exterior steps, then level; toilet for disabled □ Other details: hall and rooms (available for hire); library □ Visiting: open all day; arranged group visits are preferred; Judaica shop*

The Liberal Jewish Synagogue, NW8

West Central Synagogue

109 Whitfield Street, W1 □ Telephone: 636 7627 □ Bus: 24, 27, 29, 73, 134, 176, 253 □ Tube: Warren Street □ Parking: on street □ Rabbi: Hillel Avidan □ Address: c/o synagogue □ Telephone: 340 8806 □ Available: Tuesday, Thursday and Saturday afternoons □ Other staff: Rev Richard Golding; Miss Wilson, secretary

The synagogue is on the first floor of the Montagu Centre. The building itself is post-war (consecrated 1954) with no frills—not unlike a school or government office.

Liberal Judaism has the same straightforward approach to services as does evangelical Christianity. At West Central you will find prayers are said mostly in English, women sit together with men, and there is an amplified choir (mixed of course) with organ music.

The synagogue was established before the Second World War (the old building was bombed with great loss of life) and its leading light from the very beginning was Lily Montagu, a great personality. She had started giving Bible classes in 1893, in the Soho/Bloomsbury area, mainly for the many Jewish shop-girls in the big stores there. Out of this developed the West Central Jewish Girls club, and a Jewish Religious Union which attracted both Orthodox and Reform. The synagogue developed out of these. In fact, even today around 35 of the members ore old girls of the club, and services are still held on Saturday afternoons, recalling the days when shops closed at lunchtime.

Lily Montagu promoted total equality for women and was the first Jewish woman minister in this country. She became a JP, she helped to found the London Society of Christians and Jews, Jewish children's Homes, and the National Association of Girls' Clubs before her death, aged 90. The Montagu Centre, which caters for non-Jews as well as those who profess Judaism, has an active evening institute offering a wide selection of courses on Jewish subjects, ranging from basic Judaism and Hebrew for beginners to Advanced bible Studies and Talmudic Texts. Each year sees about 100 students enrolled.

Membership of the West Central Synagogue has now declined to under 200 from a peak of 500 in the 1960s. This is, after all, no longer a residential area. Attendance each week is around the 25 mark, with up to 100 turning up at the major festivals. As in all synagogues, different readers will be chosen each week, and different people for the other honours, such as opening the Ark. People from other traditions sometimes come to observe the Sabbath service, which is followed by tea.

The Montagu Centre is the headquarters of the union of Liberal and Progressive synagogues, which provides general information and publications on Judaism in general and the Liberal and Progressive movement in particular.

Services: Sabbath 3—4pm, (Services mostly in English) □ Wheelchair: no ramp □ Other details: committee rooms, etc □ Visiting: open 9am-5pm weekdays, ULPS books available

United Synagogue

The Central Synagogue

33 Hallam Street, W1 □ Telephone: 580 1355 □ Bus: 3, 18, 27, 30, 137 □ Tube: Great Portland Street □ Parking: very difficult □ Rabbi: Cyril Shine □ Address: c/o synagogue □ Telephone: 636 3195 □ Available: after services or by appointment □ Other staff: secretary

The Central Synagogue with its tall, slender stained glass windows, is an imposing building worthy of its distinguished pedigree. Founded in the 1850s by the Rothschild family, it continues to be patronised by the most notable and influential members of the Jewish faith, including Cabinet ministers and Members of Parliament. As a result security is strict so, although all are welcome to the services, expect a search on entry. It is only possible to visit outside of the normal service times by special arrangement.

The quality of the services, which follow the orthodox tradition, is considered to be particularly high. Two interesting features are a professional choir, and a weekly English sermon. Although it has seating for up to 1,000 people, the synagogue is often filled to capaity. Many members have strong family attachments and it is quite common to find three generations of the same family at a service. Men and women are segregated. Many travel here from well outside London because of the fine reputation of the synagogue.

In the basement there are rooms providing facilities for a school teaching the Hebrew language and a charming chidren's synagogue with all the usual features built entirely to scale. Here, the children, under supervision, conduct their own service.

The synagogue was completely rebuilt in 1958 and its most intersting feature is now the central reading desk, a modern square design in marble. The carved panels on each side depict, through symbolic carvings the stages in life, including circumcision *Barmitzvah* and a marriage. The stained glass windows are also impressive and again of a modern design.

Services: Weekday 8am; Friday 9.30am □ Facilities: amplification □ Children: own services (times as above), Hebrew lessons □ Wheelchair: several steps, help available □ Other details: small hall □ Visiting: open for services (head covering necessary, provided at door) or by prior arrangement

Chelsea Synagogue

Smith Terrace, SW3 □ Bus: 11, 19, 22 □ Tube: Sloane Square □ Parking: on street □ Secretary: Mr M Friedman □ Telephone: 458 6222□ Available: evenings (except Friday)

The present synagogue, situated in a quiet residential street behind the busy Kings Road, was erected in 1959. It was built on the site of the original one which was itself a converted artist's studio. first opened in 1917.

It is a small and unobtrusive building in a moderrn style. The architect, Cyril Adler, was the son of the old synagogue's first President and co-founder. Generally quite plain inside it, it has an Ark, however, of unique design. Facilities

include a communal hall and classrooms for regligious instruction.
The synagogue serves a community of some 250 individuals, originally locally based, but now drawing its membership from several outlying boroughs.

Services: Sabbath 10.15am (mostly in Hebrew) □ Children: youth group, Wednesday evenings □ Wheelchair: 2 very shallow steps, level access inside □ Other details: hall and classrooms o *Visiting: open only for services; telephone first*

Golders Green Synagogue

41 Dunstan Road, NW11 □ Telephone: 455 2460 □ Bus: 26, 226 □Tube: Golders Green □ Parish Priest: Rabbi Binstock □ Address: c/o synagogue □ Available: ring for appointment □ Other staff: secretary; Cantor, Rev M Binstock

The north London suburb of Golders Green is a well-established Jewish neighbourhood, with a bookshop, kosher food stores and restaurants. There are Jewish schools, and any Friday an observer might note the air of expectation as families, their preparation complete by early evening, welcome the end of the working week and the arrival of the Sabbath.

This local member of the United Synagogue group is a stately building in Georgian style, set in gardens which are kept up so as to be attractive and pleasant all year round. The architect was Digby Solomon, and it was officially opened in 1922, for a congregation who were having to meet at the Hippodrome theatre opposite the Underground station. The complex includes the large prayer hall, a small one, two classrooms, and a reference library.

The Sabbath morning service begins at 9.15 and lasts two and a half hours. Around 200 men and 100 women attend, with a growing number of young families at the core. Each week, before the portion from the Scroll of the Law is read, a member of the congregation gives a short summary. After the reading the rabbi gives a sermon. The service as a whole is lively, with children participating as well; however a choir is now only used on special occasions.

Good education is very important in Judaism, and this synagogue is able to offer a number of classes throughout the week. There are, for instance, three sets of Hebrew classes: regular lectures discuss Judaism in relation to modern-day life; there are bible classes; and open to all is the class in basic Judaism, led by the rabbi and his wife, which is held every Sunday morning from 11.45 to 12.45pm.

Inside, the synagogue is decorative, with a *bimah* or platform on which the cantor stands to lead prayers and to read from the Law. A striking feature of the synagogue is the marble pulpit. Curved steps also of marble lead up to the Ark of the Covenant. Above this is the perpetual light, the *norah tamid*, which burns as a reminder of the Jewish religious commitment, to serve and honour God in all one does.

The synagogue is a popular and pleasant venue for wedding ceremonies. Kitchen facilities are available within the complex and a 'brides room' is located on the gallery level. There are special monthly services held by children and by teenagers many of whom are members of the youth club. There is also a senior citizens' club, and at the other end of the scale, a kindergarten meets in the premises. Information on the weekly lectures is published in the *Jewish chronicle*.

Services: Sabbath 9.15am, Mincha ¼ hr before Sunset; Sunday 8.30am; Weekdays Mon & Thu 7.20am, Tue, Wed & Fri 7.30am, (All services in Hebrew) □ *Children: special weekly services for children and monthly services for teenagers, Bible studies, youth clubs* □ *Wheelchair: caretaker available to assist—1 step to main entrance* □ *Other details: 2 halls (available for hire for weddings, charity functions etc); small hall contains synagogue library* □ *Visiting: orthodox and non-orthodox Jewish people welcome; visits from schools and groups welcome*

Hampstead Synagogue

1 Dennington Park Road, NW6 □ *Telephone: 435 1518* □ *Bus: C11, 46* □ *Tube: West Hampstead* □ *Parking: on street* □ *Rabbi: Saul Aranov* □ *Address: c/o synagogue* □ *Telephone: 435 5708* □ *Available: ring for appointment*

It has been said that should the Queen ever wish to attend a Jewish service, then Hampstead Synagogue would be the ideal place. Amongst its members are many prominent British Jews, and the building itself, if not palatial, is most dignified and large enough to seat 1,200 people. (A prayer, for the good health of the Queen is of course recited here every Sabbath, as it is in all the synagogues of the land).

This is one Jewish house of worship where a devout atmosphere always prevails, and at least one book has been written on the history of the congregation and its notable ministers. Currently, the rabbi is Saul Aranov, a widely travelled New Yorker, who replaced the much-loved Rabbi Norman Solomon in 1985. The interior of the main synagogue is octagonal with a beautiful marble reading platform and pulpit flanked by four long delicately shaped pillars. High above the Ark is a gallery for the choir, framed by an ornate golden rail. The ladies' gallery extends on all sides, and light filters in through some beautiful stained glass. Many of the windows were designed by B Sochachewski after the originals were lost in the Blitz.

Services at Hampstead Synagogue follow the Singer's Prayerbook. During the week they are held in the junior synagogue upstairs which, as its name implies, is used for children's services on the Sabbath. The Saturday afternoon service and discussion also take place here. The premises also contain a library, the rabbi's offices, the Eli Chinn Hall which is used for various functions and club meetings, and the offices of the local Council for Christians and Jews.

Services: 9.15am, 4.45pm; Weekdays except Fridays 7.15am, 6.30pm; Fridays 8am, 6am; Sundays 8am, 6.30am, (Weekday services held in Junior Synagogue) □ *Children: Sunday school* □ *Wheelchair: 2 small steps* □ *Other details: hall (for hire, subject to dietary laws, etc)* □ *Visiting: open outside service times only by arrangement; men must cover heads*

Marble Arch Synagogue

32 Great Cumberland Place, W1 □ *Telephone: 723 7246* □ *Bus: 6, 7, 8, 15, 16, 16a, 30, 36, 36b, 73, 74, 137* □ *Tube: Marble Arch* □ *Parking: difficult* □ *Rabbi: Dr Johnathon Sacks* □ *Address: c/o synagogue* □ *Available: ring for appointment* □ *Other staff: Rev E Freilich, minister; Mr M Bitani, secretary*

Marble Arch Synagogue, a part of the United Synagogue, was built in 1957. It was officially opened in that same year by the Hon E S Montague, President of the synagogue from 1954 to 1961. Before 1957 members had worshipped here in a basement on this site.

Members arrive from all over London for the Sabbath morning service, and take the opportunity to socialise afterwards. The service is traditional in format. For the most part Hebrew is the language of prayer, but the Singer's Prayerbook used by the United Synagogue gives a page by page translation. A trained *Baal-koreah* reads the weekly portion of the Law from the Scrolls. A relaxed atmosphere prevails during this very tuneful service, where children are encouraged to joint in singing the psalms and everyone raises their voices at the end with the resounding Hymn of Glory.

After the service everyone gets together in the hall for wine and cakes. There is another short service later in the day. Following the Jewish calendar, special prayers are said at all the festivals, the biggest celebrations, of course, taking place at New Year and the Day of Atonement *(Yom Kippur)*. Marble Arch Synagogue, in the heart of the West End, receives many occasional visitors and tourists, including business people who stay at the nearby hotels.

The synagogue building, on the outside, is elegant and graceful. A bright and spacious foyer gives access to the main block downstairs, as well as the small chapel, the office, cloakrooms, and the ladies' gallery which are on the first floor. Inside the main prayer room, though, one finds a very geometrical and angular influence, which might have been refreshing in the 1950s but today seems rather harsh. The fixtures are in dark wood and chrome, and navy-blue soft furnishings are set off by plain white walls. An Israeli artist, Azaz, was the designer of the brightly-coloured stained glass windows, cubist in style, which are on Biblical themes.

Weekday morning services are attended by about twenty members, but on Saturdays there are about 200 people, including visitors, to what is one of London's most important and most representative centres of Jewish orthodoxy.

Services: Saturday 9.15am and Sunset; Friday Sunset; Sunday 8.30am; Weekdays 7.30am and Evening Service (6pm summer, Sunset winter), (Services are in Hebrew) □ *Wheelchair: easy access, lift* □ *Other details: hall (not for hire), reception rooms, etc* □ *Visiting: visitors welcome, tours on request; men and married ladies must cover heads*

New West End Synagogue

St Petersburgh Place, W2 □ *Telephone: 229 2631, 727 3480* □ *Bus: 12, 88* □ *Tube: Queensway, Bayswater* □ *Parking: on street* □ *Rabbi: M Turetsky* □ *Address: c/o synagogue* □ *Available: contact Beadle, Mr Harry Lee, at synagogue*

The name is misleading; this is actually one of the oldest synagogues in London! It was built in 1877 for the families who were moving to the newly fashionable area north of Kensington Gardens.

Today this is no longer so much a settled residential area. Hotels line the streets. Some, mainly elderly, Jewish people still live here though, and around 35–45 adults (only very rarely do you see children) is the average for Sabbath morning worship. This figure will include visiting Americans, who stay at the

New West End Synagogue, W2

local hotels. The choir adds a professional musical touch to the service.

Across Petersborough Mews, with its entrance in Park Place, is the Herbert Samuel Hall. Built in 1959 as a community centre, in addition to the hall there is a library, a suite of rooms, and a small synagogue *(Beth Hamidrash)*. This latter is used for private prayer and study during the week, and occasionally for Sabbath services. It is also leased to an accountancy school, who vacate the premises an hour before the Sabbath begins, that is, before the nightfall on Fridays. The business school does not interfere with worship, since in Judaism the main prayers of the day are always said, shortly after rising, early in the morning.

As well as Viscount Samuel, the Liberal Peer and Viceroy of India, many distinguished names are associated with this synagogue. None, though, can be more important than that of the first minister here, the Rev Simeon Singer, translator of the authorised Daily Prayerbook. He was a great scholar, preacher, and man of open-minded views, and he has left his mark on the building by selecting the Hebrew texts, mainly from the Psalms, whose golden letters adorn the walls and the front of the galleries like those of the famous Abulafia synagogue in Toledo.

The architecture of the synagogue is indeed indebted to Moorish models for its towers and horseshoe-shaped arches. The floor plan, however, is that of a basilica, and the cupolas above the Ark are Byzantine. The ornate Victorian splendour has been well-maintained up to the present day, and for this alone it is well worth making the trip to St Petersburgh Place.

Services: Friday Evening; Saturday 9.30/10.30am–midday, 4.30pm or at close of Sabbath □ *Facilities: amplification* □ *Wheelchair: several steps into synagogue; no lift to women's gallery* □ *Other details: hall (used for accountancy school)* □ *Visiting: open for services only—may be able to view by arrangement; women and men should cover heads*

St John's Wood Synagogue

37–41 Grove End Road, St John's Wood, NW8 □ *Telephone: 286 3838/6333* □ *Bus: 2b, 13, 46, 113* □ *Tube: St John's Wood* □ *Parking: limited space available (but not for attending services)* □ *Rabbi: Cyril K Harris* □ *Address: 126a Hamilton Terrace, NW8* □ *Telephone: 625 5093* □ *Available: almost always (do not contact by telephone on Fridays or the Sabbath)*

St John's Wood is an elegant, middle-class area in north west London with a large Jewish community; it is fitting that the synagogue which serves them is also elegant. It is also a modern building, built in 1964, the successor to an earlier building in Abbey Road, which had served since 1882. (The Jewish community had first mooted the setting up of a synagogue in 1872, and had formed their first congregation in 1877).

The large, attractive exterior has a magnificent doorway, a large brick archway enclosing an impressive wrought iron railed screen, at the base of which are the entrances themselves. Inside, the staircases in the roomy entrance hall lead to the synagogue itself. Whilst the style and materials are modern, the layout is traditional, with an upstairs gallery for the ladies and the *Chupah* at the centre, surrounded by flowers. The doors of the Ark are intricately decorated. But by far the most impressive feature is the set of stained glass windows, which run along both sides of the synagogue. Designed by David Hillman in the 1930s, originally for Abbey Road, they add to the building immensely, lending it colour, character and beauty.

The synagogue seats 1,750 people. Average attendance for the Sabbath worship is around 450, predominantly elderly; 90% of the congregation live locally. Attendance has remained constant over the years, and new members join annually. This reflects the fact that the area has changed little over the years. Services are traditional, and are both devotional and educational, with much reading from the scripture and the Scrolls of the Law. Almost all is in Hebrew.

The synagogue has a wide range of facilities. There is one very large, and two medium-sized halls, a lounge, a kitchen and a Jewish library. It contains rooms which are used for the Hebrew school, held on Sunday morning and one evening (some 100 children attend this) and rooms used for the synagogue's kindergarten. Events which take place on the premises are a mixture of educational, cultural (such as concerts), fundraising (bazaars), charity meetings and a full range of social purposes. The synagogue was designed to be more than a place of worship, but as a centre for Jewish people to hold meetings, conferences and other events. Among the various societies which meet here are several elderly clubs, including an Over Sixties Club which holds regular meetings, JACS (the Jewish Association of Cultural Societies) and the weekly Friendship Club.

Services: Sabbath 9.15am, Evening Service (times vary), Daily morning and evening worship (times vary) (Services mostly in Hebrew) □ Children: Hebrew school (Sunday morning and one weekday evening), kindergarten □ Wheelchair: easy access except to ladies' gallery (1st floor); toilets for disabled □ Other details: large hall, two smaller halls, classrooms, library, etc □ Visiting: open for services, during office hours or by appointment; women should cover heads during services

---

Independent Synagogues

New London Synagogue

33 Abbey Road, NW8 □ Telephone: 328 1026 □ Tube: St John's Wood □ Parking: on street □ Rabbi: Dr L Jacobs □ Address: c/o synagogue □ Available: ring for appointment

The New London Synagogue was established in 1964, and represented a departure from the fundamentalist orthodox Judaism practised elsewhere in London. Its founder, Rabbi Dr Jacobs described the synagogue at that time in terms of 'an independent orthodox congregation'; independent in the sense of taking control of one's destiny, and orthodox with respect to their belief in God, the Torah and Israel.

The building which houses the synagogue is a former music hall built over one hundred years ago by Collins, the acknowledged specialist in such buildings. Its conversion to a place of worship did not involve too much alteration of the charming interior. The carvings of fruit and flowers on the balcony, the fine fluted columns, the restful shades of grey, pink and cream—these features do not clash with the modern ark and seating, and do not detract from the necessary dignity of a synagogue. A modern extension was added in the early 1970s to cope with a growing congregation which again is taxing the building's resourses. This extension includes a hall used for functions and Sunday school classes.

Worship is traditional by nature, with men and women segregated at the statutory services. Hebrew and English versions of the Singer's Prayerbook are used. Lectures are regularly held covering a wide range of subjects, both religious and secular. Emphasis is also placed on the artistic and intellectual pursuits. Concerts are often staged; Yehudi Menuhin and the King's Singers have performed here.

Services: Sabbath 9.15am–12 noon and evening; Friday evening □ Children: Sunday school, for ages 4–16 □ Wheelchair: a few steps but help available □ Other details: extension, dining area, classrooms, etc □ Visiting: most days by arrangement; head coverings provided

Sandys Row Synagogue

Sandys Row, Middlesex Street, E1 □ Bus: any to Liverpool Street □ Tube/BR: Liverpool Street □ Parking: nearby car park □ President: Mr Louis Brookarsh □ Telephone: 554 1078 □ Available: ring for appointment □ Other contacts: Treasurer, Mr G B Pollack (247 7988); Resident Caretakers, Mr and Mrs Spowart (377 5854)

There is a small but stable congregation here. This is the area of Spitalfields, just outside the City, where Jews, like nonconformists before them, were first allowed to set up houses of prayer without restrictions. In Victorian times this was the centre of the old clothes trade (Mayhew's *London* gives a vivid portrait), and today it is famous for the Petticoat Lane markets. There are still quite a few Jewish traders here, though not many live in the neighbourhood now. For those who do, this is the synagogue they attend.

For the past forty years, Rev David Newman has been minister of the synagogue, giving a great service to the community. The Friday evening service is a thank-you to God for the week that has passed and whatever it brought. It begins with the traditional song of welcome to the bride, the Sabbath, who brings repose and delight after the toil of the weekday routine. Afterwards is wine and whisky and the journey home in an uplifted mood. A similar number of members, not much more than the required ten, will attend on Saturday mornings. Some women will also come and sit in the gallery, but this is an orthodox synagogue (though not affiliated to any grouping) and orthodox Judaism sees married life as a division of labour—prayer is the responsibility of men alone, while a man must always respect the woman's authority in the home.

The synagogue was founded by Dutch immigrants in 1854. These Jews were Ashkenazim (north European rite) rather than Sephardim (Spanish and Portuguese) and this is the first Ashkenazi synagogue of any consequence in east London. It provided a model for the waves of immigrant groups who came later in the 19th century and on into the 20th century. It is a large terraced building with a fading blue facade, and inside it boasts a marble floor and a fine stone stairway, which is overlooked by a branched candlestick in handcrafted metal.

Services: Friday 7pm; Saturday 9am; Monday–Thursday 1.30pm during winter months □ Wheelchair: many steps—no access □ Other details: small hall (not for hire) □ Visiting: open at service times or by arrangement

West End Great Synagogue

21 Dean Street, W1 □ Telephone: 734 0633 □ Bus: 1, 7, 8, 25, 73 □ Tube: Tottenham Court Road □ Parking: on street □ Rabbi: Alan Burns □ Address & Telephone: c/o synagogue office □ Available: all day □ Other staff: secretary

The history of this synagogue goes back to 1880 when a congregation called the West London Talmud Torah was established off Brewer Street. The name West End Great Synagogue was adopted in 1948, seven years after moving to the present Dean Street site, following a series of amalgamations with other congregations.

The building was damaged during the War and was totally re-built in the early 1960s. Its austere rectilinear facade is very typical of that architectural era. The synagogue itself is on the ground floor of this six storey building, and the ladies' gallery along with all other floors can be reached by lift. The interior is light and uncluttered having clean lines and a good deal of clear glass; there are gallery pews for up to 500 people.

Sabbath day services begin at 9.30am and usually around 100 people attend. There is no choir, but guest cantors are occasionally invited to sing. *Kiddush* is held afterwards in the David Cohen hall on the lower ground floor. A larger hall on the same floor called the Royalty Suite, is used for weddings, *Barmitzvahs* and other functions. The remainder of the building houses the Ben Uri gallery, with its fine collectio of Jewish art, and the synagogue offices. Two regular social groups meeting here are the Ladies Guild, founded in 1880 and still going strong, and the Friendship Club for retired and elderly members of the congregation.

Services: Friday Sunset; Saturday 9.30am □ Wheelchair: 1 shallow step only, lift to ladies' gallery □ Other details: 2 halls □ Visiting: office open 9.30am–5pm Monday to Thursday, and 9.30am–12 noon Sunday and Friday; visiting by arrangement

Western Synagogue

39 Brandon Street, W1 □ Telephone: 258 0179 □ Bus: 6, 7, 8, 15, 15a, 16, 16a, 18, 27, 36, 36b, 176 □ Tube: Edgware Road (both stations) □ Parking: on street □ Rabbi: Jeremy Rosen □ Address: c/o synagogue office □ Available: ring for appointment

This is a place for traditional services without much in the way of formality. There is separate seating and the occasional top hat may be seen (these are usually the wardens or other dignitaries) but on the whole Western Synagogue has a modern approach, orthodox but independent. Around 70 people attend here every Sabbath. The synagogue is modern, with some very good stained glass.

A large proportion of members are elderly, in common with most of London's synagogues. Many are council tenants from the nearby Westminster estates. This synagogue also draws a lot of people in the low income groups, and the unemployed, to its Sabbath and Sunday morning services. There is even a resource group (JUG) for the unemployed, which offers counselling, support and job search skills. As might be expected from this, there is a significant minority of young people (teens and twenties) at the synagogue, and Jeremy Rosen, the rabbi, organises a full range of interesting activities with them in mind.

The many synagogue groups include West One, a Jewish Theatre group; the Rally Club, for those with learning difficulties; the Graduate Group; and entrance is free to the regular general lunchtime discussions. On the last Friday of each month is an *Oneg Shabbat,* which means a short service with songs, home cooking, and a social get-together.

Services: Friday ½ hour before Sunset (7pm summer); Saturday 9.30–11.30am; Sunday 8.30am, (Services in Hebrew) □ *Children: Western Jewish Youth Centre: theatre group* □ *Wheelchair: 6 steps; caretaker can assist* □ *Other details: hall (available for hire)* □ *Visiting: open at service times or by arrangement; men and women must cover heads*

Westminster Reform Synagogue

Rutland Gardens, SW7 □ *Telephone: 584 3953* □ *Bus: 9, 52, 52a, 73* □ *Tube: Hyde Park Corner* □ *Parking: on street* □ *Rabbi: A H Friedlander* □ *Address: c/o synagogue* □ *Available: during day at synagogue*

Housed in an elegant building that once belonged to Queen Victoria's father, the Westminster Reform is the only independent Reform synagogue in the country. It was founded in 1957 by a group of 50 families who left West London Synagogue, and whose aim was to create 'an instrument for the pursuit of religous truth, a source of encouragement to human progress, and a comfort and inspiration to individual men and women'.

At services, prayers are in both English and Hebrew, and sermons are in English. The rabbi Albert Friedlander tackles large subjects such as 'Fighting Oppression' and 'Love and Hate'; great contemporary Jewish thinkers such as Martin Buber and Leo Baeck have influenced his approach. There is a strong tradition of congregational participation in the services, and the singing is to organ accompaniment. Over 300 member families pay yearly subscriptions—the synagogue's sole income—though no-one is barred from membership due to inability to pay, and there are some unemployed members here. On average 100 worshippers come to the main service. A small number of Indian and Black Jews attend.

The Reinhart Library is well stocked with several thousand books available for reference or borrowing, and there is a special children's section. Anyone is welcome to make use of the library, which is housed in an attractive room with Chagall prints on display. The synagogue also runs a full complement of social and study groups, and programmes for the Jewish festivals. A children's religion class is held on Sunday mornings, and a youth club meets regularly; adult education classes meet every week, and there are monthly talks by members of the Council of Christians and Jews.

In 1964, 1,564 Sacred Scrolls from the ravaged communities of Bohemia and Moravia were entrusted to this synagogue for safe-keeping and restoration. Looted by the Nazis, these *Sifre Torah* were to be exhibited by them as examples of the art work of 'an exterminated ethnographical group'. Instead many people now come here to view them with mixed feelings of wonder and grief.

***Services:** Friday evening 6.30pm; Saturday morning 11am–12.30pm, (Services in Hebrew and English) □ **Children:** creche; Religion school Sunday 10am–12 noon for ages 6–15 □ **Wheelchair:** lift □ **Other details:** meeting rooms, classrooms, reading room/library, hall (not for hire) □ **Visiting:** open 10am–6pm every day*

7 SIKHISM

Sikhs follow the teachings of a succession of ten Gurus who lived in the Punjab region of India. The first was Guru Nanak, born in 1469 into a Hindu family. He came to believe that the dominant religions of India, Hinduism and Islam, should come to respect and learn from each other, in spite of their differences. The following Gurus, all nominated by their predecessor, each contributed more to the faith. Guru Angad, for example, formulated the Gurmukhi alphabet in which all the hymns and teachings are written and which all Sikhs must learn, while Guru Arjan built the Golden Temple, still the major holy shrine. The last human leader, Guru Gobind Singh, did not name a successor but declared that a book containing all the writings of the Gurus would be the final and permanent Guru.

This book, the *Guru Granth Sahib,* is accordingly treated with the same respect as were the human Gurus. It is kept in a special room and is present at all ceremonies, when any Sikh man or woman may read from it. It contains 5,894 verses and hymns, and all copies are identical.

The Sikh people believe that there is only one God, who created the universe and everything in it. There are many possible kinds of life and our human life is only of of them. They believe that all of us have lived before, maybe as animals, plants, or even rocks. But it is only when we are born into human bodies that we can respond to the love of God. However, our attachment to this life keeps us in the cycle of rebirth, and it is necessary for God to show grace *(nadar)* to us in order for us to live totally with God.

If a Sikh is a member of the *Khalsa* (brotherhood of Sikhs), he will be found wearing five signs to show this. These signs are known as the five K's—*kesh* (uncut hair); *kanga* (hair comb); *kara* (steel wrist band); *kirpan* (sword); and *kaccha* (short underpants). The turban itself is not one of the signs which Guru Gobind Singh told the Khalsa to wear but most (male) Sikhs wear a turban to emulate the Guru himself who wore one as a sign of authority.

The *gurdwara* is the place of worship for the Sikhs and means 'door of the Guru' or 'God's house', and is the very heart of the Sikh community. It is the gathering together of Sikhs in the presence of the Guru Granth Sahib which makes the gurdwara such a special place. It is also a place where one can teach Gurmukhi, and often acts as a community social centre for Sikhs. One is welcome to attend services, but they are rather long and it may be advisable to arrive some time after the service has begun; this is not a sign of disrespect. Visitors are asked to take off their shoes and to cover their heads. Men and women usually sit apart though this is a custom rather than a rule. After the service sweet, sticky food called *karah parshad* is handed round, and one will be invited to the langar-room, a kind of open kitchen.

Most gurdwaras in the Greater London area are in Southall, where the vast majority of the community live. It is estimated there are some 180,000 Sikhs in Britain. The major festivals are Baisakhi (April), Diwali (October/November) and Holi (February/March).

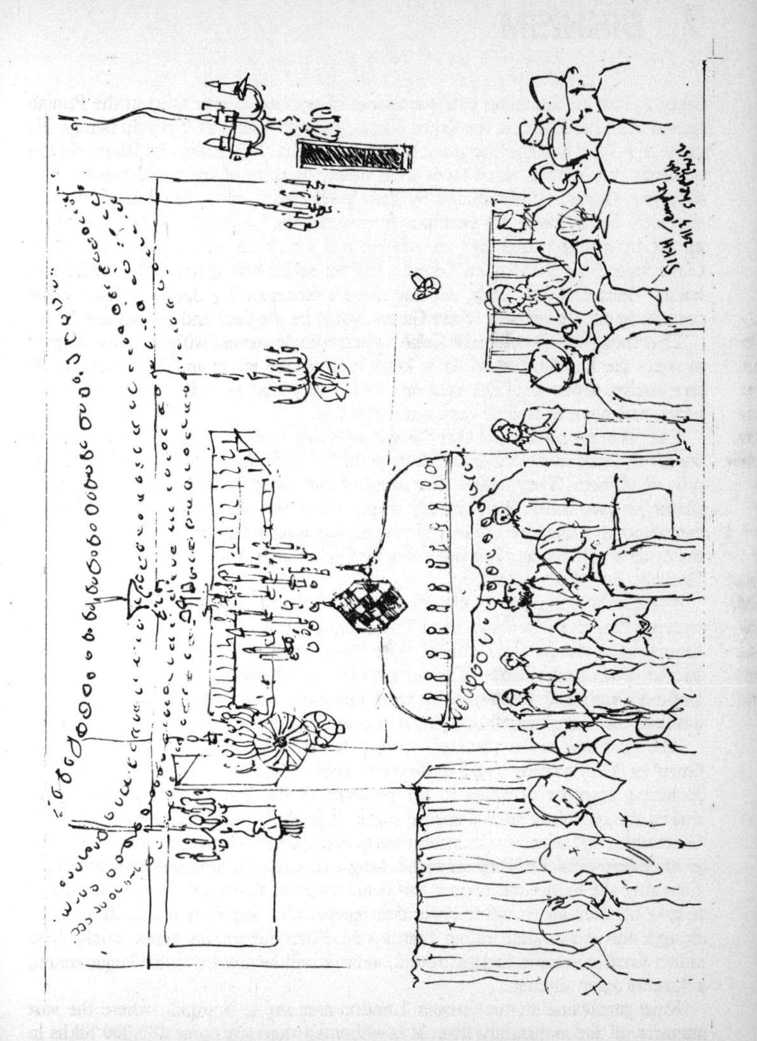

Interior, Central Sikh Temple, W11

The Central Sikh Temple

62 Queensdale Road, W11 □ Telephone: 603 2789 □ Bus: 12, 49, 88, 295 □ Tube: Shepherds Bush, Holland Park □ Parking: on street □ President: Mr Gurman Singh Sahani □ Telephone: 571 2751 (office), 904 4191 (home) □ Secretary: Mr Gurpreet Singh Anand □ Available: by appointment

The Central Sikh Temple in Shepherd's Bush is a modern square, brick building situated in the residential area of Holland Park. It is a fairly large building with several floors for all the necessary rooms of a gurdwara, and includes a large worship room and langar hall. On entering the building there are several noticeboards informing one of the times of services and of any other events happening in the community, and they are written in both English and Gumurkhi.

The worship room itself is plainly decorated with a white sheet covering the floor and coloured beads hanging from the ceiling. All emphasis is on the special platform which holds the Guru Granth Sahib during the service. The book is placed on a quilt of three cushions *(Manji Sahib)* covered in shawls, and a gold-laced canopy *(channani)* lit up with coloured bulbs hangs above it. During a service musicians play traditional Indian music by the side of this platform, chanting verses from the Guru Granth Sahib, whilst the *granthi* (reader) waves a fan over the book, thereby emulating the human gurus who had fans waved over them as a sign of respect. Many different musicians may be invited to play during a service.

The services at this temple are on Wednesday and Sunday evenings from 7pm and can run for several hours. One is welcome to attend and one will find many a friendly face. After the service one will no doubt be invited to join in the langar in a separate room. Here is an opportunity to share specially prepared food which one scoops up by hand with chappati and roti, and talk with members of the temple.

Services: Sunday & Wednesday 7pm □ Wheelchair: many steps, very difficult access □ Visiting: open most days; it is polite to make an appointment to visit or to attend services

8 SUFISM

Sufism is popularly regarded as the mystical heart of Islam, but in fact it pre-dates that religion. Certainly its most famous exponents, the Dervishes and such like, developed within Islam but other groups and traditions with a claim to the title have grown up in various places, encompassing a wide range of beliefs and practices. Of those present in the West, the example included here, with its pan-religious stance, is not untypical.

London Sufi Centre

21 Lancaster Road, W11 □ Telephone: 221 3215 □ Bus: 7, 28, 31 □ Tube: Westbourne Park, Ladbroke Grove □ Parking: on street □ Leader: Nigel Hamilton □ Available: by appointment

The London Sufi Centre is the base for a range of activities including inter-religious worship, healing and meditation classes. This is not part of the strictly Islamic Sufi tradition, but a much more open order based on the teachings of Hazrat Inayat Khan of the ancient *Chisti* Sufi line, founded in India. His work has been continued by his son Pir Vilayat Khan who travels all over the world to teach and conduct inter-religious retreats.

Central to Hazrat's teachings, found in the 12 volumes of *The Message,* is the unity of all faiths and, accordingly, there is a Universal Worship Service held each month to which people of all beliefs are welcome. At this service, six candles are lit for the great world religions of Hinduism, Buddhism, Judaism, Zoroastrianism, Christianity and Islam, and a seventh for all other faiths not mentioned. Then there follows 'attunement to the spirit of each religion' by means of dances, chants, prayers etc and readings from the Scriptures. A pot-luck supper follows the service.

The 'soul' of the order is held to be the Sacred Healing Service which concludes the healing class each Monday evening. Names of those to be healed can be submitted before the service and the healing practices include the use of breath, colour, light and movement.

Classes are also given in the sacred dance of the Sufi tradition (a fee is charged). This has long been regarded as a means of 'communicating' with and experiencing the Absolute. Sufi meditation is also taught, and other topics studied here include the spiritual dimensions of psychology, alchemy and personal unfoldment. Seminars and retreats are regularly held. In all, the Centre offers a varied programme expressed in the broadest terms through worship and teaching.

Services: 1st Sunday 5pm Universal Worship service; Monday 7pm Sacred Healing Service □ Wheelchair: very difficult—steep steps □ Other details: therapy rooms □ Visiting: open 9am–5pm daily; call before travelling

9 ZOROASTRIANISM

Zoroastrianism is the ancient religion of Persia (Iran) and was founded by the prophet Zarathustra (or Zoroaster in its Greek form). Opinions vary as to Zarathustra's dates between the Parsi tradition of 6000 BC and current Western academic views of 14–1700 BC. Whichever, he can be regarded as the first prophet in the history of religion and the first proponent of monotheism. He also propounded belief in free will, the judgement of heaven and hell, resurrection and the coming of a messiah. His teachings are preserved in five *Gathas*, ancient hymns which form a central part of Zoroastrian liturgy and of the holy book, the *Avesta*.

For over a thousand years (550 BC to 642 CE), Zoroastrianism was the official state religion of successive Iranian empires which spanned from Turkey to Pakistan. It can thus be seen as a unique bridge between the major Eastern and Western religions on which, it can be argued, it exerted a profound influence. The empires finally crumbled in the face of the inexorable advance of Islam and now there are very few Zoroastrians remaining in Iran. Many departed in the 10th century for India where, known as Parsis, they have grown to be an affluent and respected community, especially in Bombay.

Dualistic is a term often applied, controversially, to Zoroastrianism because it teaches that the wholly good God, Ahura Mazda, is pitted against the evil Ahriman. However it is a central tenet that evil will be defeated—'I have the remedy', affirms Ahura Mazda in the Gathas. An essential feature of worship, along with physical and moral purity, is fire, though it is totally wrong to imagine Zoroastrians worship fire. The religion is optimistic and urges full involvement with the world which is essentially good; asceticism and celibacy are viewed with some suspicion.

The Zoroastrian Association has been established in Britain for over 125 years. There are 3–5,000 Zoroastrians in Britain today, many of whom are highly qualified and professional people. It may come as a surprise to most people to learn that, earlier this century, there were three Indian MPs at Westminster. One was a Conservative, one a Liberal and the third a Socialist, but each was a Parsi Zoroastrian.

Zoroastrian Association of Europe

Zoroastrian House, 88 Compayne Gardens, NW6 □ Telephone: 328 6018 □ Bus: 28, 159, C11 □ Tube: West Hampstead □ Parking: on street, difficult □ Secretary: Mr Fily Maravala □ Address: c/o Zoroastrian House □ Available: office hours

A large Victorian house in West Hampstead has since 1969 been headquarters of the Zoroastrian Association of Europe—a vital social, cultural and religious centre. All the festivals of the Zoroastrian calendar are celebrated here, the best attended being the New Year festival on 21st March when around 600 people can be expected.

At the time of writing there are no full-time priests in the UK so ceremonies are

Priests, Zoroastrian House, NW6

led by part-time priests, all of whom must be members of the priestly class. Any number of priests from two upwards may officiate at a ceremony. Many rites are for Zoroastrians alone, when the small flame room may be used, but some, such as the *Jashan* ceremony, which marks the birthday of the Prophet Zarathustra, have become open to invited guests.

The ceremony takes place in a functional worship room at the rear of the house, which has a raised area (complete with extractor fan over the fire urn) where the priests perform the rites. Dressed all in white, their mouths covered with a piece of white cloth, called a *padan,* so as not to pollute the flames, the priests intone ancient prayers in the Avasta and Pazand languages. Throughout the ceremony the priests maintain the fire which is regarded as a symbol of divine qualities and as the clearest manifestation of 'life energy'. The prayers include homage to the seven Ameshaspends, which are to be understood both as archangels and as attributes of Ahura Mazda. The soul of the prophet Zarathustra along with other great souls from the faith's long history are also remembered and revered.

During the Jashan ceremony, which is one of thanksgiving and blessing, the worshippers may sit quietly or follow the prayers from books. It is intended to create an atmosphere whereby those present feel a mystical link both with each other and with the Divine. After the service, refreshments are served downstairs; guests are made very welcome.

Zoroastrian House is also used for a variety of functions, including weddings, social events and lectures. Children attend for language and religion classes, and they are initiated into the faith in a ceremony held here. The vast majority of Zoroastrians in Britain are Parsis from Bombay and the Gujarat, though there are some Iranians. Visitors will find that Zoroastrians, priests and laity alike, are most open and willing to discuss their faith.

Services: no regular services, but all festivals of Zoroastrian calendar celebrated □ Facilities: amplification □ Children: language and religion classes □ Wheelchair: several steps; assistance required □ Other details: various rooms □ Visiting: anyone interested in Zoroastrianism should apply to secretary

BIBLIOGRAPHY

We found the following works to be invaluable in the compiling of this book:

Oxford Dictionary of the Christian Church; ed. Cross & Livingstone
Penguin Dictionary of Religions; ed. Hinnels
International Church Index (Doctrinal); ed Sacey (Index Publ.)
London, all vols; Pevsner (Penguin)
A Guide to London's Churches; Blatch (Constable)
UK Christian Handbook 1987/88 Edition; ed Brierley (MARC Europe)

The following were also useful:

The Good Church Guide; ed. Kilmister (Penguin)
Welcome to London's Churches; Mason (Norheimsund Books)
The City of London Churches; Betjeman (Pitkin Pictorials)
London City Churches; Cobb (Corporation of London)
Visit some London Catholic Churches; S & E Usherwood (Mayhew McCrimmon)
A Methodist Guide to London & the South East; comp. Vickers & Young (WHMS Publ.)
Jewish London; Zeff (Piatkus)
Islam in Focus; Hammudah Abdulati (American Trust Publ.)
Alternative London: ed. Downes, Holme & Handley (Otherwise Press)
Faith in the City; (Church House Publishing)
The Church in Crisis; Moore, Wilson & Stamp (Hodder & Stoughton)

INDEX

KEY TO ABBREVIATIONS USED IN INDEX

B	Buddhism
BP	Baptist Churches
CB	Christian Brethren
CC	Christian Community
CE	Church of England
CF	Congregational Federation
CS	Church of Scotland
EFCC	Evangelical Federation of Congregational Churches
ELCE	Evangelical Lutheran Church of England
FCS	Free Church of Scotland
FIEC	Federation of Independent Evangelical Churches
FPCS	Free Presbyterian Church of Scotland
H	Hinduism
I	Islam
ID	Interdenominational
JF	Federation of Synagogues
JI	Independent Synagogues
JLP	Union of Liberal and Progressive Synagogues
JR	Reform Synagogues
JS	Sephardi Synagogues
JU	United Synagogue
JW	Jehovah's Witnesses
LC	Lutheran Churches
LCD	Lutheran Church of Denmark
LDS	Latter Day Saints
MC	Methodist Church
NC	The New Church
OBU	Old Baptish Union
OC	Orthodox Churches
OO	Oriental Orthodox Churches
PC	Pentecostal Churches
PCW	Presbyterian Church of Wales
QK	Quakers
RC	Roman Catholic Church
SA	Salvation Army
SBP	Strict Baptists
SDA	Seventh Day Adventists
SP	Spiritualists
SRC	Swiss Reformed Church
UC	Unitarian Churches
UEC	Union of Evangelical Churches
URC	United Reformed Church
UUCC	Ukrainian Uniat Catholic Church
UWI	Union of Welsh Independents